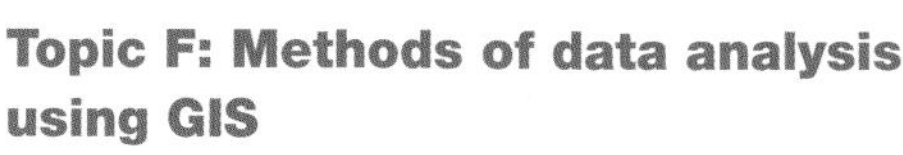

Topic F: Methods of data analysis using GIS

Topic G: Advanced techniques in GIS analysis

Topic H: GIS output

Topic I: GIS applications

preface

The completion of this book has been a significant effort involving contributions from many people. At ESRI (UK), Roy Laming's enthusiasm for GIS and commitment to provide schools with access to the technology has been fundamental in driving forward the GIS agenda in UK secondary education. Without Roy this book would have never happened. Angela Baker continued this role after Roy moved on from ESRI (UK), coordinating all aspects of ESRI input to the project. Angela's zeal and commitment has kept the book on track and I am very grateful for all her significant contributions. Also at ESRI (UK), Tim Burnham proofed the exercises and Sorcha Kennedy helped with the supply of police data and case study material. I am also indebted to the Technical Solutions Group for the ESRI (UK) diagrams.

At the Geographical Association, Fran Royle coordinated the production with significant input from Andrew Shackleton, Bryan Ledgard and Dorcas Turner.

I have been able to pull together a book like this because of my GIS work with the pupils and staff at Bishop's Stortford College (BSC). Without the help of Keith Irvine and Steve Bacon I would have never been able to deliver GIS in a classroom context. Matthew Drury and Naomi Byart have been very supportive in helping to develop and evolve teaching ideas using GIS.

I would like to thank Joseph Kerski for his feedback and comments on earlier versions of this book. His observations were extremely helpful and what changes I could not make this time round will hopefully be in the next edition!

I am very grateful to all those people who have tested the practical exercises for me; pupils at BSC, colleagues in the Cambridge GIS in Education Project, and the PGCE trainees at the University of Cambridge. Thanks also to Liz Taylor for her positive support and encouragement in all things GIS over the years.

This is not an academic book, so full references in the text to supporting research would be inappropriate. However, as a geography teacher attempting to interpret the work of GIS experts for school geography, I have found some sources very helpful and influential in the development of the book: Longley *et al.*, (2005), Heywood *et al.*, (2006) and Burrough and McDonnell (2000). In particular, Longley *et al.* (2005) was a central source for the development of chapters 12-17. The ASET GIS learning materials, which I first used in teaching the ASET Level 3 qualification in GIS, have been a great unpublished source of information in helping present the theoretical section of this book. Finally, I made extensive use of the ESRI manuals in pdf format that come with ArcView to source illustrations and help explain GIS theory. ESRI (2004a, 2004b and 2004c) were the primary sources for the development of chapters 8-11. A full reference list is provided at the end of this book and I am very grateful to those authors for the use of their work.

I would like to dedicate this book to Ramona: *te iubesc asa de mult*.

Peter O'Connor
October 2008

GIS for A-level geography

Peter O'Connor

Geographical Association

contents

ISBN 978-1-84377-210-1
First published 2008
Impression number
10 9 8 7 6 5 4 3 2 1
Year 2011 2010 2009 2008

Published by the Geographical Association,
160 Solly Street, Sheffield S1 4BF.
Website: www.geography.org.uk
E-mail: info@geography.org.uk
The Geographical Association is a registered charity: no 313129.

Copy editing: Andrew Shackleton, Asgard Publishing Services
Copyright permissions: Dorcas Turner
Design: Bryan Ledgard
Illustrations: Paul Coles and Kim Farrington
Printed and bound in China through Colorcraft Ltd

The GA's Publications Board would be happy to hear from other potential authors who have ideas for geography books. You may contact the Publications Board via the GA at the address above.

How to use this book

Why use this book?

The role of geography in society is perhaps more important than ever. Governments, organisations and individuals are having to grapple with increasingly complex social, economic and environmental problems. Population growth, global warming, poverty, dwindling energy resources, and the degradation of environments and habitats are issues that touch the lives of all of us on the planet. An important dimension in all these issues is space. Recognising where events are happening and how processes vary spatially is a first step in trying to resolve many of the impacts associated with human activity.

Currently, Geographical Information Systems (GIS) are the most powerful set of tools that exists for the analysis and visualisation of spatial information. Therefore GIS is at the heart of the applied application of geography to real-world problem solving. GIS is to geographers what the calculator is to mathematicians and the pen is to writers. It is therefore very likely that any student who wishes to follow a career in geography will at some point have to use GIS technology.

The growing awareness of the importance of GIS is reflected in the new specifications for A-level, with all the exam boards making reference to the technology. Additionally, all new specifications have modules that revolve around teaching and understanding methods of geographical investigation. An understanding of GIS plays a crucial role in introducing students to modern methods of spatial data capture, processing, analysis and presentation. Therefore many of the chapters in this book could be used as case study material to reinforce students' learning about the different stages of a geographical investigation. The practical exercises in this book give students the opportunity to develop their GIS skills and to gain hands-on experience of the technology.

The structure of the book

The book is divided into two units:

- **Unit 1: GIS theory and applications**
- **Unit 2: Practical exercises in GIS using ArcView 9.2**

Unit 1 provides students with a theoretical background to GIS use. While many of the topics covered illustrate the benefits of GIS use, there is also an attempt to consider the limitations of the technology.

This unit has three main aims:

- To provide students with a theoretical understanding of spatial data.
- To examine methods of spatial data capture, processing and analysis.
- To provide a range of examples of how GIS can be used to solve practical problems.

The unit is divided into nine topics labelled A to I. Topics A, H and I provide discussion on why GIS is important, how GIS can be used in practical problem solving, as well as case studies of GIS use.

Topics B, C and D describe the basics of how spatial data is stored and how geographic projection and coordinate systems work. These topics are important reading for those students who intend to collect their own fieldwork data and import it into GIS for analysis.

Topics E, F and G have two functions. Firstly, the materials covered include detailed examples of how geographical data can be captured, analysed and presented, providing case study material for the new **investigations modules** at A-level. Secondly, these topics will be useful to students designing and planning their own geographical investigations with GIS.

It is the intention of this unit that students should be able to dip in and out of the different topics as and when required. In this context, the book is perceived as a resource to support independent research, to help with the planning of individual geographical investigations and to identify modern methods of data capture, analysis and presentation. The unit is therefore not simply about GIS theory but also describes how professionals use geography to tackle real-world problems today.

Unit 2 introduces five practical exercises that aim to develop students' GIS skills in the area of data manipulation, presentation, analysis and output around four geographical themes. The exercises are designed to be carried out by students with no previous experience of GIS use. Each exercise is provided in PDF format on the accompanying CD.

Each of the exercises is independent, although exercises 2 and 3 are linked by the topic of crime. The exercises only use a small part of the data that is included with the book. However, students and teachers should not feel limited by the nature and extent of the exercises, because once they have mastered some of the techniques, they can go on to ask more complicated geographical questions. In this way, the exercises are intended to get students and teachers started with GIS. The data included is extensive and can be fully explored as individual confidence grows.

While the early stages of learning to use GIS are mainly about knowing which button to press next, the long-term goal is to reach a stage where the majority of time is spent thinking about the geography which GIS allows students to explore. I would therefore encourage students and teachers to try and stretch themselves beyond the content of the exercises in order to realise the full potential of the data contained on the accompanying CD.

CD content

This book comes with two CDs. One contains the data and digital copies of the exercises. On the data CD are five activity sheets, to be used in conjunction with the GIS exercises. The activity sheets are for students to record written responses to the questions posed in the GIS exercises. The numbered steps in the activity sheets correspond to those in the exercises. The other CD contains a trial version of ArcView 9.2 and a series of extensions. You will need to install the software and the data in order to perform the exercises in the book. Instructions for installing the two CDs that come with this book are given in the CD case.

I hope that your exploration of GIS will be enjoyable and stimulating but most of all will encourage you to think spatially!

Unit 1:

GIS theory and applications

Topic A: An introduction to GIS

Geography, information and technology

The importance of information

The exchange of information between organisations is essential to the successful development, operation and maintenance of many modern economies. High-quality information is required to make effective decisions in all sectors of business and government. Manufacturing industries use information about where to source the cheapest raw materials so that they can reduce costs and increase profits. Supermarkets collect information about what shoppers buy and where they live through the use of loyalty cards (Figure 1.1). They use this information through advertisements sent to the home in the form of letters to help sell other products such as house insurance, home loans and credit cards. Governments will collect statistics on where people live so that they can decide where to build new hospitals and schools. Information has become so important to governments and organisations that they have spent billions of pounds collecting and managing it. As a result, companies specialising in the collection and analysis of information have become an important economic sector in the global economy. Information has become a new raw material for many types of business activity.

Figure 1: Loyalty cards are often used as a source of data input for analysis in Geographical Information Systems. This can give retailers information about what they should stock in their shops in relation to different market areas.
Photo: Bryan Ledgard.

Geographic information and the technological revolution

The United States Government has estimated that 80% of all information exchanged around the world has a geographical component. A geographical component is any information that provides details of a location (Figure 1.2). For example, an estate agent may be trying to sell a house for a client. The agent may produce a leaflet describing the number of rooms in the house, the size of the back garden and other features of the property. The fact that the house details will be linked to an address and postcode adds a geographical component to the description of the house.

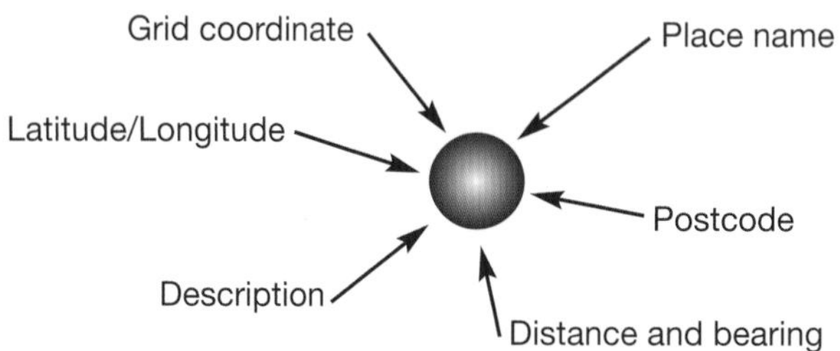

Figure 1.2: Information that can provide details of location. Source: ASET (2005).

The general growth in the use of geographical information can be linked to the development of new information technologies. Central to the expanded use of technology in geography has been the rapid improvement in the processing power of computers (Figure 1.3). Twenty years ago it would have cost tens of thousands of pounds to display and analyse a simple aerial photograph, whereas nowadays the same can be done for a fraction of the cost. Relatively recent technologies such as remote sensing (RS) and global positioning systems (GPS) have also enabled the relatively cheap collection of geographical information from large areas. As RS and GPS technologies became established, new software systems became necessary in order to analyse the information collected. These factors together led to the further development and use of Geographical Information Systems (GIS).

In recent years the growth in the use of GIS technology has been extremely rapid. It is now estimated that GIS is used by about 1 million regular users and 5 million casual users across the globe. The use of GIS is growing at more than 10% per annum and is worth in excess of £4 billion a year on a global scale. GIS technology has also become much more accessible to the general public through the development of the world wide web. There are now many examples of GIS technologies that can be accessed via the internet (Figure 1.4). GIS is

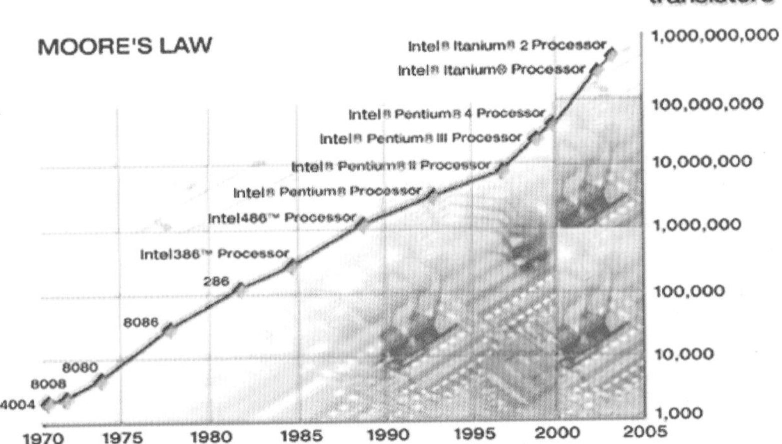

Figure 1.3: Moore's Law describes the increased processing power associated with computers between 1970 and 2005. Processing power is measured in millions of instructions per second (MIPS) and has risen because of increased transistor counts that occur within a micro-processor. Source: Intel.com

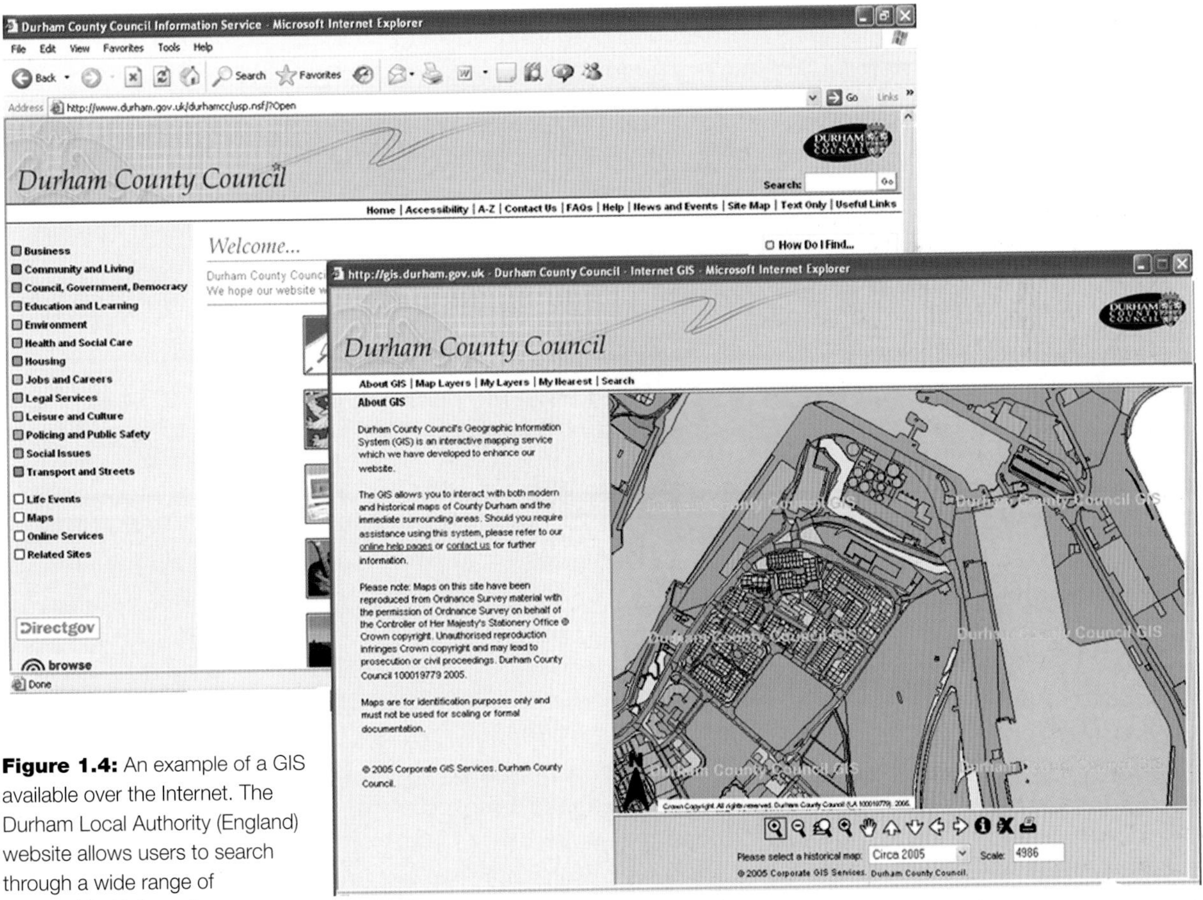

Figure 1.4: An example of a GIS available over the Internet. The Durham Local Authority (England) website allows users to search through a wide range of geographical information. Source: Durham County Council. OS base mapping reproduced with permission.

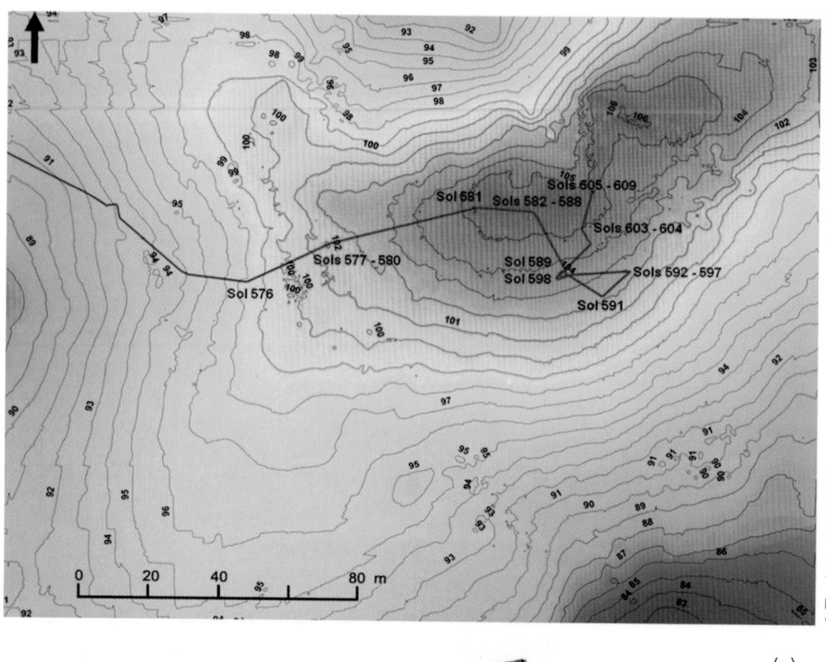

(a)

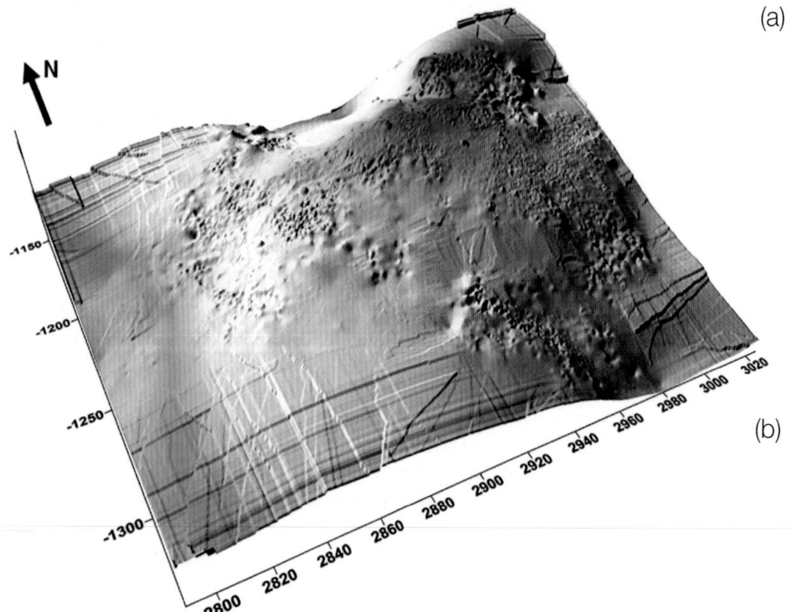

(b)

Figure 1.5: (a) Scientists have used GIS to help generate Digital Terrain Models of Mars from multiple photographs taken by the Rover Missions; (b) a 3D view of image (a) in the Husband Hill summit area of Mars. Source: Di *et al*. (2008).

used by a diverse range of organisations, and the number of people using the technology is growing all the time (Table 1.1; Figure 1.5). Clearly the use of GIS extends beyond traditional geographical organisations such as the Ordnance Survey, and it is becoming a common business management tool. Thus knowledge of GIS provides individuals with a set of skills that are highly valued by employers and transferable between different sectors of economic activity.

Areas where GIS is used	Application of GIS
Agriculture	Monitoring of crops and farm size in relation to the management of European Union subsidies.
Archaeology	Site description and analysis. Frequently used on the 'Time Team' television programme.
Environment	Used by the Environment Agency to monitor and model air and water quality.
Health	Used to analyse the location of disease in relation to environmental factors. For example, do people who live next to nuclear power stations have a higher risk of developing cancer?
Forestry	Management, planning and optimising extraction and planting of trees.
Emergency services	Optimising fire, police and ambulance routing; improving understanding of crime and its location.
Navigation	Over air, sea and land.
Marketing	Many shops now use store loyalty cards to record information about the way people shop. This information can then be mapped and used to locate new stores, market new products to certain income groups and optimise the delivery of goods.
Real estate	Calculating property values in relation to location, and for insurance.
Regional and local planning	Used by many local authorities to plan the regeneration of urban areas and manage local services.
Road and rail	Planning and management.
Tourism	Location and management of facilities and attractions.
Utilities	Location, management and planning of water, drains, gas, electricity, telephone and cable services.
Population and social studies	Government Census data is used to analyse demographic trends and developments.
Anti-terrorism	The CIA, FBI, MI5 and MI6 all use GIS to monitor and analyse the possibility of terrorist attacks associated with geographical location.
Military	GIS was used extensively in the Iraq War by both the US and UK military to plan missions.

Table 1.1: GIS use in different areas of economic activity. Adapted from Burrough and McDonnell, 2000.

Questions

- Why is information important to society?
- What is geographic information?
- How is the growth of GIS linked to changes in technology?
- Use the website *www.esri.com* to investigate how at least two different industries use GIS to manage their business.

What is GIS?

2

GIS can be thought of as a system for managing the input, processing and output of geographical data. The system at a simple level usually contains computer hardware, a spatial database, software and, perhaps most importantly, a thinking operator (Figure 2.1).

Spatial/geographical data

GIS

?

Computer hardware /software tools/people

Specific applications/ decision-making objectives

Figure 2.1: The basic components of a GIS. It is vital to note that people are also an essential component of any GIS. People are at the heart of GIS as they make the decisions that affect the quality and utility of GIS applications. Adapted from ASET (2005).

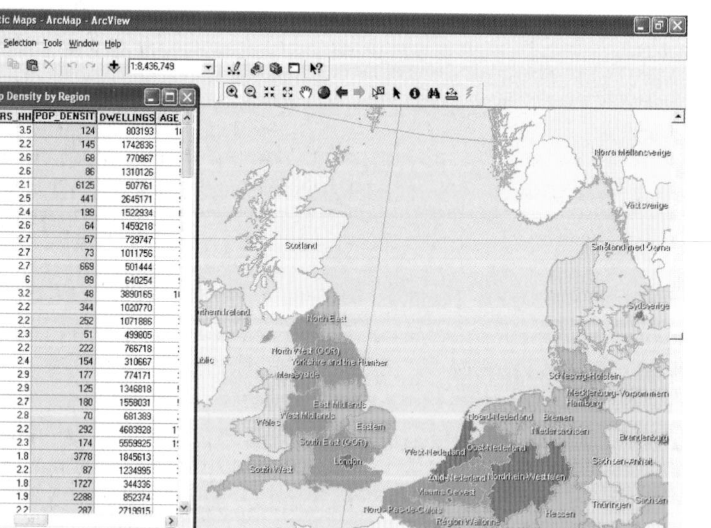

HOUSEHOLD	PERS_HH	POP_DENSIT	DWELLINGS
1009391	3.5	124	803193
1530136	2.2	145	1742836
680094	2.6	68	770967
1145088	2.6	86	1310126
480097	2.1	6125	507761
2427489	2.5	441	2645171
1401039	2.4	199	1522934
1153460	2.6	64	1459218
588819	2.7	57	729747
888184	2.7	73	1011756
343810	2.7	669	501444
753240	6	89	640254
3121811	3.2	48	3890165
945721	2.2	344	1020770
980553	2.2	252	1071886
330269	2.3	51	499805
676868	2.2	222	766718
281210	2.4	154	310667
677985	2.9	177	774171
1111204	2.9	125	1346818
1298881	2.7	180	1558031
553852	2.8	70	681389
4777349	2.2	292	4683928
5387746	2.3	174	5559925
1830209	1.8	3778	1845613
1169359	2.2	87	1234995
354560	1.8	1727	344336
902419	1.9	2288	852374
2763430	2.2	287	2719915

Figure 2.2: A map showing population density across a small area of Western Europe. Note that the data used to produce this map comes from the attributes table. It would be difficult to visualise patterns associated with the data by looking at the table alone. The map adds value to the data by making the patterns it displays easier to understand and recognise. Such actions applied to data create information. Therefore the creation of information requires some processing of raw data. There is always a link maintained between the map and the data. In this example only the data highlighted blue in the table is displayed on the map. However, GIS gives the user the opportunity to display other attributes that are held in the database table. Created in ArcView using ESRI Data and Maps.

The number of hardware components, the sophistication of the software and the complexity of the geographical data will vary greatly between different GIS users (see Table 1.1 in the previous chapter). However, the main functions of all GIS are the handling, manipulation and visualisation of data that are geographically referenced. In this way when you look at a map within a GIS it frequently has a database linked to it (see panel below). When data is summarised or changed in the database, the linked map that is viewed on the computer screen will also change (Figure 2.2).

What is a database?
A database is one or more structured sets of data, managed and stored as a unit and generally associated with software to update and query the data. A simple database might be a single file with many records in a series of rows and columns, each of which references a field title that describes the nature of the data.

While the above statements about the nature of GIS are correct, it should be borne in mind that scientists and geographers have not been able to agree on a universal definition of GIS. This is because people's views of GIS change depending on how they apply the technology. Also, with the rapid advance of information technologies, the capabilities of GIS are constantly evolving, so applications in the future might include many new uses. Despite these concerns, one of the most frequently used formal definitions of GIS is:

'A set of tools for collecting, storing, retrieving at will, transforming, analysing and displaying spatial data from the real world for a particular set of purposes.' Burrough and McDonnell (2000).

Importantly, the tools aspect of this definition provides a framework for thinking about how GIS works. Tools are used in GIS to complete a particular task or job. Within GIS there are four main jobs that need to be carried out in relation to the management of spatial information:

- Geographical data needs to be input into the GIS. Therefore GIS contains tools for taking data from sources such as satellites, paper maps and surveys into the computer while trying to maintain or improve the quality of the original data.
- Geographical data needs to be stored in the GIS in a manner that allows for retrieval, updating and editing. As a result GIS contain database tools that allow these functions to be carried out.
- Geographical data needs to be manipulated and analysed. The tools that allow this to happen are similar to those found in Microsoft

Excel. In GIS, however, actions such as calculating the mean, mode or medium are applied to a spatial set of data.
- Geographical data needs to be displayed. Therefore a set of tools needs to be available that displays all or part of the database in tabular, graphic or map form.

All of these tools enable GIS to take difficult to understand raw spatial data and turn this into usable **information** (see Figure 2.2). In this way GIS adds value to data and provides information to organisations that informs the decision-making process. Data in the form of tables of numbers is of little value as it is difficult for a person to process numbers shown in this format. However, GIS analysis provides information by revealing patterns in the data through the production of maps and other media. The information then provides a means to make decisions. **Thus the transformation of data into information is one of the most important functions of GIS (Figure 2.2)**.

What makes data spatial or geographical?

GIS can be used effectively in any business or organisational environment where it is necessary to support decision-making by means of geographical information. Most recordable data can be placed in a spatial context. For example, a police force could simply record the different types of crime that occur within a town. From their recording of this data the police will be able to recognise which crime occurs most frequently within the town. However, the simple tallying of crime incidents (as in Table 2.1) does not offer much assistance in deciding where resources such as police officers and patrol cars can be deployed to tackle crime incidents directly. Linking the crime incident data to a map would give senior officers a clearer picture of where patrols can be routed to discourage or capture the criminal (see Figure 2.3). **It is this attempt to link the data to a location that makes the data spatial.** The accuracy of the spatial data will be determined by how the data is linked to the map. For example, the linkage could be defined precisely using a coordinate system such as a six-figure grid reference, or a less accurate frame of reference might be used such as a street address or a postcode. It is also important to recognise that, when people use the terms geographical data or spatial data, they effectively mean the same thing.

Table 2.1: The number of crime incidents over a one week period in Kent, England. Source: Kent Police.

House burglary	Car theft	Violent crimes	Vandalism	Street robbery
43	72	12	87	18

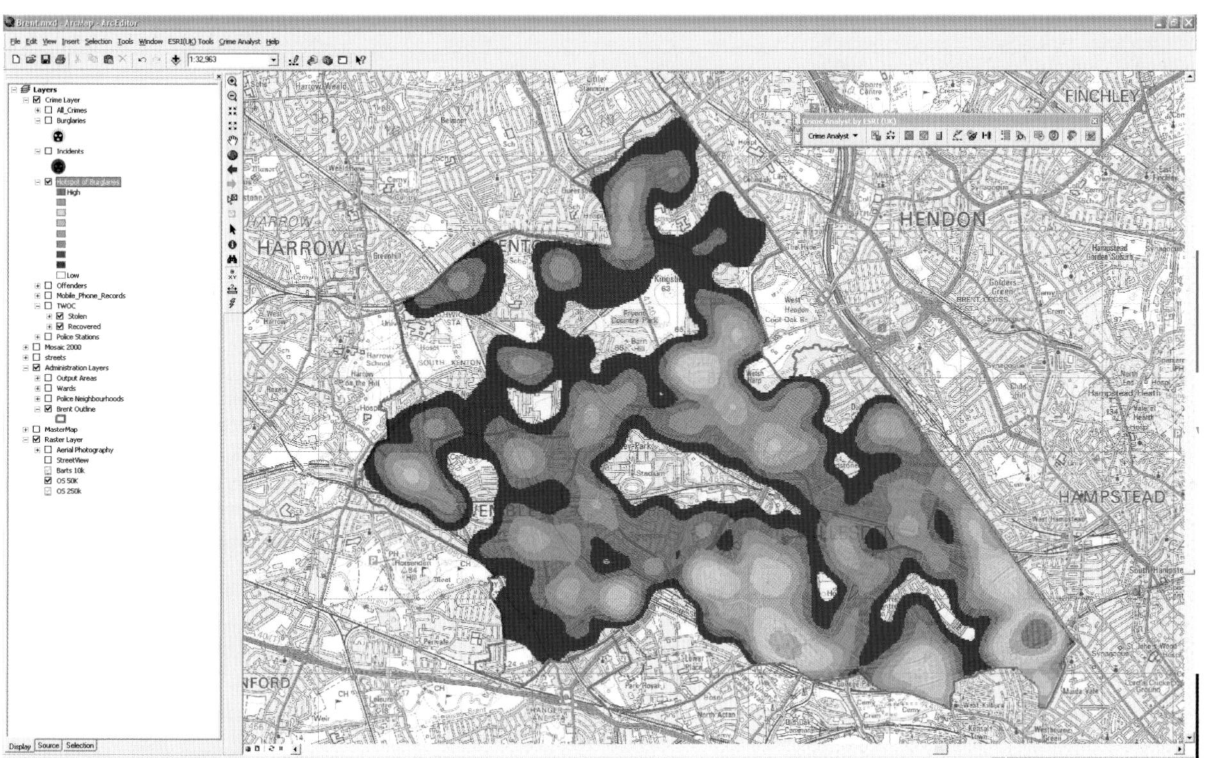

Figure 2.3: A map showing burglary densities in an area based on the London Borough of Brent, England. The redder the colour, the more burglaries occurred in that area. Source: ESRI (UK).

Questions

- What is GIS?
- What tools for handling data will most GIS contain?
- What is the difference between information and data?
- Of the data presented in Table 2.1 and Figure 2.2, which do you think would be more helpful for managing crime? Explain your reasons fully.

Mapping, GIS and society

Maps by their very nature simplify the world in which we live in an attempt to represent that world on a piece of paper or digitally within GIS. As a result, the person constructing the map will have to make decisions about what information to include or leave out. In carrying out this process, mapmakers can in part construct their own view of the world. This means that maps can be used as propaganda (Figure 3.1) or to present an incomplete or distorted view of the world that suits the aims of the mapmaker. Maps created in GIS can be used in many ways, some of them contributing to the general good of society while others may marginalise certain social and economic groups or certain points of view.

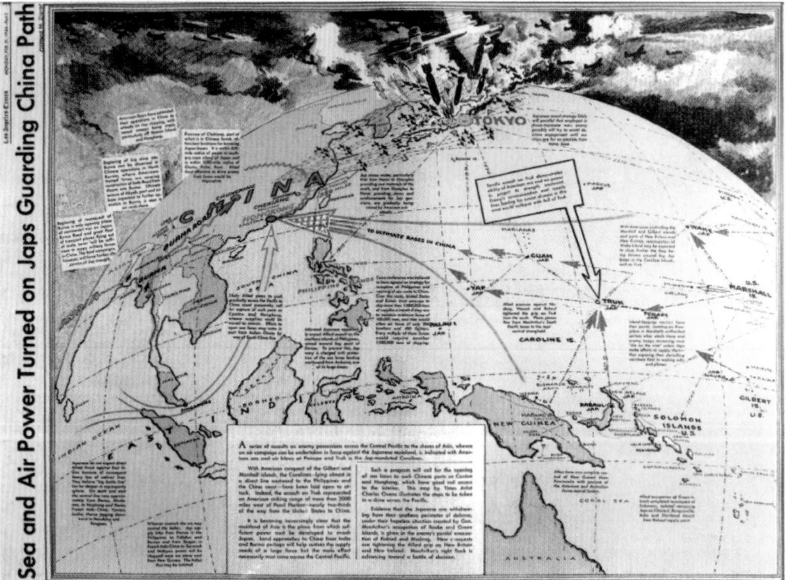

Figure 3.1: This map was used during World War II as propaganda by the United States. Charles H. Owens. 'Sea and air power turned on Japs guarding China path' Copyright 2008 *Los Angeles Times*, 21 February 1944. Reprinted with permission.

The need for map awareness

The widespread integration of GIS mapping into everyday society is taking place at a rapid rate with the advent of virtual globes like Google Earth that stream vast amounts of geographical information across the internet. Clearly there are many opportunities for GIS mapping to play a positive role in society. For example, GIS was used effectively to manage and mitigate the impacts of the 9/11 terrorist attacks (Figures 3.2 and 3.3 overleaf).

Figure 3.2: The photo right shows 'ground zero' in New York City. Maps were produced quickly using GIS to help the police enforce no-go areas and inform the general public as to which areas were accessible to them after the 9/11 terrorist attacks in 2001. Source: Kevany (2003).

PEDESTRIAN AND VEHICULAR TRAFFIC RESTRICTIONS
Effective 9/17/2001

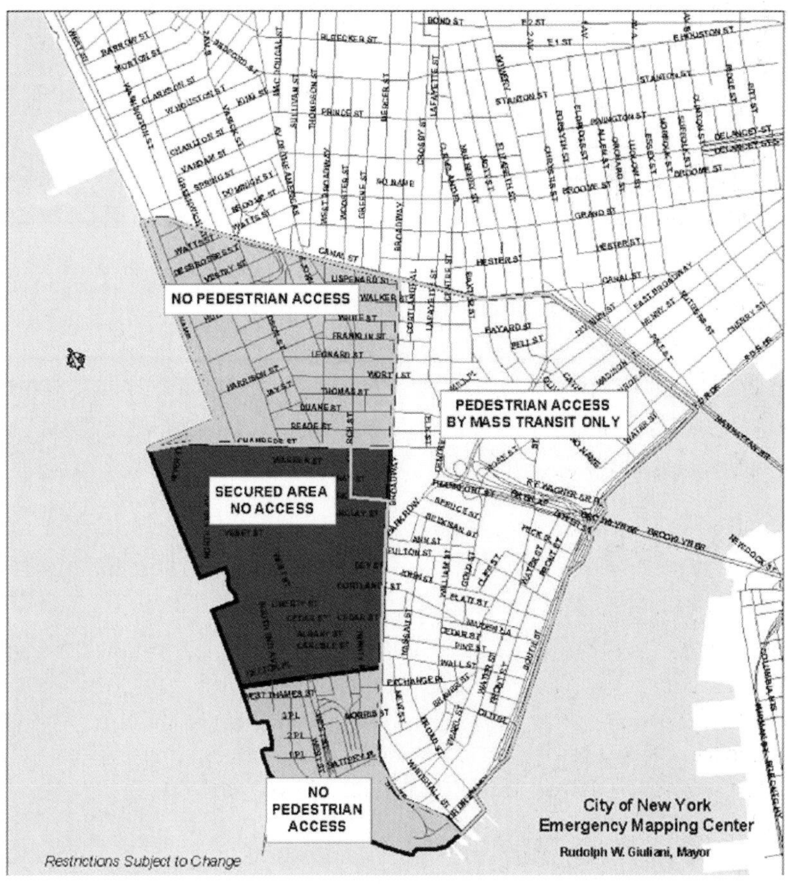

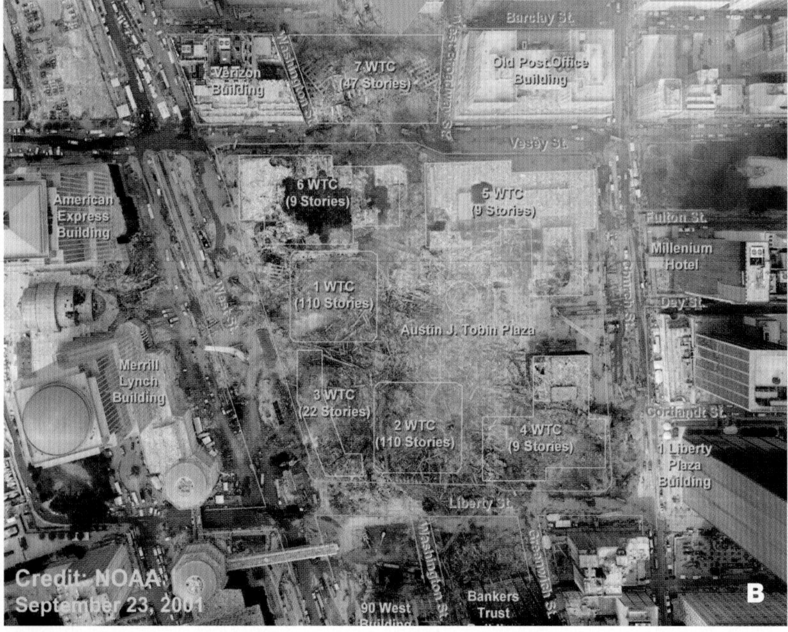

Figure 3.3: Satellite imagery (A) and GIS mapping (B) were used after the 9/11 terrorist attacks to map key features of the cityscape. The results could then be used to coordinate search and rescue operations as well as restoring key services to the city. IKONOS satellite image courtesy of GeoEye. Copyright 2008. All rights reserved. Source of outline map: *http://wtc.nist.gov*.

GIS mapping was used to plan programmes of work to restore electricity, gas, water and the return of New York's transport system. The police, fire and ambulance services used the technology to manage the clean-up operation and define areas of access and risk (Figure 3.2). Examples of the positive ways that GIS can contribute to society are numerous, including activities such as monitoring rainforest destruction (Figure 3.4), groundwater vulnerability (Figure 3.5), sea-level rise (Figure 3.6), food production (Figure 3.7) and changes in fertility rate (Figure 3.8).

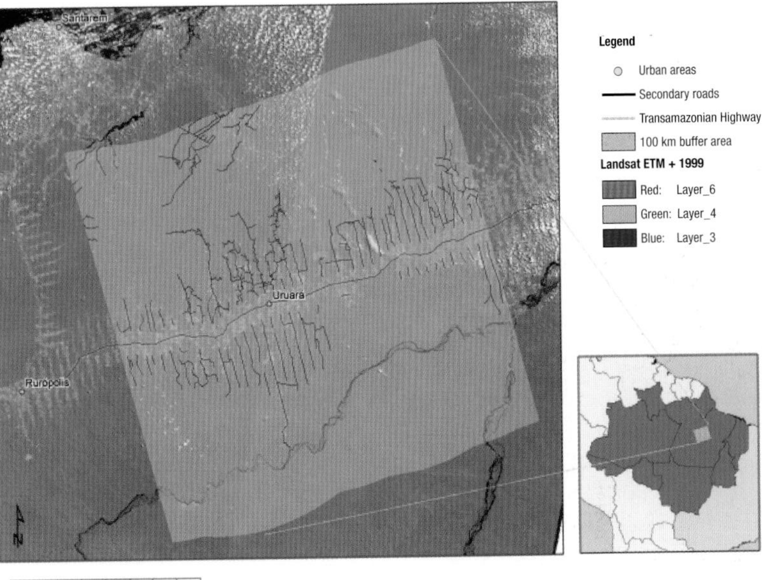

Figure 3.4: Satellite and GIS technology is being used to monitor the destruction of rainforest in the Amazon Basin. The pattern of destruction closely mirrors the road network. Scientists are using this knowledge to model how the rainforest will break up in the future and to predict the impacts of these changes on biodiversity. Source: Arima *et al.* (2005).

While GIS has been fundamental in providing new ways of examining spatial patterns, and in helping to unpack the complexities of human and environmental interactions, the limitations of the technology need to be clearly visualised so that GIS output can be applied in a context of understanding and critical awareness. Without a critical eye, GIS output could be utilised in ways never intended, leading to poor policy decisions on the part of organisations and governments.

It is important for users of GIS output to be literate in the technology so that they can select the correct GIS tools for the tasks required, maximising the positive contribution of GIS to society.

Much of the rest of this book will consider these issues directly but the examples below provide a brief introduction to areas that GIS users need to be aware of when considering the ways in which GIS can impact on society.

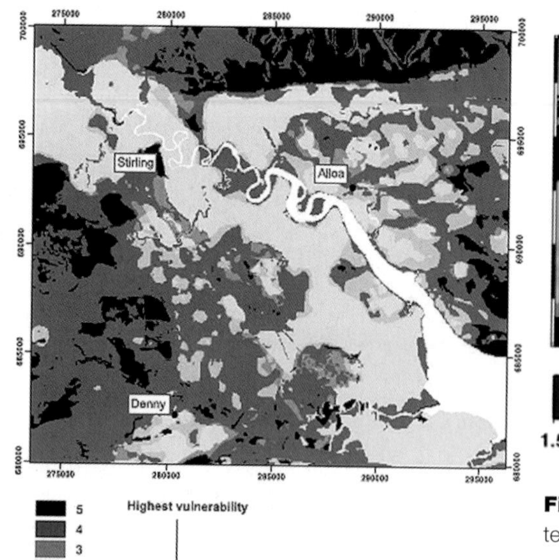

Figure 3.5: Map showing groundwater vulnerability in the area around Stirling, Scotland. Such maps are used to identify areas at greatest risk from the potential effects of groundwater contamination. Planners will use such information to restrict the location of activities likely to result in groundwater contamination. They can also use it as a basis for placing extra restrictions on activities in areas of highest risk to reduce the likelihood of pollution occurring. Source: Ó Dochartaigh *et al.*, (2005).

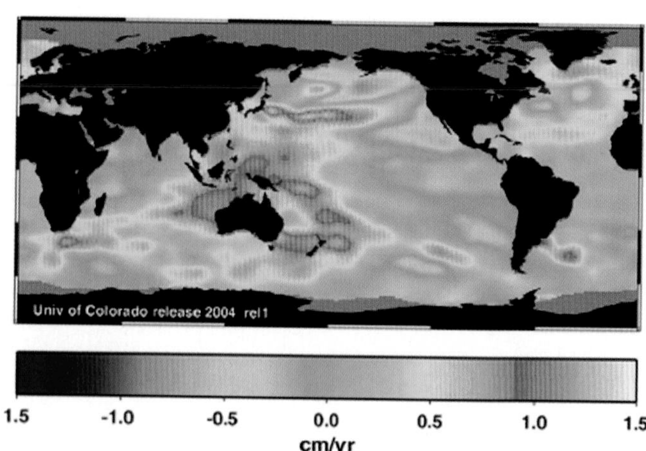

Figure 3.6: Sea level trends produced from remote sensing and GIS technologies for the period 1993–2003. Source: Tralli *et al.* (2005).

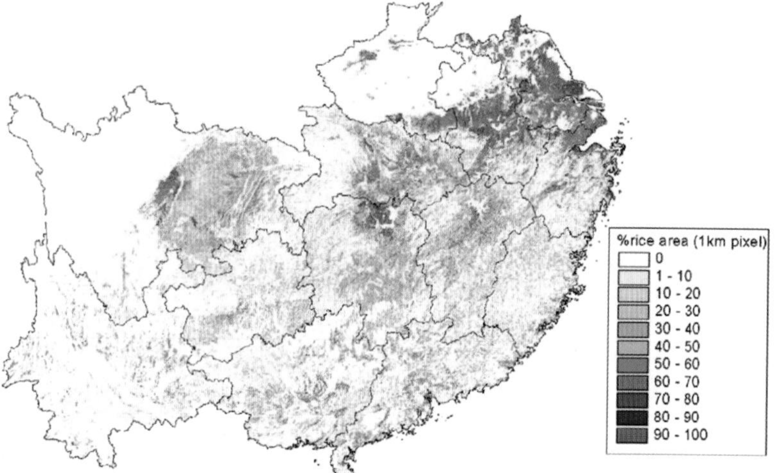

Figure 3.7: A map produced using remote sensing and GIS techniques to show areas of rice production in China. In a country with a population greater then 1.3 billion people the monitoring of food production has been identified as a priority by the Chinese Government. Source: Xiao *et al.* (2005).

Figure 3.8: Spatial variability in total fertility rate (TFR) in Greater Cairo, Egypt, between 1986 and 1996. Typically in the past, fertility rate differences would have only been analysed for differences between rural and urban areas. With the use of GIS it is now possible to break down urban areas into smaller units for analysis. The results of such analysis provide important information for planners and government departments. Source: Weeks *et al.* (2004).

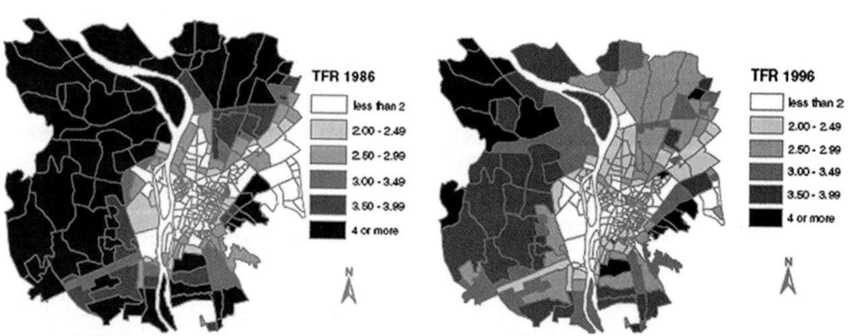

Projection systems are used to transform a three-dimensional object – the Earth – into a two-dimensional flat piece of paper. The paper map resulting from this process of the Earth is a distortion of reality (Figure 3.9).

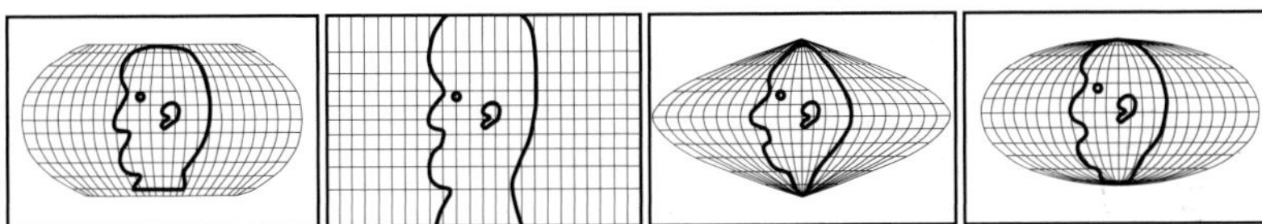

Figure 3.9: Four different projection systems commonly used to transform a 3D Earth into a flat piece of paper. A head drawn on one projection (Robinson's) has been transferred to a Mercator (centre left) and a sinusoidal (centre right), and finally to a Mollweide (far right).The 'natural' profile could have been drawn on any of these and then plotted on the others. This simple exercise clearly shows that the shape of the face produced depends on the projection system used. Source: Kaiser and Wood (2001).

In Figure 3.9, each projection system presents an approximation of how the original face would have looked, but none shows it perfectly. Therefore, when any map is examined, questions have to be asked about how true, how complete, how accurate and how precise it is. In all circumstances the answers given will depend on the purpose for which the map is to be used. Maps are at their most flawed when they are used in functions for which they were never designed (Figure 3.10).

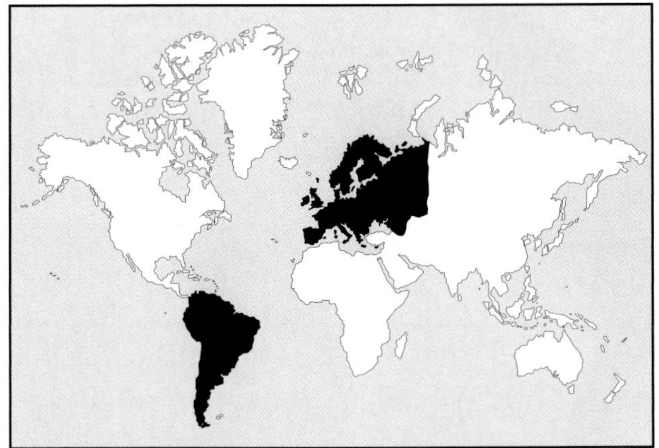

Figure 3.10: The Mercator projection makes Europe look larger than South America. In fact, Europe only has 3.8 million square miles and there are 6.9 million square miles in South America. Of course, the projection was never designed to facilitate the comparison of areas. Source: Kaiser and Wood (2001).

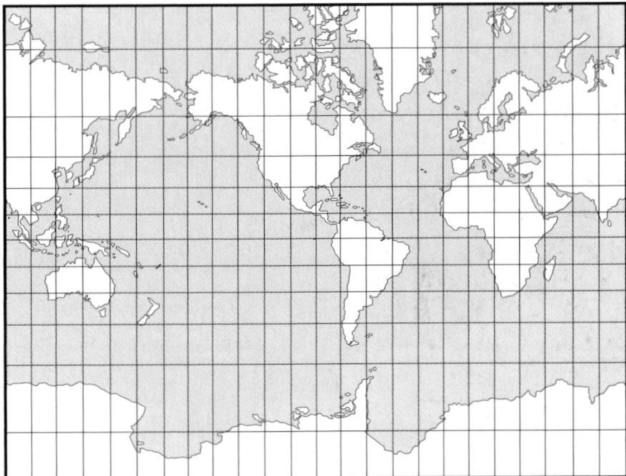

Figure 3.11: This Mercator projection is centred on the United States. This type of image has been argued as helping to reinforce the United States as the only remaining superpower. Countries like China appear marginalised and even physically divided to the eastern and western portions of the map. It is important to consider how such constructions affect the views of individuals. Source: Kaiser and Wood (2001).

Governments, organisations and individuals have exploited the limitations of maps in accurately representing reality in order to construct and communicate their own world view.

Figure 3.11 shows a map centred on the United States. Some academics would argue that the types of maps individuals are exposed to profoundly affect their world view. American students studying this map may be reinforced in their view that the United States are at the centre of the global economy. The map could be used to diminish the perceived power and size of Asia by splitting the continent to the east and west of the United States. Someone living in Australia may look at this map and think that the person who constructed it has marginalised the importance of Australia in global politics. Maps have to be interpreted, and the way information is presented affects how different societies view the world.

Examine Figure 3.12, which shows the results for the 2004 Presidential election in the United States. The map gives the impression that George Bush won a landslide victory over John Kerry as the 'red' states dominate the country by covering a far greater area than the 'blue' ones. However, this is very misleading because it fails to take into account the fact that most of the red states have small

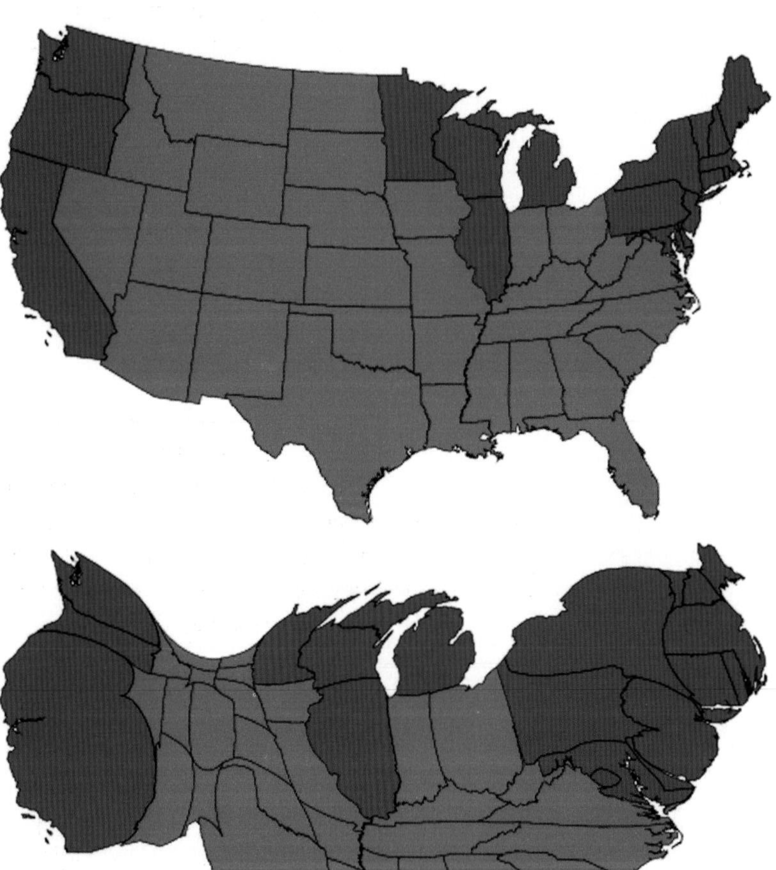

Figure 3.12: Results for the 2004 US Presidential elections by state. The states of the country are coloured red (Republican candidate, George W. Bush) or blue (Democratic candidate, John F. Kerry) to indicate where candidates won across the country. Source: Gastner *et al.* (2005).

Figure 3.13: The 2004 presidential election results as illustrated by a population cartogram (red = win for George W. Bush; blue = win for John F. Kerry). Source: Gastner *et al.* (2005).

populations. The blue ones may be small in area, but they have large populations, which are what matters in an election.

The limitations of Figure 3.12 can partly be addressed by producing a cartogram, which is a type of map that distorts geometry or space. Figure 3.13 is a space cartogram that rescales the areas of states so as to be proportional to the number of people living in them. As a result, Figure 3.13 gives a truer picture of the closeness of the American election in 2004.

It is clear from Figures 3.12 and 3.13 that techniques of map construction can be selected to communicate the same data with different meanings. In examining a map's meaning, users should attempt a critical assessment of the techniques chosen to construct the map. They must also consider whether the map's content is appropriate to its intended function. By considering these questions, individuals will be enabled to make value judgments and make the right choices when using maps to address environmental and social problems.

Issues of technology access and GIS

In the more economically developed countries (MEDCs), GIS is increasingly becoming essential as a decision-making tool for commercial organisations, governments and even individuals. It is being used to classify, standardise, judge, measure, describe and analyse the social, economic and environmental nature of the places in which we live. While these measures can be used effectively to help governments choose the best sites for new schools and hospitals, and commercial organisations to select locations for maximum profit, there are concerns about how GIS may remain inaccessible to large sections of society at a range of different scales.

Figure 3.14 (overleaf) shows a screenshot of the MAGIC (Multi Agency Geographic Information for the Countryside) website (*www.magic.gov.uk*). This site was created by a partnership of UK government departments and agencies in order to provide access to rural and countryside information for use by the general public and other organisations. While the website provides a wealth of information about the English countryside, this resource is inaccessible to a large section of the population. For example, Figure 3.15 (overleaf) shows that in December 2003, only six out of every 100 people in the UK had access to broadband internet, which is the level of service required to

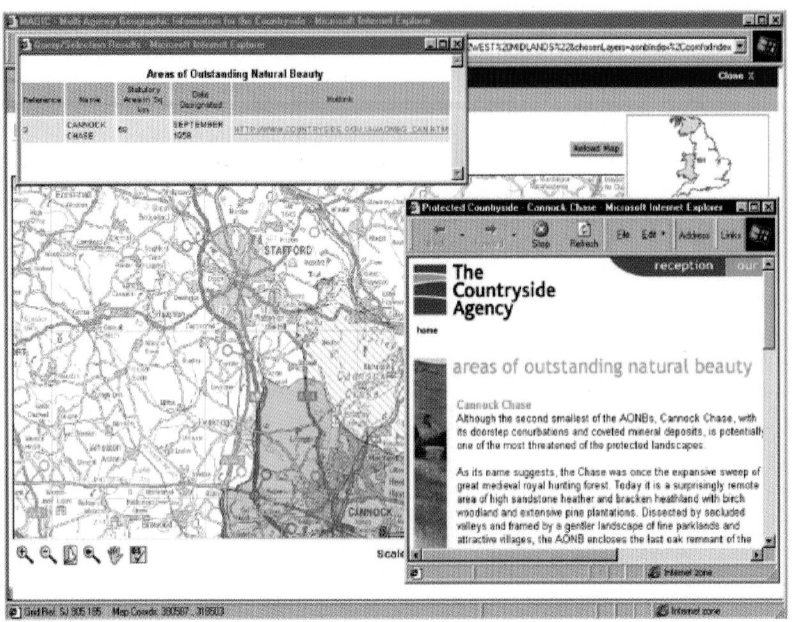

Figure 3.14: A screenshot of the MAGIC (Multi Agency Geographic Information for the Countryside) website showing areas of outstanding natural beauty that are accessible to the general public. Source: Askew *et al.* (2005). OS base mapping reproduced with permission.

use the MAGIC website efficiently. This pattern of limited access to potential GIS resources is repeated across many countries and is worse in areas that are less economically developed. There can also be significant variations within a single country in terms of access to computer hardware and the internet for different sections of society (see Figures 3.16 and 3.17). This in turn greatly affects their ability to exploit the benefits of internet GIS. Thus the provision of internet GIS by governments offers enhanced service provision to the most economically favoured groups in society, while doing little for the prospects of marginalised communities.

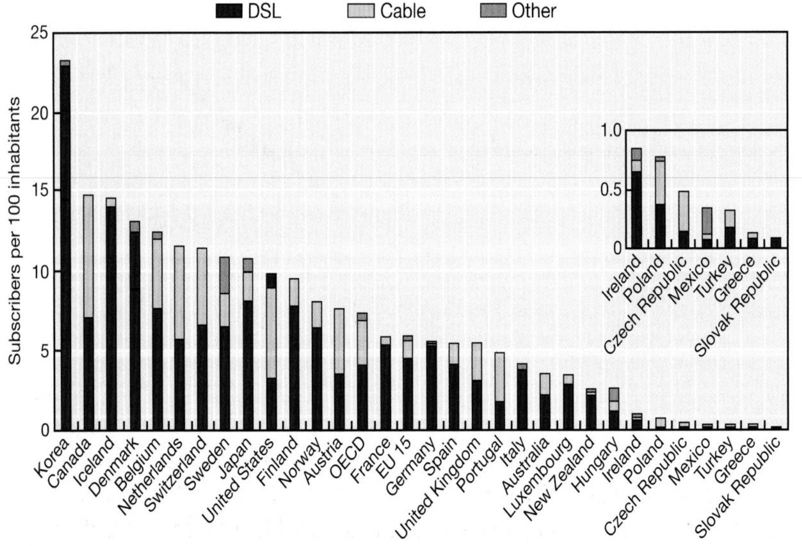

Figure 3.15: Broadband access per 100 inhabitants, December 2003, p. 147, *OECD Information Technology Outlook* 2004, © OECD 2004.

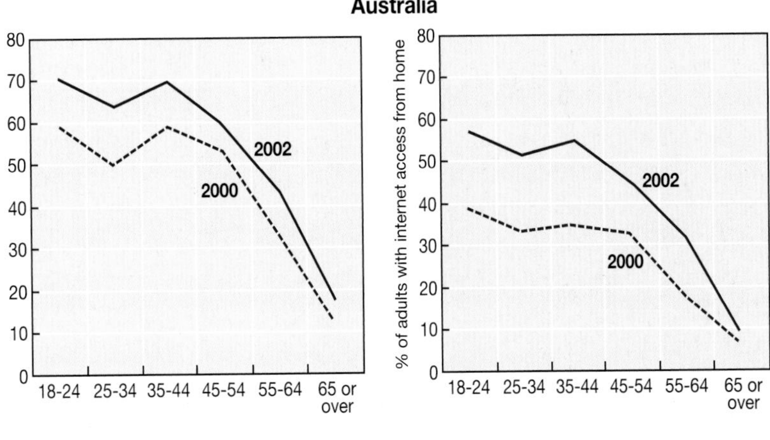

Figure 3.16: ICT access by age in selected OECD countries, as percentage of population, p. 152, *OECD Information Technology Outlook* 2004, © OECD 2004.

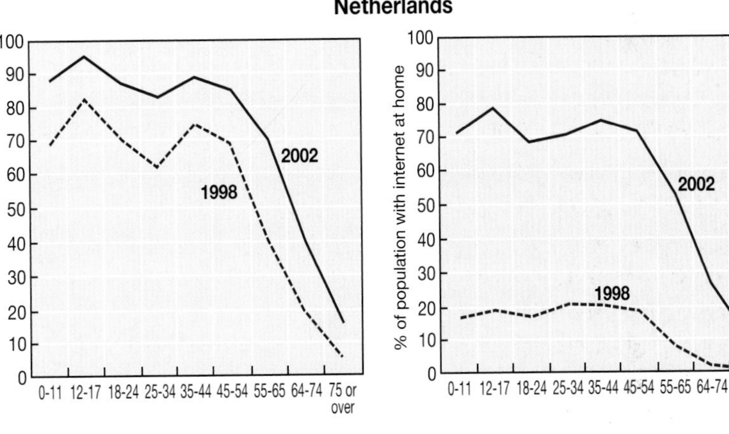

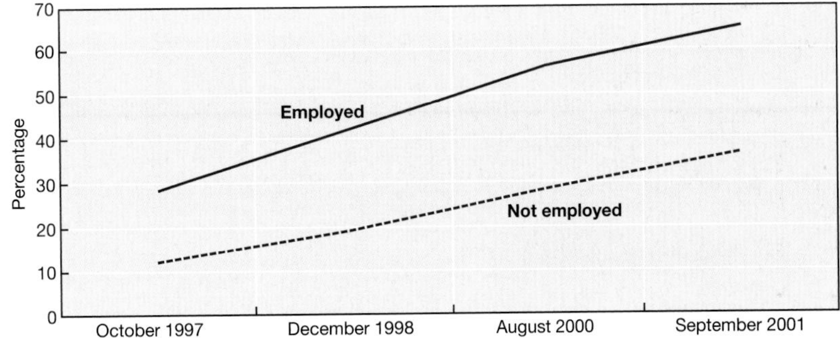

Figure 3.17: Internet use in the United States, 1997-2001, p. 157, *OECD Information Technology Outlook* 2004, © OECD 2004.

GIS and social structure

GIS representations of cities are increasingly affecting how places are used and accessed by different sectors of society. For example, the large volumes of information readily available via GIS-based internet services make it possible for GIS-literate groups to identify 'suitable' communities in which to live and socialise. In this way the simplified representations of community as constructed by GIS are made more real by groups choosing to access only those places whose attributes meet their perceived needs.

GIS-based websites like UpMyStreet (Figure 3.18) in the UK provide sophisticated postcode-searching tools that can define the nature of places on the basis of attributes such as crime rates, school performance, house prices, environmental quality, hazards, pollution and access to services. If individuals choose to use this information to select communities that most closely mirror their own values, this could lead to self-reinforcing social groupings. In essence the GIS database could play a part in constructing the social structure of the city.

A further consequence of GIS is that commercial service providers are overwhelmingly selecting sites for new outlets that reflect the places in which the most economically active and favoured groups live. This approach could work to undermine the prospects of marginalised groups and communities if, for example, a new cinema or shopping

Figure 3.18: UpMyStreet provides detailed statistics on the nature of places to postcode level. Source: *www.upmystreet.com*.

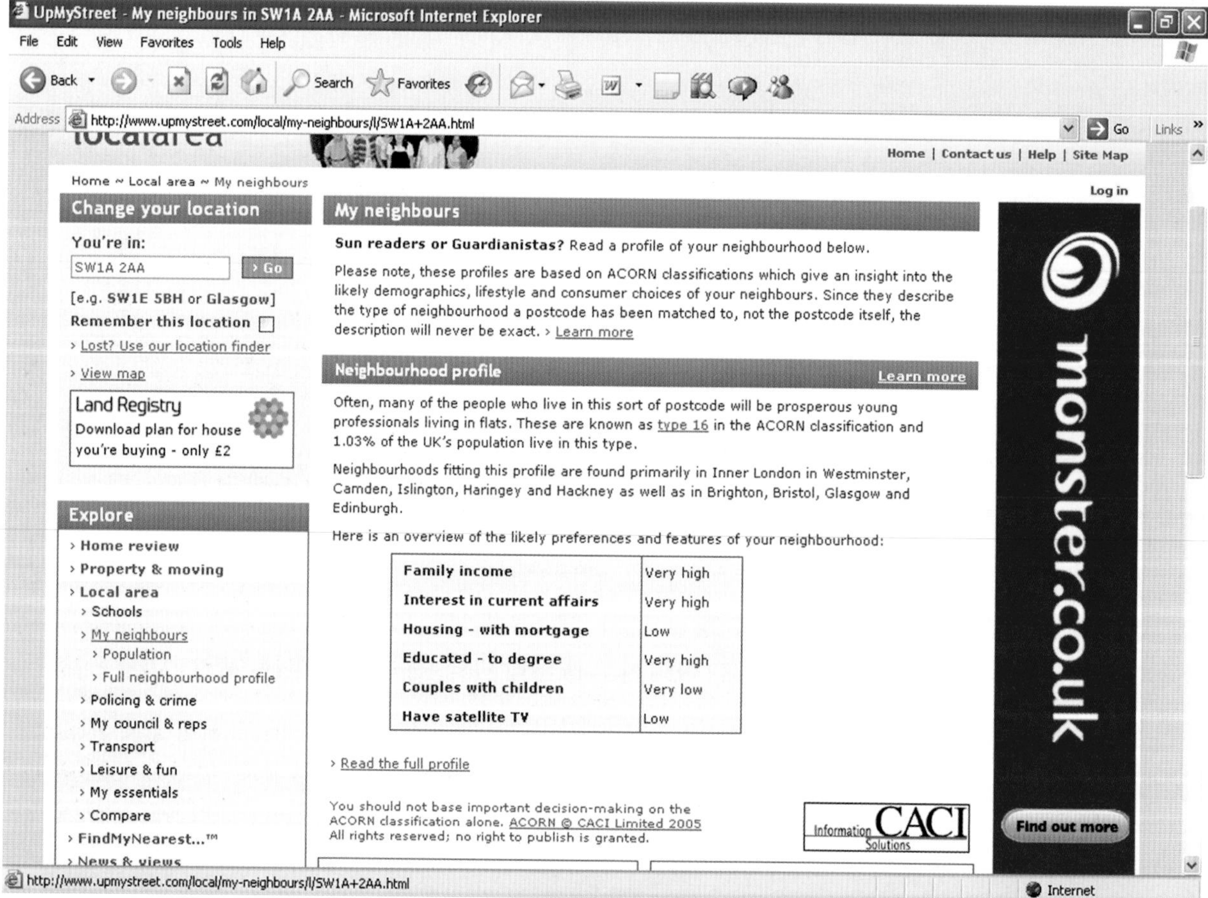

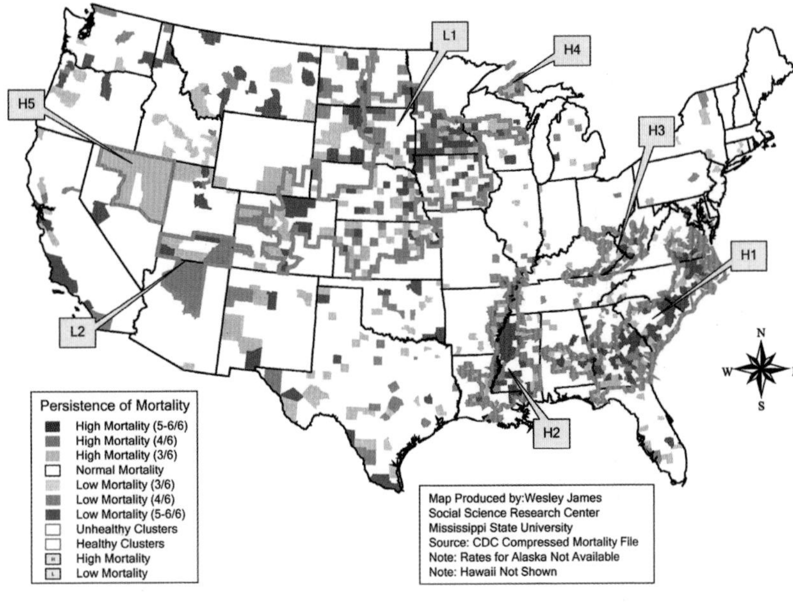

Figure 3.19: Clusters of persistent mortality in the United States: 1968–1997. Source: Cossman *et al*. (2003).

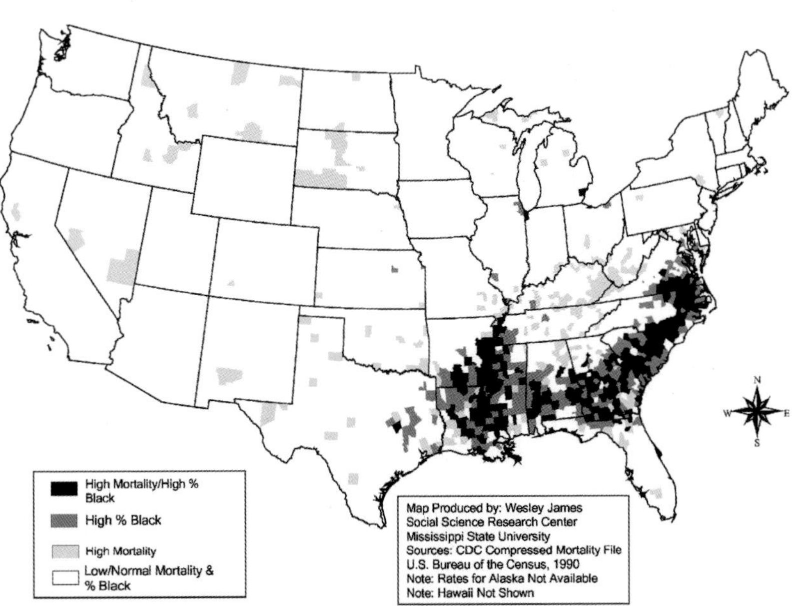

Figure 3.20: High-mortality and high-percentage black counties in the United States: 1988–1992. Source: Cossman *et al*. (2003).

centre is located in an area which they cannot easily access. However, GIS can also be used to identify patterns of deprivation (Figure 3.19) and explore which groups in society live in these locations (Figure 3.20). Understanding where the worst-off groups in society live enables national and local government agencies to initiate change if the political will exists. Positively, the information that GIS provides can be used to place pressure on policy makers to develop strategies that promote social inclusion.

The future

At the moment GIS captures a picture of society that is rather static and lumpy, where community representations are linked to areas like census and postcode zones. However, a future is approaching rapidly where a vast range of tracking systems will mean that very soon real-time geographical simulations of places will be accessible over the internet. For example, it is now possible to track the movements of individuals through the signals emitted from their mobile phones. It is just a small step from this to mapping the characteristics of that individual and others as they move around the environment. The question is, once these processes become routine, how will this information be used? Will it be used by governments to engineer a society that is inclusive? Or will commercial interests predominate in creating a spatial structure that excludes and divides? In this context it is worth remembering that rarely has new technology been introduced without creating new problems for society to manage and consider. There is no reason to think that GIS will be any different.

Questions

- How do you think maps could be used to influence your world view?
- Which groups in society are least likely to be able to access the benefits of GIS?
- How can GIS have potentially positive and negative impacts on society?

Topic B: What are the characteristics of geographical data?

4

Location

If geographical data is going to be used successfully within GIS, the nature of the data must be properly understood so as to avoid any unnecessary errors. Geographical data can have three major characteristics that can be regularly stored in most GIS databases:

- Location
- Geometry
- Topology

The nature of these factors will be considered in this chapter and the next one.

The location of a place can be expressed in many ways (see Table 4.1 and Figure 1.2 on page 10). For example, if the President of the United States was visiting the United Kingdom's Prime Minister, there are many ways in which the location of the proposed meeting place could be communicated. The simplest way would probably be to provide an address for the location:

Prime Minister
10 Downing Street
London
United Kingdom

Table 4.1: Different ways of expressing the location of No 10 Downing Street.

Locational system	Locational data used	Locational accuracy
Ordnance Survey X coordinate	530047	Point
Ordnance Survey Y coordinate	179951	Point
Postcode	SW1A 2AA	Area
Latitude (WGS84)	N51:30:13 (51.503540)	Point
Longitude (WGS84)	W0:07:40 (-0.127696)	Point
Landranger series	TQ300799	Map sheet
Lower super output area	018C LSOA	Area

Names of places and addresses are frequently used to enable different groups of people to meet in the same place or location. The advantage of addresses or place names is that this type of information is easy to understand and everybody has some experience of using it. For this reason many organisations use names and addresses for attaching other information to a location; later this information can be mapped.

For example, after attending a fire, the fire brigade will want to record information about how the fire started, the number of fatalities and injuries. This information will then be attached to an address for future reference. Another advantage of this type of referencing system is that it tries to tie information or data to a point. The disadvantage of using this type of locational information within GIS is that, for the information to be displayed on a map, the address or place name has to be converted to an X and Y coordinate. In order to tackle this problem a **gazetteer** has to be constructed. A gazetteer is a database of geographical places or addresses that are then each supplied with a set of individual X and Y coordinates. In GIS the generation of an X and Y coordinate from an address is often called **geocoding**.

If the President of the United States wanted to send a letter, he would probably add a postcode to the address of the Prime Minister. A postcode is another type of locational information that can be used to find a place. The postcode location for number 10 Downing Street is shown in Table 4.1.

The UK postcode system

About 25 years ago, the Royal Mail developed the postcode system for the sorting and delivery of post in the United Kingdom. There are over 27 million delivery points for mail in the UK. To help find these places, each code has two parts – the outward code and the inward code. The first two letters refer to a postcode area; these are followed by subsequent numbers and letters subdividing this into districts, sectors and unit postcodes. The physical area covered on a map gets smaller as you move from districts to units (Table 4.2). Using the Prime Minister's postcode it breaks down as follows:

- SW denotes the South West London postcode area – there are currently approximately 124 postcode areas in the UK.
- SW1A denotes district 1A in the South West London area – there are currently approximately 3,000 postcode districts in the UK.
- SW1A 2 denotes sector 2 in district 1 of the South West London postcode area – there are approximately 10,000 postcode sectors in the UK.

Table 4.2: There are four hierarchical levels to postcodes in the UK. Source: Office for National Statistics (ONS) (2004).

Example	Geographic Unit	Number in UK (August 2003)
PO	Postcode area	124
PO16	Postcode district	2,932
PO16 7	Postcode sector	9,750
PO16 7DZ	Unit postcode	1.75 million

Postcodes have become a common basis for organising other information collected by public and private sectors. For example, market research organisations frequently map the results of surveys by postcode. It is essential for a user of GIS to understand what boundaries are being used to map any collected data as this will affect how the resulting maps can be used. For example, it may not be possible to compare maps based on postcode district boundaries from different years as the physical shape of boundaries frequently changes. If these circumstances arise, this will introduce error into the analysis regardless of the quality of GIS being used.

Output areas and census data

Another very important geographical boundary used in the UK to locate information is the output area (Figure 4.1). These boundaries and locations are used by the Office for National Statistics to display data collected during the 2001 Census.

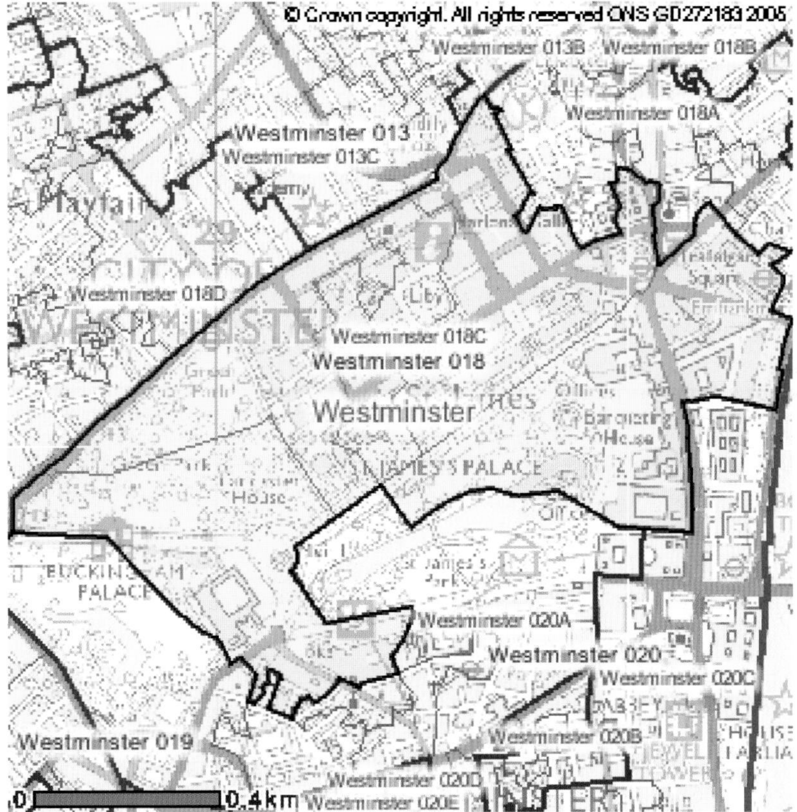

Figure 4.1: Lower Super Output Area 018C for the Area of Westminster, which includes No 10 Downing Street. Source: ONS. © Crown Copyright and/or database right. All rights reserved. Licence number 100017849.

For analysis purposes, the country has been divided into small blocks of land called output areas. These allow us to look in more detail at smaller local areas. Output areas have been combined to form two layers of super output areas known as lower-layer super output areas (LSOA) and middle-layer super output areas (MSOA). There are 34,378 lower super output areas and 7,193 middle super output areas in England and Wales. The output areas allow the data that was collected from individual households during the census to be joined together. This process in GIS is called **data aggregation**. Joining together all the data for households and averaging it out over the larger physical space of the output area offers a number of advantages. Aggregating the data protects the privacy of individual households by preventing anybody from identifying the answers that were given in relation to the census questionnaire. However, the physical size of the output area is still small enough to identify meaningful patterns that could be used by local authorities in making important policy decisions. Postcode SW1A 2AA is located in the lower-layer super output area referred to as Westminster 018C (see Figure 4.1 on previous page).

Other locational information

Table 4.1 on page 31 provides yet further locational information that could be used to help find the Prime Minister's residence. This includes Ordnance Survey X and Y coordinates, and coordinates for latitude and longitude. The advantage of using this type of locational system is that it is very accurate because it provides an exact geographical location. The further characteristics of coordinate systems will be explored later in the book.

Questions

- What systems are used to locate places in the UK?
- What is data aggregation?
- What are the advantages of data aggregation?
- Although they are not discussed in this chapter, what do you think might be the disadvantages of data aggregation?

Geometry and topology

Geometry

Geographical information often has shape associated with it. For example, buildings may be square, circular or rectangular. Shape may also relate to other physical aspects of the landscape such as the course of a river or the topography of a rural area.

Looking at Figure 5.1, it is clear that the buildings around 10 Downing Street have a vast range of shapes and sizes, and that these features are an important part of defining the nature of this landscape. Likewise, when inputting information into GIS, it is important to ensure that the **geometry** of the area under investigation is accurately recorded. If the geometry of places was not accurately recorded this would make certain uses of GIS impossible. For example, imagine trying to plan the laying of electrical cables in terms of spacing and materials required without an accurate map showing the size and shape of buildings, roads, bridges and footpaths.

Figure 5.1: An aerial photograph of Westminster Bridge and the area around 10 Downing Street. Try and examine the geometry of the features in the photograph. Source: *www.citiesrevealed.com*.

Topology

Topology is concerned with connections between features in the landscape and not their physical shape. Topology is important in GIS as it gives direction to the data. For example, it could be used to indicate the direction in which a river will flow. More importantly, the topological information in GIS describes how all the different parts on a map will fit together when they are displayed. If all the features that make up a map such as roads, rivers, houses, fields and lakes were considered as a jigsaw puzzle, topology is the information used by the GIS to put the map together in the fastest possible way. Figure 5.2 illustrates the four main aspects of topology:

- **Connectivity**: Downing Street and Kings Charles Street are connected to Parliament Street.
- **Containment**: 10 Downing Street is wholly contained within the boundary of map square A.
- **Adjacency**: The Conference Centre is adjacent to Storey's Road.
- **Direction**: 10 Downing Street is northwest of Westminster tube station.

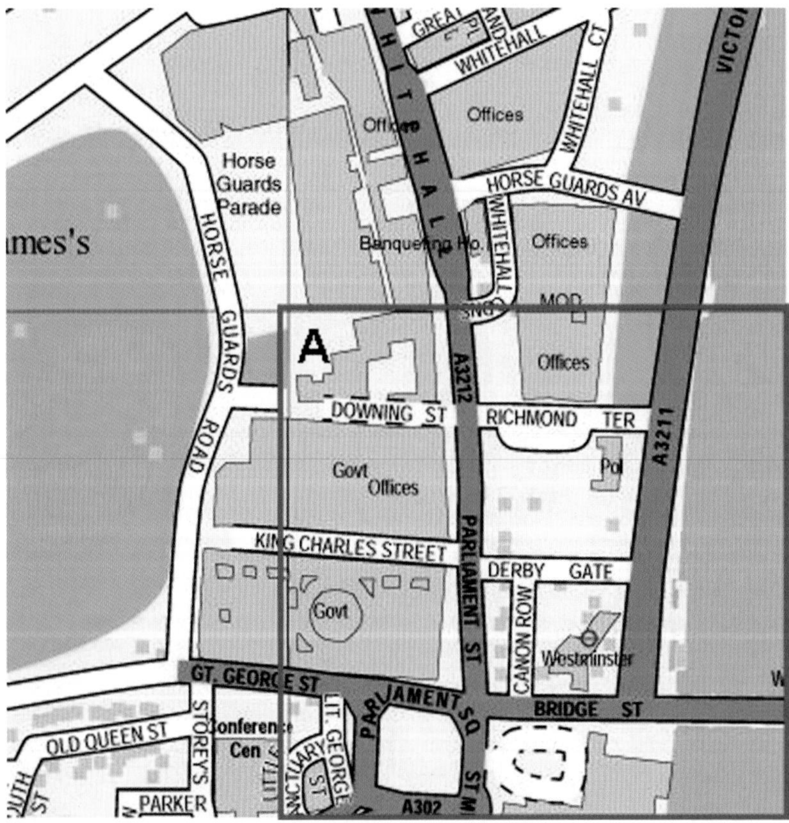

Figure 5.2: A street map of the area surrounding 10 Downing Street. © Crown Copyright and/or database right. All rights reserved. Licence number 100017849.

Some of the most famous topological maps ever created are for various underground railway networks (Figure 5.3). Distances between stations on this map are not correct. However, the stations and lines are all topologically correct. For example, the stations are all correctly located relative to one another. They are all correctly connected to one another by the train lines on the map.

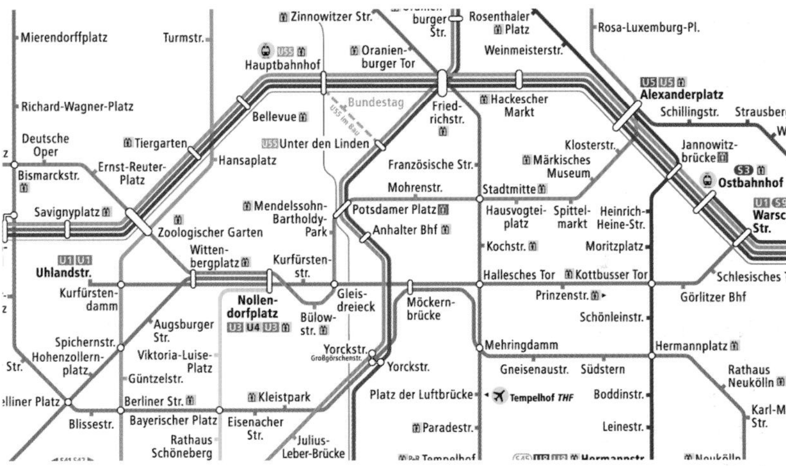

Figure 5.3: A section of the Berlin Underground map. This map is a type of cartogram, distorting the geometrical relationships between the stations but retaining their correct topological relationships.

Non-geographical data

GIS also has the facility to display non-geographical data when it is linked to a point, line or area. In GIS this is called **attribute data**. For example, a line displayed on a map could be a road, river or power line. Attribute data is used within GIS to describe the exact nature of the line. Each physical feature represented on a map can have more than one attribute associated with it. For example, the attributes for 10 Downing Street might include the number of rooms and exits, who is usually present in the building, the number of surveillance cameras and other security information. The linking of attribute data to features on a map is one of the most commonly used functions within GIS. The Census is an excellent example of attribute data. When census data is linked to counties (areas) it can become apparent which parts of the country are poorest or have the highest house prices, and a whole host of other economic and social patterns can be examined.

Questions

- What is the difference between geometry and topology in GIS?
- Describe and explain the function of attribute data in GIS.

Topic C: Digital storage and representation of geographical information

6

Introduction

Computers are frequently used to model the human and physical worlds. For example, even a trip to the cinema is likely to result in an encounter with computer-generated effects. However, no matter how sophisticated film makers tell us their digital effects have become, it is nearly always possible to tell the real world from a computer-generated environment. One of the difficulties of replicating the real world within a computer is the problem of capturing the infinite detail in the places and spaces that exist around us. Any information that is captured for use in GIS will always be a simplification of the real world. In computing, these simplified realities are called **models**. Given that all models are a simplification of reality, these models will have a series of limitations associated with them that will affect how they can be used.

It is necessary to use models in GIS because it is not possible to represent the infinitely complex world in a computer system with limited processing and data storage capabilities. When selecting a data model for use within a GIS, it is important to realise that each type of model will have a series of advantages and disadvantages associated with it.

How is the real world modelled?

When we attempt to model the earth there are three main stages:

- **Definition:** What features are we interested in mapping and how are they defined? This is an important question because the feature that is of greatest interest will receive the most resources in terms of data collection.
- **Classification:** How do the features being mapped relate to one another?
- **Representation:** How can the features being mapped be represented in a computer?

The decisions made during each of these stages associated with the building of a GIS model will affect how that model can be used. The information collector will make decisions at each of the three stages above. Each decision the collector makes will limit how the data can be used and how the information can be represented in the computer. It is necessary to explore these ideas further.

Definition and classification decisions in modelling

The first stage in the creation of a GIS model requires us to define the objects that we want to map. We might, for example, consider the need to map the location of a number of factories. Defining the nature of a factory in a GIS is not as simple as it sounds. For example, does the definition include all types of factories such as car manufacturing, iron and steel production, food packaging, and computer assembly in the same classification? Or will the way we define 'factory' enable us to see where these different types of manufacturing are located on a map (see Figure 6.1)? By thinking this way we have introduced the concept of classification – we have a class of features defined as 'factory', within which there are number of subclasses.

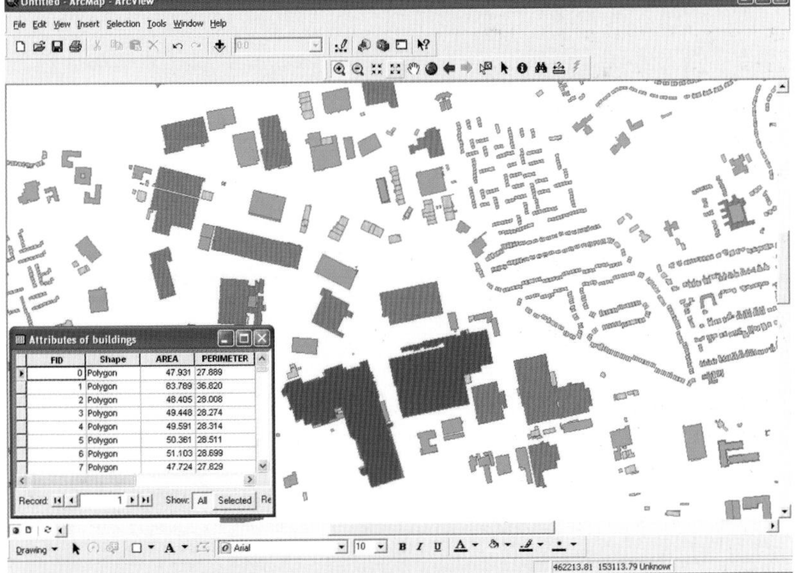

Figure 6.1: A vector map of an area of Basingstoke, England. The attributes attached to each of the buildings only include data that describes size, therefore we do not know how any of these buildings are used. This affects the range of ways that this map can be applied before extra information has to be collected. OS base mapping reproduced with permission.

Representing data within GIS

If we want to represent a factory as a model in a computer, a number of further choices have to be made. The first concerns the level of detail that we want to associate with the mapping of each factory. At small scales it may only be necessary to show the location of the factory as a single dot. However, at larger scales (e.g. Figure 6.1) a more detailed plan of the extent of the factory may be required. These types of decisions fundamentally affect how the information can be used.

Consider an example: you are responsible for planning the security of 10 Downing Street. Having a map that simply locates number 10 by a dot would not be very useful for managing the evacuation of the building in an emergency. It would be better to know how many floors and exits there are in the building. Given certain types of incidents, it would be good to have routes of escape mapped over the building plan and linked to other features such as roads, paths and gardens. Therefore, deciding how you are going to represent features on a map will largely determine the use of the data within GIS and how much it will cost to collect that data.

Figure 6.2: The two main types of data structures used within GIS. Raster data structures are made up of grids. Vector data structures are made up of points, lines and areas. Source: ASET (2005).

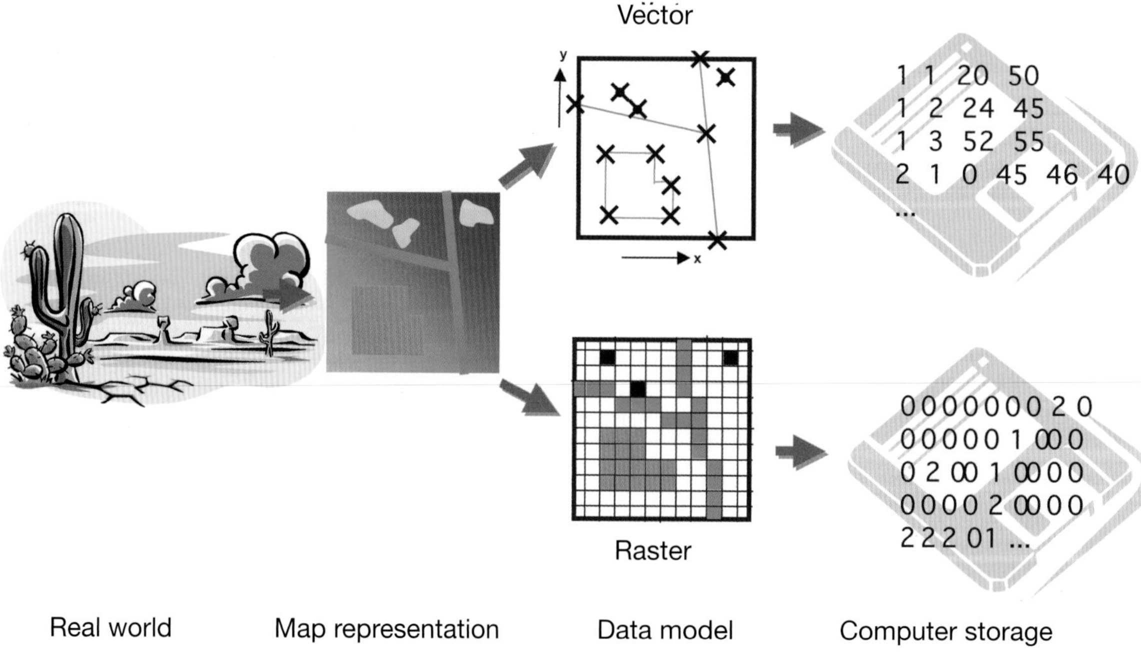

Finally, it is necessary to encode the information digitally within the GIS so that we have a computer record of the house and all the information we need about it. When data is encoded digitally, it is necessary to create a **data structure** so that the information is stored efficiently and can be easily retrieved. In GIS there are two commonly used data structures: **vector** approaches and **raster** approaches (Figure 6.2). These data structures are examined in the next two chapters.

Models vs structures

In GIS, 'model' is the word used to describe how information is displayed by the computer to represent the real world. The word 'structure' refers to how data is stored on the computer's hard drive or associated databases. Data structures not only contain the data which is to be displayed but also contain information to make the storage of data as efficient as possible. The volume of data stored within raster and vector data structures will depend upon cell size and the density of vertices respectively. This is because the vector structure requires a smaller volume of data to redraw the image every time that it is required. The nature and structure of the data model impact on how vector and raster data systems can be used.

Questions

- Why are models necessary in GIS and what are their limitations?
- What is data classification?
- What is the difference between a model and a data structure in GIS?

Vector data structures

Vector data models represent features on the ground by using three simple building blocks: **points**, **lines** and **areas** (see Figures 6.2 and 7.1). For the points, lines and areas to have meaning, it must also be possible to attach attribute data to these features.

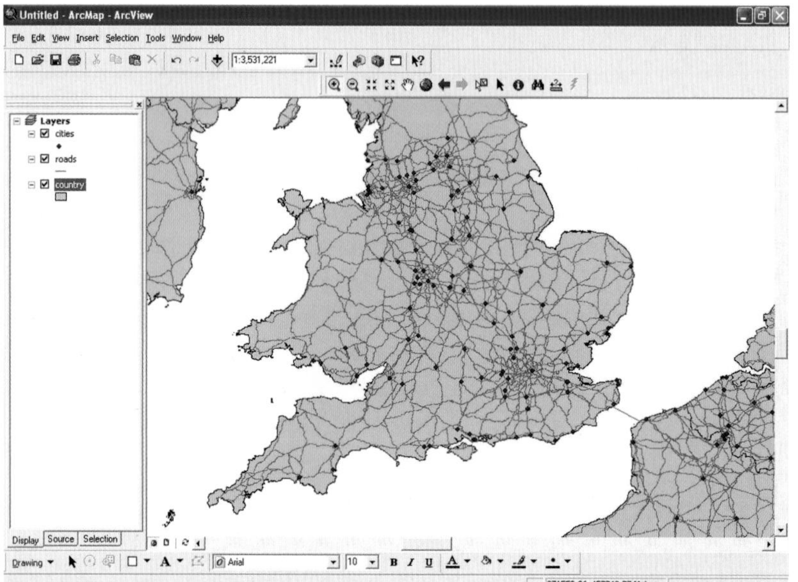

Figure 7.1: An example of a vector map and data model with the points representing cities, the lines representing roads and the areas representing countries. Created in ArcView using ESRI Data and Maps.

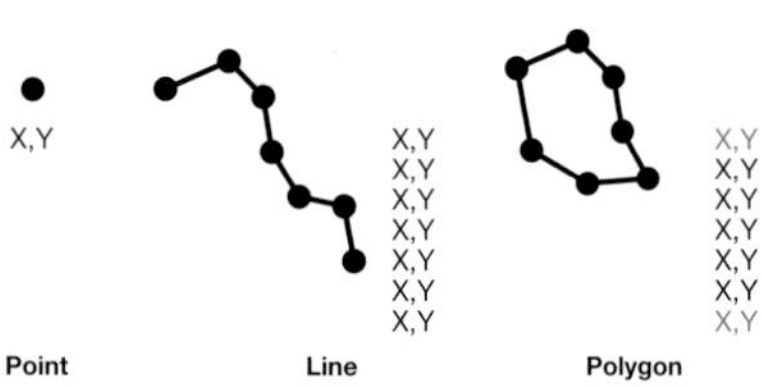

Figure 7.2: Vector data are located in space using a series of X and Y coordinates. Source: ASET (2005).

Using the vector data structure, a point is located by a single X and Y coordinate (Figure 7.2). Line features such as roads are two or more straight line segments joined together. These line segments are often referred to as **vertices**. The more vertices used to construct the line, the more accurately the feature will represent reality (Figure 7.4). The points where lines are joined together are called **nodes** (Figure 7.3). An area is made up of a series of connecting lines that closes. In GIS, closed areas are often referred to as **polygons** (Figure 7.2).

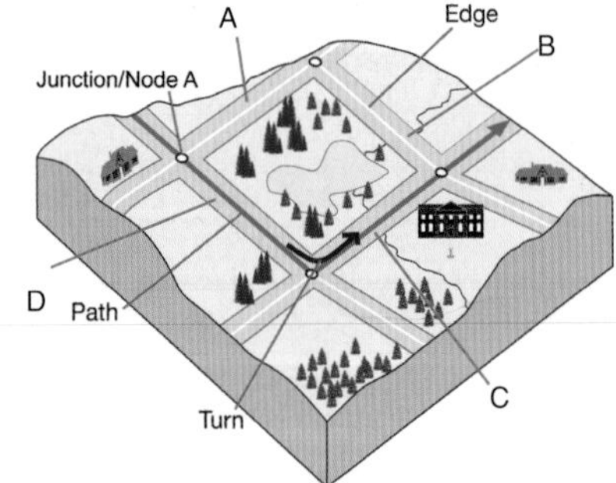

Figure 7.3: Vector data structures can contain excellent topological descriptions of the spatial relationships between related features. In this example, paths are represented by lines that connect at their endpoints (called junctions in real life but referred to as nodes in GIS). Adapted from ESRI (2004a).

Vector data also has topology. Consider Figure 7.3, which shows how a series of lines are linked together by junctions, also known as nodes. Because the data structure records how these lines are connected together, the spatial relationship between objects can be stored or investigated. For example, topology records how all the features fit together to form an image. Topology is like a set of rules that allow a jigsaw puzzle to be rapidly put together. For example, the database for Figure 7.3 will not only record that there are four lines named A, B, C and D, but that line A and D are connected together at Junction/ Node A.

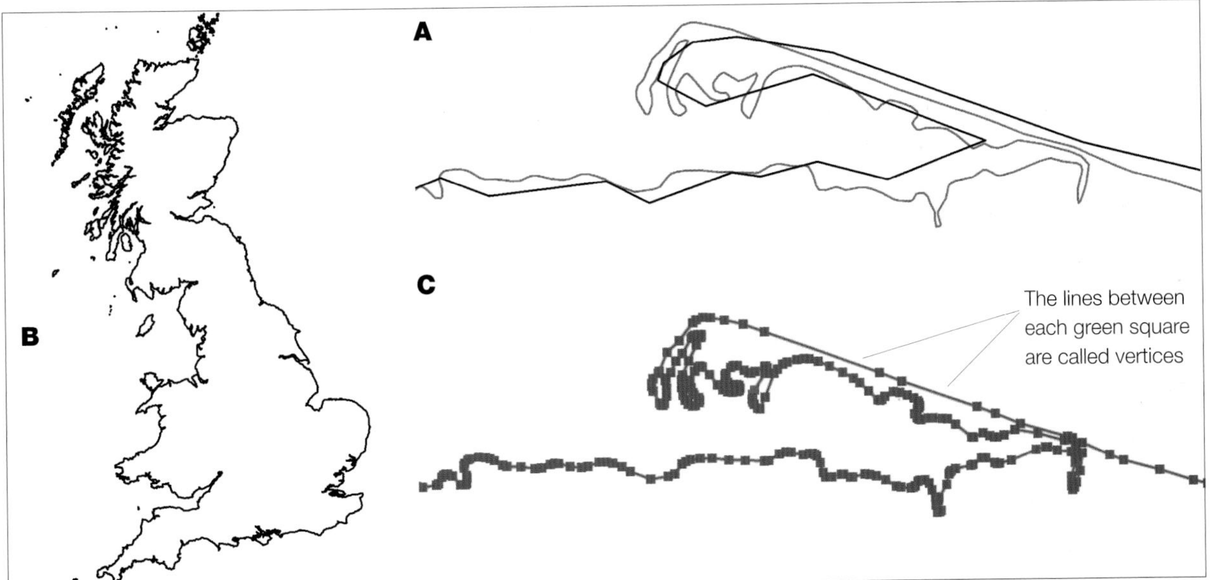

Figure 7.4: (**A**) shows an area of the UK coastline (red line) and its approximation by a vector line (black line). Notice now the vector line does not capture the complexity of the coast's variations. Such simplification of features is common in vector GIS, with the level of simplification often determined by the scale at which the data set is to be used. For example, the same black line shown in (**A**) has been zoomed out to show the entire coast of the UK in (**B**). When used at this scale the number of vertices used to capture the coast is probably appropriate. With the ability to zoom in and out of maps in GIS it is very important to think about what scale the data was intended to be used at. (**C**) shows a section of UK coast. With the increased complexity of the coastline, more vertices must be used to improve accuracy. Created in ArcView using ESRI Data and Maps.

The nature of vector data presents a number of advantages and disadvantages associated with this structure:

Major advantages

- The precision of the vector structure allows for a high level of cartographic accuracy in the representation of geographical data (see Figure 7.1).
- The data structure makes it relatively easy to describe the topological relationships that exist between features in a GIS database.
- The vector data structure can cope with the storage of a wide range of attribute information about the feature of interest.
- This type of data structure requires little duplication of data and therefore is very efficient when it comes to storing information.
- The vector data structure is good at analysing discrete data.

Major disadvantages

- The topology associated with vector data structures makes it difficult to carry out certain types of geographical analysis such as overlay.
- Vector data can give a false sense of accuracy. For example, vector data will often record coordinate information with a precision of five or six decimal places. This would give the appearance that measurements could be carried out accurately to one thousandth of a millimetre. However, the Ordnance Survey of Great Britain quotes an average accuracy of 0.4 metres for its

large-scale landline data sets. So at this point in time the data structure offers a capability greater than the best survey techniques currently available.

- The boundaries represented by vector data are sharp. This works well for mapping the built environment but is not very good for representing physical geography. For example, changes in soil and vegetation type across a landscape usually occur gradually and do not relate well to sharp boundaries (see Figure 7.5).

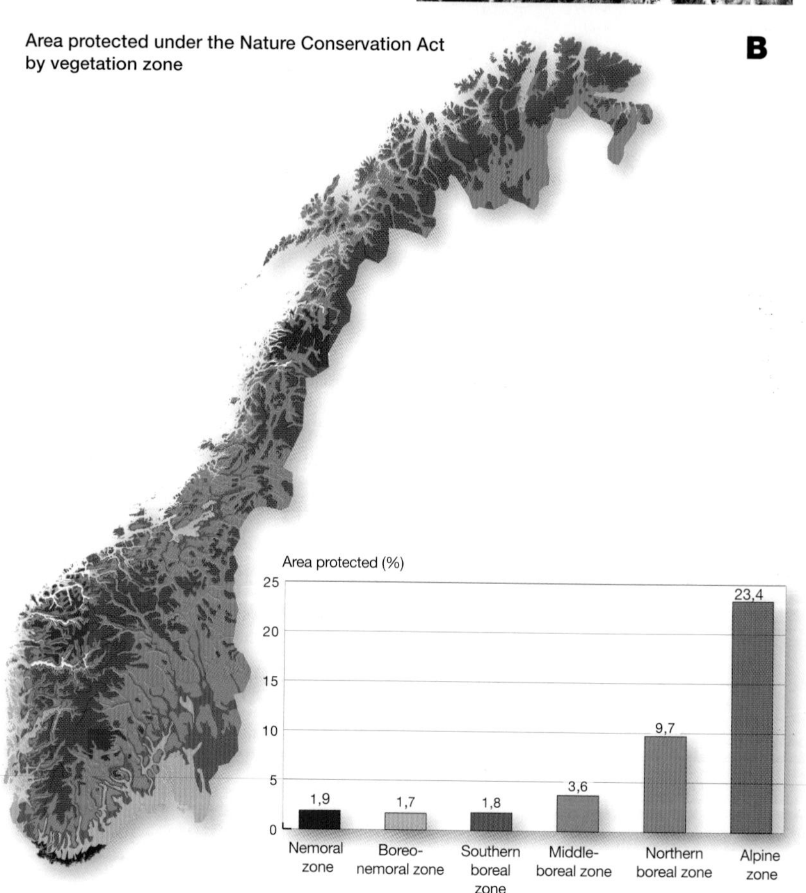

Figure 7.5: (**A**) Boundaries represented by vector lines and polygons will often not accurately reflect the gradual changes that occur in natural landscapes. For example, in this image of southwestern Norway vegetation patterns represented by the different shades of brown and green change gradually with altitude. Consider whether representing such patterns in a GIS with sharp, simple boundaries would affect how we think about such places. Would representing and simplifying the vegetation shown in this image with a vector map lose the awe and wonder of this place? Would we be able to make suitable management decisions about this environment if we only used vector based mapping? Source: *http://landsat.usgs.gov/images/gallery/108_L.jpg*. (**B**) A vegetation map of Norway with sharp polygon boundaries between vegetation types. Think about how this map simplifies reality and how such simplification affects the utility of the map and the user's perception of the places represented. Source: *www.environment.no*

Questions

- What are vector data models?
- Why is it important for vector data to have topology?

Raster data structures

In a raster model the world is represented as a surface that is divided into a regular grid of **cells** (see Figure 8.1). Each cell is a square that represents a specific area.

In a raster all cells must be the same size. Cells are organised in rows and columns. Each cell has a value to describe the zone, class, category or group the cell belongs to.

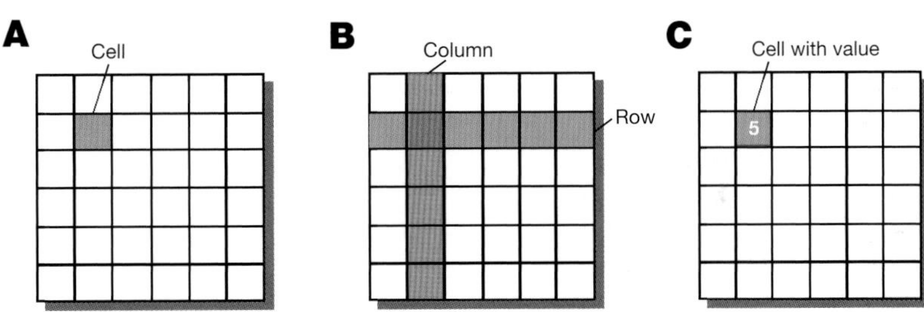

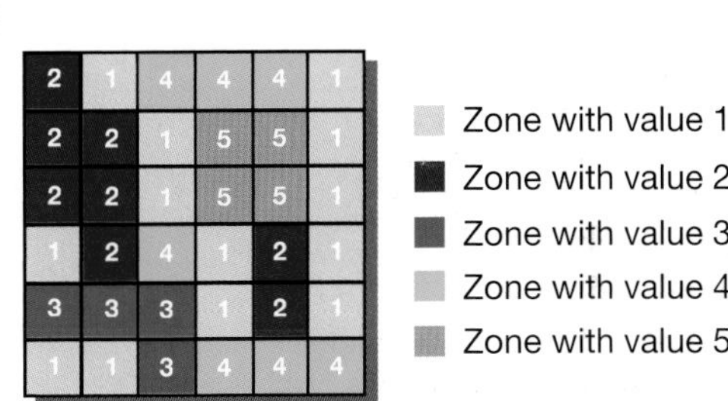

Figure 8.1: Raster data model showing (**A**) the cell, (**B**) the rows and columns that make up the raster, (**C**) the value attached to the cell and (**D**) the values that combine to create a map showing different zones. Adapted from ESRI (2004b).

For example, part D of Figure 8.1 contains five zones that range in value from 1 to 5. A value of 5 could represent a land cover of water, while a value of 3 could show an area of forest. When cells of the same value are located next to one another they are called **zones**, **classes**, **groups** or **areas**. These terms are often used interchangeably. Whereas a single raster typically represents a single theme such as land use, multiple raster data sets should be produced to depict a whole environment. Therefore, a typical raster database may contain many layers, each consisting of thousands of grid cells.

Raster data is generally divided into two categories:
- Thematic data
- Image data

The values in all **thematic** raster data represent some measured quantity of a feature such as elevation or population density (e.g.

Figure 8.1, part D). The values of cells in an **image** represent reflected light or energy as measured by satellites and other remote sensing technologies (see Figure 8.2).

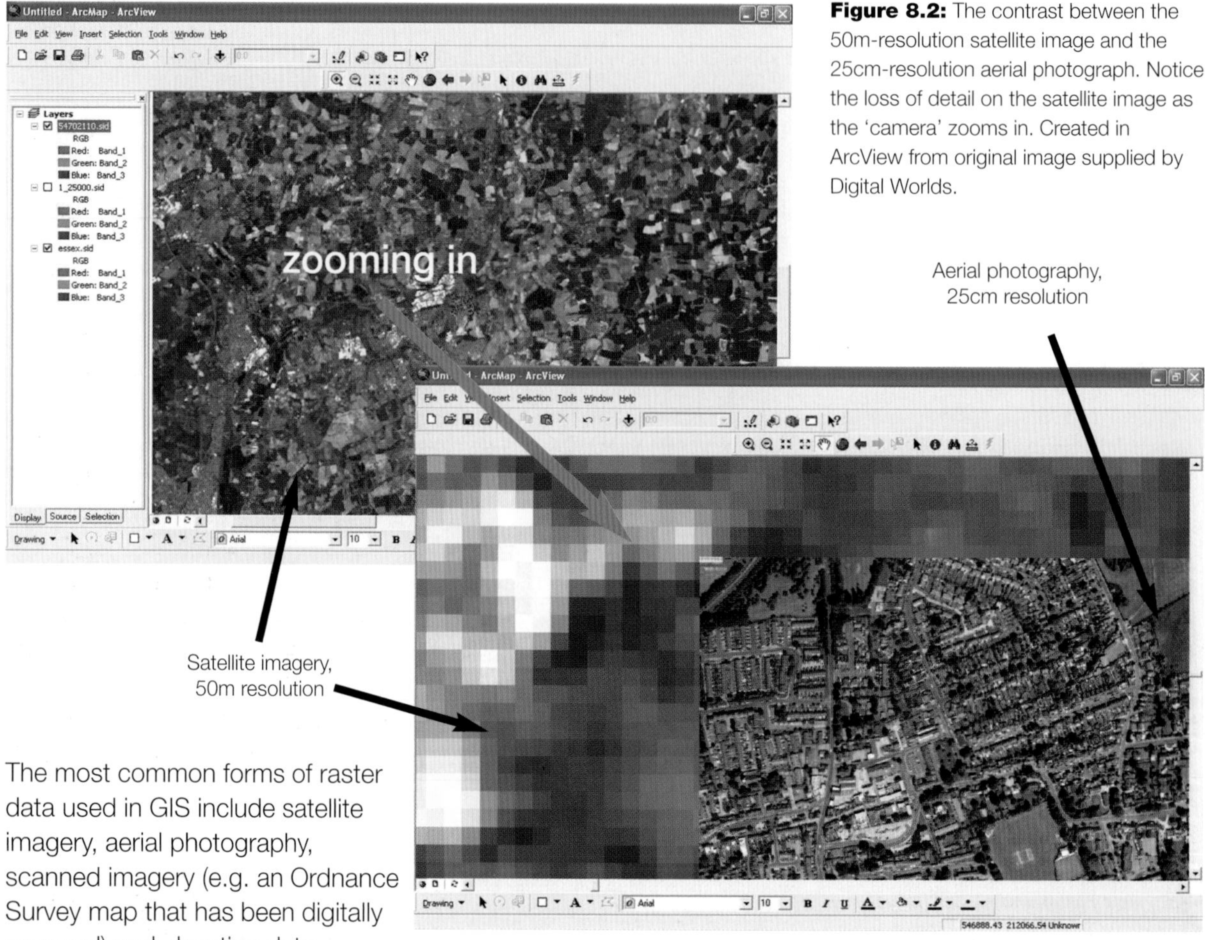

Figure 8.2: The contrast between the 50m-resolution satellite image and the 25cm-resolution aerial photograph. Notice the loss of detail on the satellite image as the 'camera' zooms in. Created in ArcView from original image supplied by Digital Worlds.

The most common forms of raster data used in GIS include satellite imagery, aerial photography, scanned imagery (e.g. an Ordnance Survey map that has been digitally scanned) and elevation data.

There are two important characteristics associated with raster layers: spatial resolution and raster orientation.

Spatial resolution

The cells that make up a raster can be of any size. Each cell could represent a square kilometre on the ground or an area as small as a square centimetre. As the size of the raster cell gets smaller, the resolution of the map or image is said to increase. The higher the **resolution** of the image, the more detail it can reveal about the area being investigated. For example, Figure 8.2 shows a satellite image of an area in Essex surrounding Harlow Town. The satellite image has a resolution of 50m. That is to say, that every cell that makes up the image covers an area of $50m^2$ on the ground. As such the image can only reveal the detail of the landscape when the features being investigated have an area much larger than $50m^2$. For example, the image shows well the variation in the size of fields surrounding Harlow. However, as we zoom in, the image starts to appear blocky and no detail about the landscape is revealed. In this way satellite imagery at this resolution would be of limited use for investigating variation in urban structure across a town. In order to investigate urban structure it would be much better to use a higher-resolution source such as aerial photography. In Figure 8.2 an aerial photograph of an area in Harlow is shown with a resolution of 25cm. This means that each cell on the image represents 625 square cm on the ground. With this sort of resolution it is easy to pick out features such as houses and cars.

It is important to consider the concepts of scale and raster resolution together when collecting data for GIS analysis. If the correct raster resolution is not selected, then much of the necessary detail about a landscape will be lost (Figure 8.3). For example, within a single cell of a low-resolution raster there may be great variation in the variable of interest. This will mean that the values may have to be averaged. In the case of classifications there may be many types of vegetation that exist in the cell but only one can be selected, thereby decreasing data resolution. Thus it is vitally important to select the right resolution of raster when considering the data requirement needs of any GIS-based investigation.

Figure 8.3: The effects of a coarse/low-resolution raster on the representation of three different geographical landscapes.
A) The shape of the tree canopy appears unrealistic at such a low resolution.
B) The relief of the land as represented by the raster will not capture the full variation of elevation within the landscape. For example, the height for each cell will have to be averaged, masking possible variations in height across the landscape.
C) The low resolution of this transformation does not convey the true pattern of vegetation change across the landscape. Adapted from ESRI (2004b).

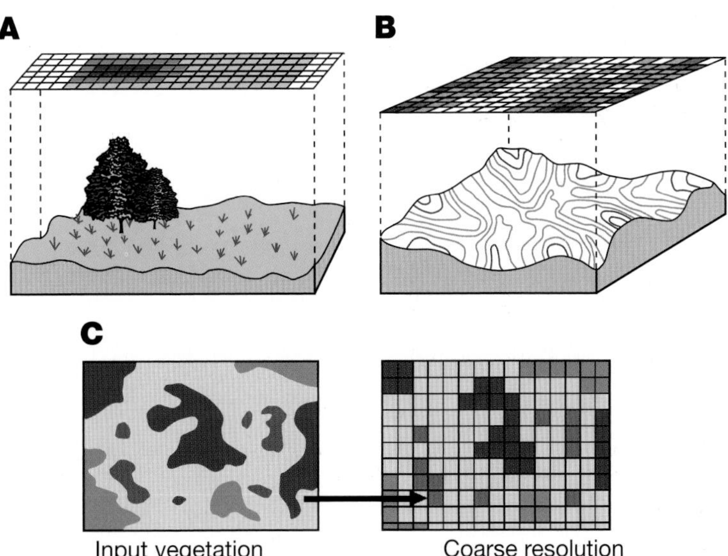

Raster orientation

Before raster data can be combined with other sources of information, it must first be correctly aligned in relation to grid north and the map projection that is being used. This is essential as most raster data is collected by satellites or aerial photography. The orientation of data collection is not standardised, neither are the paths taken by satellites and aeroplanes, so the orientation will have to be determined for every raster loaded into GIS. To determine the correct geographical location for a raster data set, usually one or more corners or points will be associated with a set of grid-referenced coordinates (see Figure 8.4). Once these coordinates are known, the data can be accurately positioned. This process is called **georectification**.

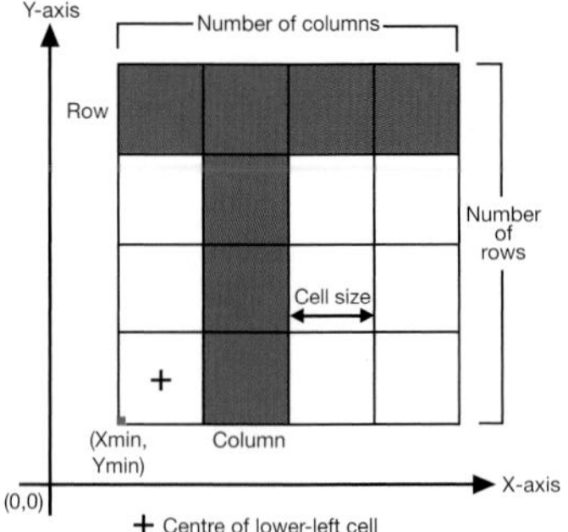

Figure 8.4: A set of coordinates is required to align the raster correctly with other sources of geographical information contained within the GIS. In this case the coordinates of the lower-left cell are known and are used to locate the raster correctly within geographical space. Adapted from ESRI (2004b).

The nature of raster data presents a number of advantages and disadvantages:

Major advantages

- Raster data structures are simple in their nature, allowing great flexibility in the types of analysis that can be carried out.
- Many kinds of spatial analysis may be used. For example, overlay operations can be carried out efficiently with this type of data. In addition, cells with the same values can be easily counted to carry out statistical operations such as averages, standard deviations and other more sophisticated mathematical operations.
- Operations requiring the recoding of cells such as reclassification or colour shading are very rapid.
- The technology is cheap.
- Mathematical modelling is simple because all cells have a simple regular shape.
- Many forms of data are available.

Major disadvantages

- Large data volumes resulting from the need to increase the resolution of data sets in order to capture sufficient detail about landscapes.
- Using large grid cells to reduce data volumes reduces spatial resolution. Much of the required information may subsequently be lost on account of the generalisations that result from the capture of data.
- Low-resolution raster data sets can appear awkward and unattractive due to their blocky nature.
- Transferring raster data sets to projected coordinates can be difficult, resulting in loss of information and distortion of cell shapes.

Questions

- What is raster data and what are its common forms in GIS?
- Define the terms spatial resolution and raster orientation.

Topic D: Geographic coordinates, map projections and GIS

Creating a simplified model of the shape of the earth

Introduction

Although often represented by a simple circle, the earth is an extremely complex shape. Our world is battered and deformed by the forces of gravity associated with the moon and sun. Additionally, tectonic processes reorganise the relative positions of continental and oceanic crust leading to the formation of a curved, irregular-shaped surface. As the shape of the earth is constantly under the influence of these processes, it is impossible to capture accurately the shape of the earth on a flat piece of paper. So every map ever produced is compromised in the way shapes, angles and distances between features are represented. All mapping, therefore, is a process of simplifying the real world, which means that all maps contain some kind of error, both in space and in how that space is represented over time.

A major discipline called **geodesy** has been developed to try and reduce the limitations associated with map production. All mapping and navigation is based on geodesy, which has two major aims:
- To determine the shape and size of the earth.
- To determine the location of the features on the earth's land surface.

To carry out accurate mapping a number of questions have to be answered:
- How do we simplify the shape of the earth to map and find locations?
- What parts of the earth do we choose to represent accurately and what features do we ignore?
- What is the best simplified shape of the earth to use when creating a model of the earth?
- What coordinate systems are going to be used to locate features accurately on the earth?
- How will features that exist on a curved irregular surface be represented on a flat piece of paper or within a GIS?

This chapter and the two that follow consider the issues involved in trying to find answers to these questions – a process that is fundamental to the successful use of GIS. In particular, understanding how GIS copes with these issues will affect how the GIS user deals with:

- data selection and data sharing
- the management of data
- the assessment of error associated with GIS analysis
- assessing the confidence of recommendations and decisions made on the basis of GIS analysis.

Spheroids and spheres

The shape and size of the earth is often represented or modelled by a sphere or spheroid (Figure 9.1). A sphere is based on a circle, while a spheroid (Figure 9.2) is based on an ellipse. Although it is a bit confusing, the terms spheroid and ellipsoid are frequently used to mean exactly the same thing. The shape of the earth is best represented by a spheroid because it reflects more accurately the bulging that occurs along the equator.

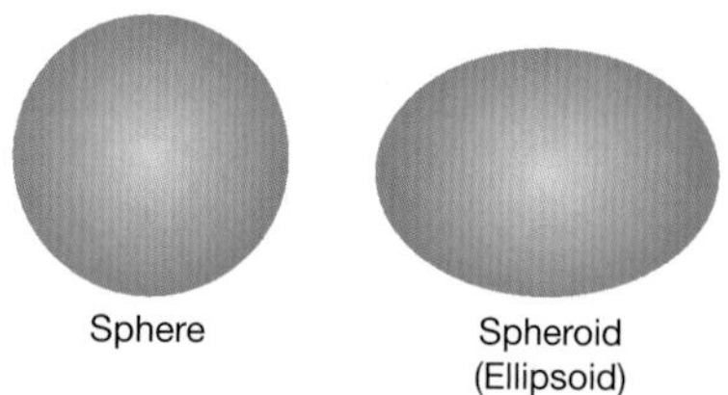

Figure 9.1: The sphere and spheroid are surfaces commonly associated with geographic coordinate systems. Adapted from ESRI (2004c).

The earth is sometimes treated as a sphere to make the mathematical calculations used in map production easier. It is often assumed that the earth is a sphere for small-scale maps because at small scales the difference between a sphere and a spheroid has little influence on map accuracy. However, for larger-scale maps (scales of 1:1,000,000 or larger), a spheroid is necessary to represent the shape of the earth in order to maintain accuracy. The final choice of sphere or spheroid will largely depend on the map's purpose.

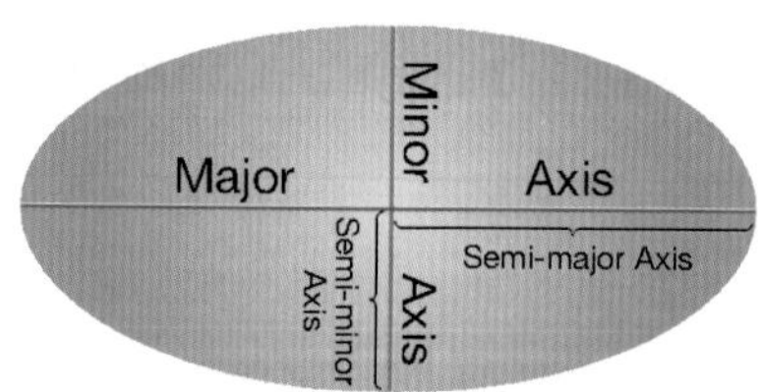

Figure 9.2: The major and minor axes of an ellipse. Adapted from ESRI (2004c).

Satellite imagery is now being used by scientists to show that the earth is neither a perfect sphere nor a perfect spheroid. For example, data collected shows that the South Pole is closer to the equator than the North Pole. Due to these advances in understanding, satellite-determined spheroids are now replacing the older ground-measured spheroids as they are much more accurate. The earth has been surveyed many times and it has been found that different spheroids are needed to fit distinct areas and countries. A spheroid that best fits one region is not necessarily the best one for another region. As a result, GIS uses many different spheroids and you need to be aware of which spheroid you are dealing with in order to accurately determine the location of objects and understand the limitations of the data sets being used.

The geoid

Maps often contain information about height and therefore this type of data has to be collected in map production. For example, height data is commonly shown on a map by contour lines. Scientists use an imaginary surface of 'zero height' to make measurements of altitude because there is no 'real' surface on the earth that is constant. For example, people often think that sea level is a constant level from which height can be measured. However, this is not the case as sea level changes with the tidal cycle and atmospheric pressure.

The imagery surface that scientists make their height measurements from is a level surface. This surface is defined as everywhere at right angles to the direction of gravity. As it is necessary to identify heights of places all over the world, the reference surface must be a closed shape, a bit like a spheroid. As the direction of gravity varies greatly all over the earth this means that a level reference surface is not a simple figure like the spheroid, but is bumpy and complex. This irregular three-dimensional shape is called the geoid (Figure 9.3).

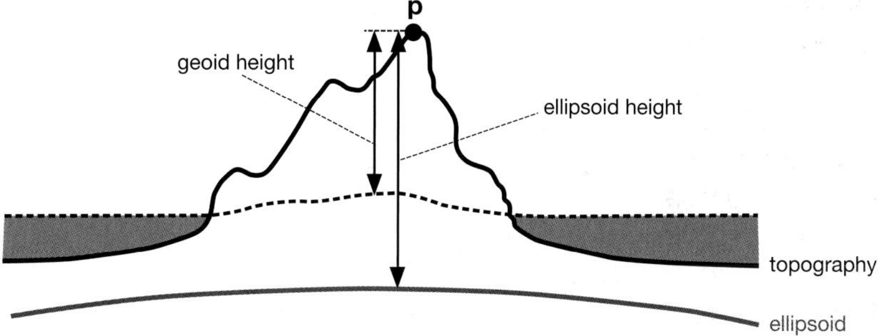

Figure 9.3: A simple representation of the relationship that exists between the geoid and ellipsoid surfaces in determining height. From *A Guide to Co-ordinate Systems in Great Britain*, Ordnance Survey, 2002.

In contrast to spheroids, of which there are many that fit different parts of the earth, there is only one global geoid. The global geoid is a level surface which is closest to the average surface of the world's oceans.

Datums

In GIS a datum is very important as it defines the position of a chosen spheroid relative to the centre of the earth (Figure 9.4). A datum is used to define the origin and orientation of latitude and longitude lines. If the datum in a GIS is not known accurate measures of location cannot be given.

The earth's centre of mass is often used to define the origin of a datum. The most widely used global datum is WGS 1984. It serves as the framework for locational measurement worldwide. Local datums

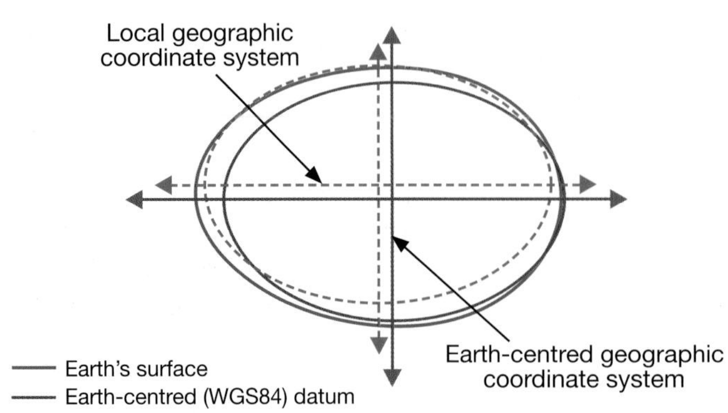

Figure 9.4: Datums are used to locate the position of spheroids relative to the centre of the earth. Adapted from ESRI (2004c).

and local spheroids are often used together to reduce the distortions associated with mapping the earth's curved surface on a flat piece of paper. Local datums are not suitable for use outside the area for which they were designed.

The spheroid, geoid and datum together form our simplified model of the earth on top of which we can lay our other geographic and projected coordinate systems to define location.

Questions

- Why do all maps contain errors?
- What is the difference between a sphere and a spheroid?
- Define the terms geoid and datum.
- What is a datum used for?

10 Geographic coordinate systems

Geographic coordinates are used to define locations on the earth. One of the most commonly used coordinate systems is latitude and longitude (Figure 10.1). Angles measured in degrees from the centre of the earth to a point on the earth's surface are used to calculate longitude and latitude values.

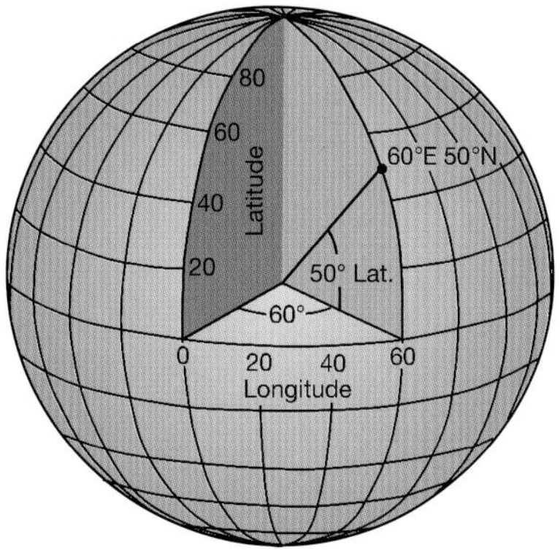

Figure 10.1: The world as a globe showing longitude and latitude values. Adapted from ESRI (2004c).

Using the spheroid, horizontal lines are lines of equal latitude (parallels). Vertical lines are lines of equal longitude (meridians). The gridded network these lines form on the globe is called a graticule. The lines of zero longitude and latitude are called the prime meridian and the equator. For most geographic coordinate systems, the prime meridian passes through Greenwich, England (Figure 10.2). For navigation the globe is divided into four hemispheres. Above and below the equator are north and south, and left and right of the prime meridian are west and east. Latitude and longitude are measured in decimal degrees or degrees, minutes and seconds. Latitude is measured relative to the equator and longitude is measured relative to the prime meridian (Figure 10.3).

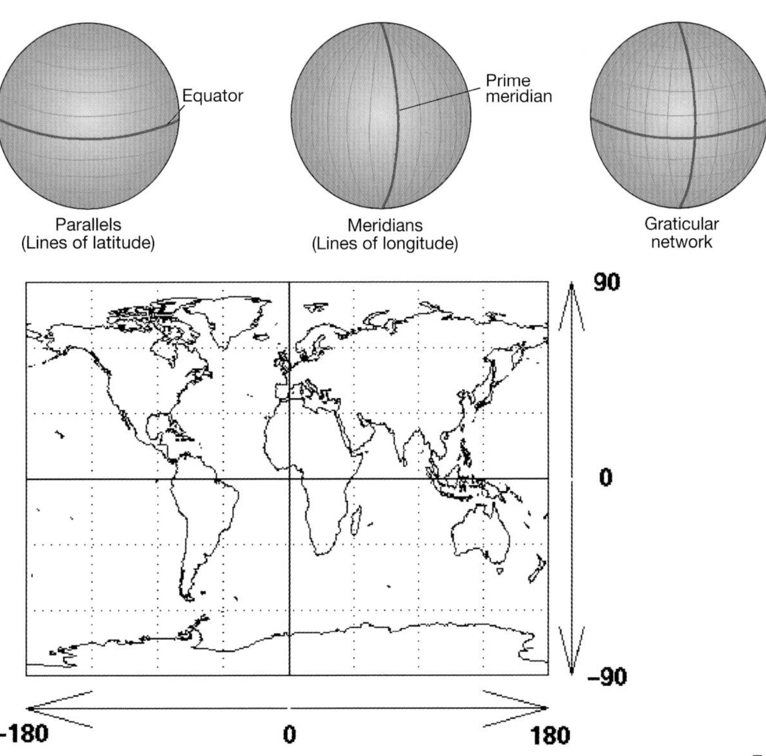

Figure 10.2: The parallels and meridians that form a graticule. Adapted from ESRI (2004c).

Figure 10.3: Latitude is measured from the equator, with positive values going north and negative values going south. Longitude is measured from the prime meridian with positive values going east and negative values going west. Source: *http://jwocky.gsfc.nasa.gov/teacher/latlonarchive.html.*

It is important to realise that latitude and longitude are not uniform units of measurement. Only along the equator does one degree of longitude approximate the distance represented by one degree of latitude. This results from the equator being the only parallel as long as a meridian. Meridians are sometimes known as 'great circles' as they all have the same radius as the spherical earth. The equator is the only parallel that is a great circle. As a result, parallels north and south of the equator get gradually shorter until they become a single point at the poles. As you move towards the poles the distance represented by one degree of latitude decreases (Figure 10.4).

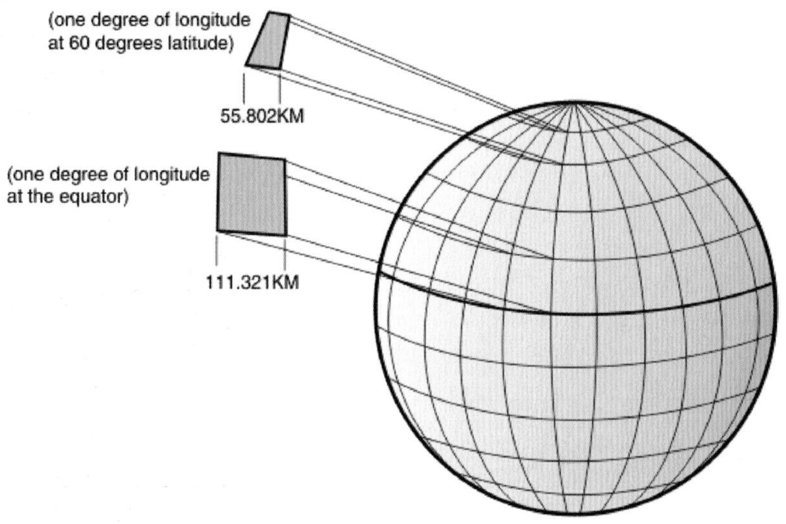

Figure 10.4: Different values of distance between locations on the graticule. At the equator, one degree of longitude is approximately 111.321 kilometres, while at 60 degrees of latitude, one degree of longitude is only 55.802 km. Source: *http://publib.boulder.ibm.com.*

Limitations of coordinate systems

Where am I really standing?

With the three elements of latitude, longitude and ellipsoid height, it is possible to determine a position. However, it is worth remembering that, when that position is given, the point is being defined in relation to a model of the earth (e.g. the selected spheroid) and not the real earth. In addition there is more than one model in use by a whole host of different organisations and governments. Figure 10.5, for example, shows three different locations for the same point of longitude and latitude.

Each of the points in Figure 10.5 uses a different datum (OSGB36, WGS84 and ED50) but they all have the same longitude and latitude values. All three datums are widely used in the UK and none of them is

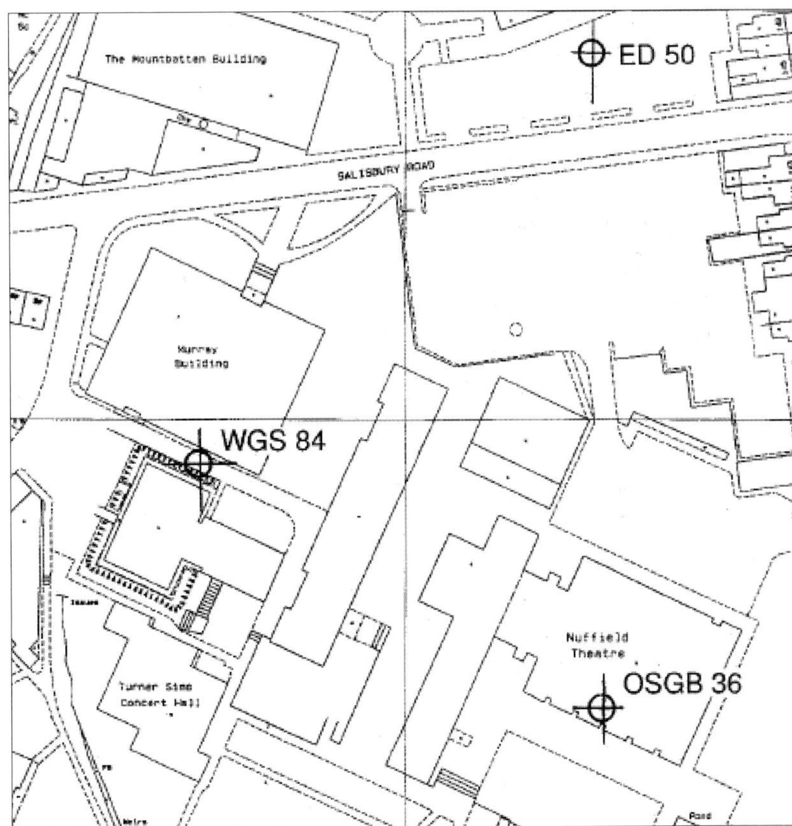

Figure 10.5: Three points with the same latitude and longitude using three different datums. The map extract is 200m square. From *A Guide to Co-ordinate Systems in Great Britain*, Ordnance Survey, 2002.

wrong. So if you are asked to find a location within the UK, where exactly you end up will be determined by what datum you are using.

The result is that different datums in common use today can disagree on the coordinates of a point by more than 200m. For any application where an error of this size would be significant, it's important to know which datum is being used and exactly how it is defined. For example, imagine that you are a member of a military group like the SAS, and you are asked to identify the coordinates of a terrorist location that is hiding weapons. The weapons are hidden in a heavily populated area. The result of your report will be that a cruise missile attack will be launched to destroy the terrorist target. However, if the coordinates are not calculated using the same coordinate system as that held by the missile, there will be little chance of hitting the military target and many civilians may be injured or killed. These types of operational issues had to be dealt with frequently during both Iraq wars and during operations in Afghanistan. In particular, where there are multinational forces operating in the same area, each group must standardise their respective datums and spheroids to minimise the effects of so-called collateral damage.

Time changes everything!
Question: If you could accurately locate the position of your house today, would it be in the same location tomorrow?

Answer: Probably not!

Explanation: The earth is in continuous motion, which deforms the surface structures and features of our world, changing the location of objects within the landscape. For example, the tidal influences of the sun and moon can cause a point on the ground to move up and down by a metre each day relative to the centre of the earth. Tectonic processes can cause continents to move apart or together by as much as 10cm a year – over a period of 50 years this can cause the relative position of objects to change by as much as 5m. The country of Britain sinks a few centimetres when the tide comes in due to the weight of water on the continental shelf. Even the weather can deform the shape of the land. High pressure systems can cause inland areas to sink by about 5mm. In Scotland the land has been rising by about 2mm per year due the release of pressure caused by the melting of glaciers since the last ice age. All these effects mean that data has to be updated regularly over time to maintain the accuracy of coordinate systems.

Questions

- What is a coordinate system?
- Why is it important to know what coordinate system is being used by a GIS?
- Why is updating information regularly important for maintaining the accuracy of maps?
- What are the limitations of coordinate systems?

Projected coordinate systems

Projections transform a three-dimensional spheroid onto a two-dimensional surface for viewing on a flat surface like a piece of paper or computer screen. Projected coordinate systems have an advantage over spheroids because they can have constant lengths, angles and areas across a flat map. It is these properties of projected maps that allow them to be used as tools in business, government planning and environmental management.

Y

$X<0$ $Y>0$ | $X>0$ $Y>0$

(0,0) X

$X<0$ $Y<0$ | $X>0$ $Y<0$

Figure 11.1: The signs of x,y coordinates in a projected coordinate system. Adapted from ESRI (2004c).

In a projected map x and y coordinates are used to locate position. Where x and y = 0 this is called the origin. The central horizontal and vertical lines on a gridded map are known respectively as the x axis and the y axis. Units of measurement are consistent and equally spaced across the full range of x and y. Horizontal lines below the origin and vertical lines to the left of the origin have negative values; those above or to the right have positive values. In Figure 11.1 the four quadrants represent the four possible combinations of positive and negative x and y coordinates.

The process of transforming a three-dimensional spheroid onto a flat map sheet is called map projection. One way to visualise this process

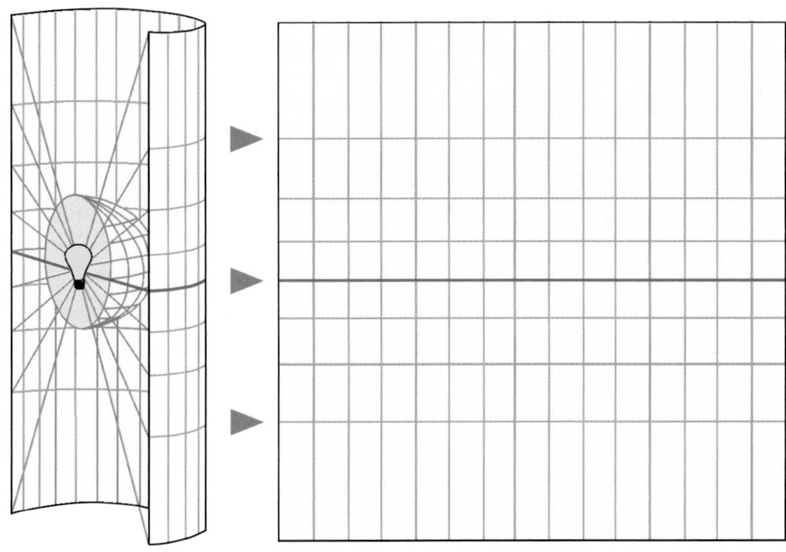

Figure 11.2: The graticule of a geographic coordinate system is projected onto a cylindrical projection surface. The graticule consists of the girded lines used to divide up the globe and map sheet. Notice that, as you move away north and south from the light, the graticule becomes more distorted. This projection method best preserves features closest to the central position of the light bulb. Adapted from ESRI (2004c).

is to imagine shining a light through the earth onto a surface, called the projection surface (see Figure 11.2). A light at the centre of the earth will cast a shadow of itself onto the piece of paper. You can now unwrap the paper and lay it flat. However, during this process the earth that is being projected will be distorted on the projection surface. As a result, representing the earth in two dimensions causes distortion in the shape, area, distance or direction of the features being mapped.

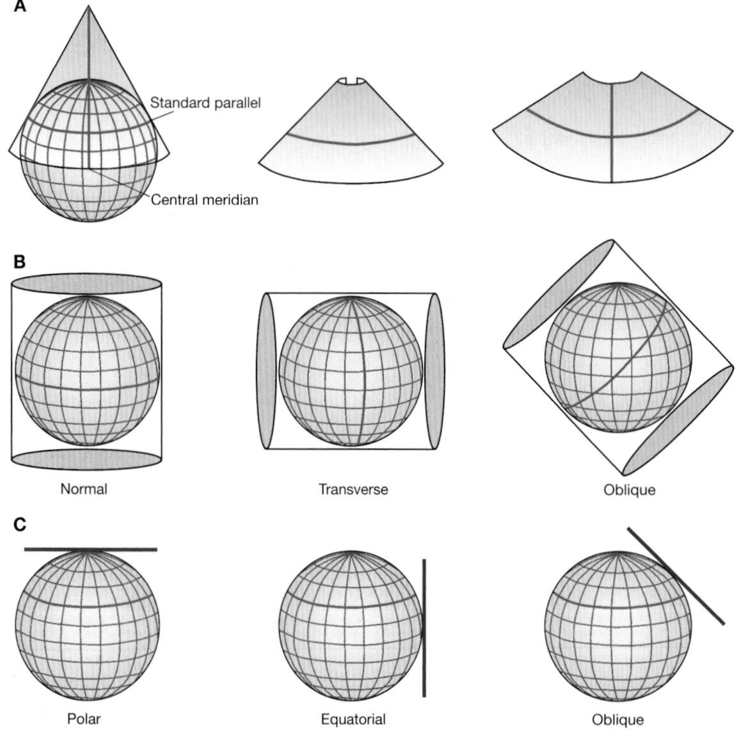

Figure 11.3: Different types of projections:
A) conical projections;
B) cylindrical projections;
C) planar or azimuthal projections.
Adapted from ESRI (2004c).

Figure 11.3 shows that there are three main ways to project locations from a spheroid onto a flat surface or display screen. Each type of projection has different properties of the original spheroid that it preserves best. In addition different projections are best suited to mapping different parts of the world. Cylindrical projections, for example, are best for lands between the tropics, while conical projections are best for temperate latitudes and planar projections are best for polar areas.

As Figure 11.3 shows, within each projection family there are many subtypes, each with its own characteristics, advantages and disadvantages. The different projections attempt to preserve area, shape, distance or direction between places on the earth. However, none of the projections can preserve all four variables. Most projections can only preserve one or two of the above variables.

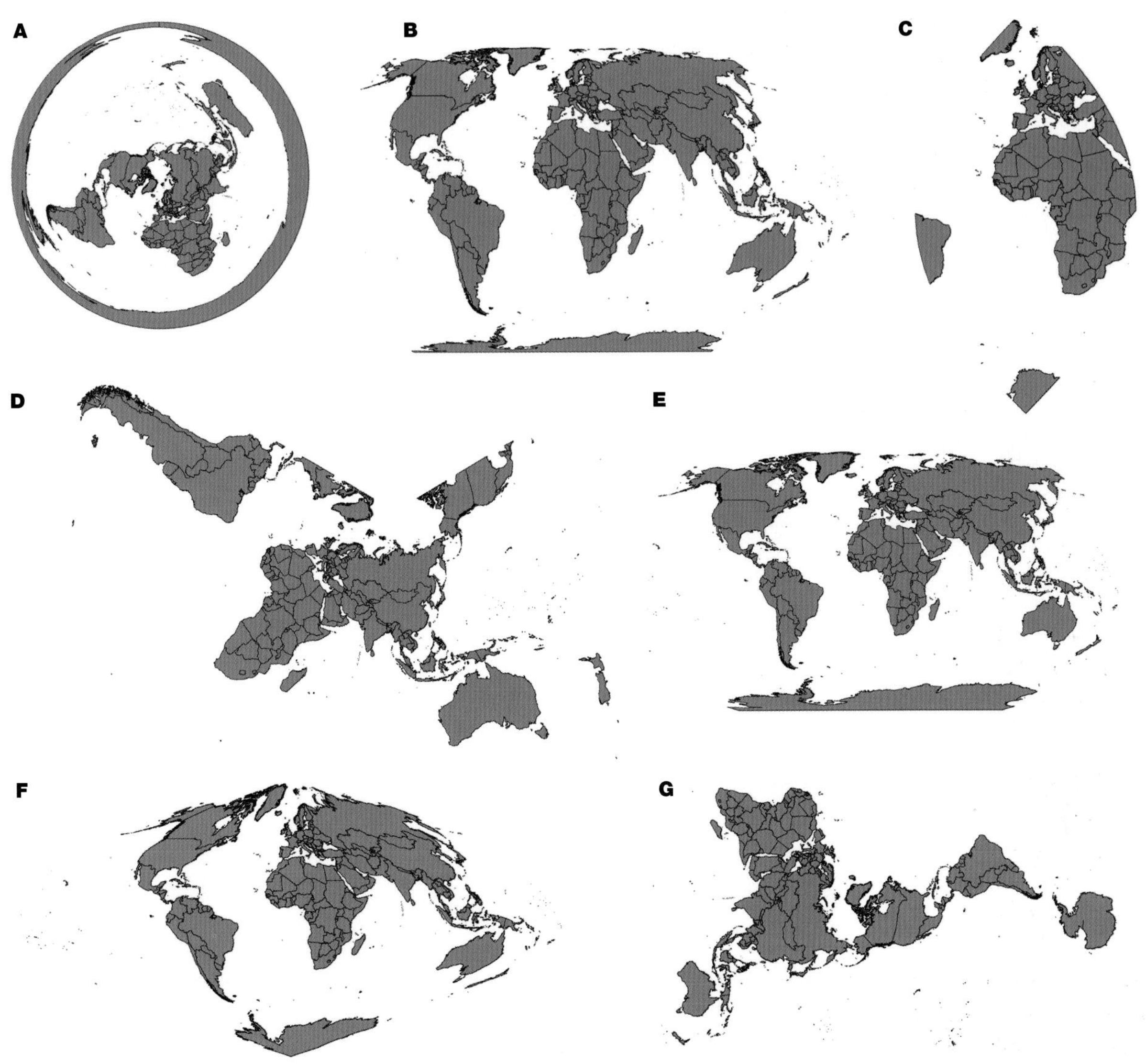

Figure 11.4: Examples of different types of projection system and their resulting maps: **A**) Azimuthal Equidistant; **B**) Eckert VI; **C**) Great Britain National Grid; **D**) Lambert Conformal Conic; **E**) Robinson; **F**) Sinusoidal; **G**) Fuller. Created in ArcView using ESRI Data and Maps.

The examples of maps produced by some different types of projections are shown in Figure 11.4. Table 11.1 (overleaf) gives an explanation of the key features associated with each type of projection. In working with GIS the map projection should be selected carefully in relation to the task at hand. If the object of a GIS session is to measure distance, then a map projection system that minimises the distortion of this variable should be selected. In GIS it is common to select projections that minimise the distortion of area, as area calculations are frequently carried out using GIS. When choosing a projection it should also be remembered that the nature of distance, shape, area and direction will not have the same characteristics all over the map. For

Projection name	Projection method	Effects on shape	Effects on area	Effects on direction	Effects on distan
A) Azimuthal Equidistant	Planar.	Except at the centre, all shapes are distorted. Distortion increases from the centre.	Distortion increases outward from the centre point.	Directions are true from the centre outward.	Distances are accu from the centre po outward. For polar the distances along meridians are accu but there is a patte increasing distortio the circles of latitu outward from the c
B) Eckert VI	Equal area.	Along the equator, shapes are stretched north–south 29% relative to the east–west dimension. This stretching decreases to zero at 49º16' N and S at the central meridian. Nearer the poles, features are compressed in the north–south direction.	Area is preserved.	Local angles are correct at the intersection of 49º16' N and S with the central meridian. Direction is distorted elsewhere.	Scale is distorted n south 29% along th equator relative to east–west dimensi distortion decrease zero at 49º16' N a the central meridia is correct only alon parallels. Nearer th features are compr in the north–south direction.
C) Great Britain National Grid	Cylindrical, transverse projection.	Conformal; therefore, small shapes are maintained accurately.	Distortion increases beyond Great Britain as the distance from the central meridian increases.	Local directions are accurately maintained.	Scale is reasonably accurate 180km ea west of the central meridian.
D) Lambert Conformal Conic	Conic projection.	All graticular intersections are 90º. Small shapes are maintained.	Minimal distortion near the standard parallels.	Local angles are accurate throughout because of conformality.	Correct scale along standard parallels.
E) Robinson	A type of cylindrical projection.	Shape distortion is very low within 45º of the origin and along the equator.	Distortion is very low within 45º of the origin and along the equator.	Generally distorted.	Generally, scale is true along latitudes and S. Scale is con along any given lat and for the latitude opposite side.
F) Sinusoidal	A type of cylindrical projection.	No distortion along the central meridian and the equator.	Areas are represented accurately.	Local angles are correct along the central meridian and the equator, but are distorted elsewhere.	The scale along all parallels and the ce meridian of the pro is accurate.
G) Fuller	This projection converts the globe into a 20-sided figure called an icosa-hedron. Each side is a geodesic triangle that is then flattened into a two-dimensional triangle. The facets are unfolded in a specific manner to keep the land masses unbroken.	Distortion increases as the distance from the facet edges increases. Because the Fuller projection is made up of 20 facets that are projected individually, overall shape distortion is low.	Distortion increases as the distance from the facet edges increases.	General directions are distorted, depending on the orientation of a facet. Angles within a facet are slightly distorted due to the flattening of the geodesic triangle.	The scale is correct the facet edges.

ons	Uses and applications
mited to 90º from e, although it ect the entire olar projections for regions within dius because there inimal distortion.	Routes of air and sea navigation. These maps will focus on an important location as their central point and use an appropriate aspect.
ly as a world	Suitable for thematic mapping of the world. Used for world distribution maps in the 1937 World Atlas by the Soviet Union. Frequently used as the main projection in school atlases.
for Great Britain. n east–west ue to distortions.	The national coordinate system for Great Britain; used for large-scale topographic mapping.
regions nantly east-west in nd located in the orth or south . Total latitude maps should not 35º.	Used for many new United States Geological Survey maps created after 1957. It has replaced the Polyconic projection.
conformal nor ea. Useful only for aps.	Developed for use in general and thematic world maps. Used by the National Geographic Society since 1988 for general and thematic world maps.
n is reduced when d for a single land ther than the entire his is especially regions near the	Used for world maps illustrating area characteristics, especially if interrupted. Used for continental maps of South America, Africa and occasionally other land masses where each has its own central meridian.
n direction is not t's difficult to directions without le on the map.	Best used for display and educational uses.

Table 11.1: Examples of different types of projection system and how they affect the characteristics of shape, area, direction and distance. The corresponding maps associated with each of these projection systems are shown in Figure 11.3. Adapted from ESRI (2004c and g).

example, some projection systems will only preserve shape along the equator or the central meridian (see Table 11.1 for examples).

The most widely used map projection system is the Universal Transverse Mercator (UTM), developed by the United States military in the late 1940s. It is now a world standard for topographic mapping and digital data exchange and forms the basis for the British National Grid. Table 11.2 identifies the key features of UTM projection.

Variables	Characteristics
Projection type	Cylindrical projection with central meridian placed in a particular region.
UTM ellipsoids	UTM uses the following spheroids: International Spheroid, Clarke 1866 (Africa), Clarke 1880 (North America), Everest and Bessel (Maling, 1992).
Suitable area of use	The projection is only intended for mapping between 84ºN and 80ºS.
Unit of measurement	Metre.
Area	Distortion increases with distance from the central meridian.
Shape	Conformal. Small shapes are maintained. Larger shapes are increasingly distorted away from the central meridian.
Distance	Accurate scale along the central meridian.
Direction	Local angles are accurate everywhere.
General description	The UTM divides the world north-south into 20 sectors of latitude, starting at 84°S. Zones 8º high, except the most northerly and southerly, which are 12º high. Each zone has its own coordinate system. Data on a spheroid or ellipsoid cannot be projected beyond 90º from the central meridian. In fact, the extent on a spheroid or ellipsoid should be limited to 15–20º on both sides of the central meridian.

Table 11.2: The key features of the UTM projection system. Adapted from ESRI (2004c) and Burrough and McDonnell (2000).

British National Grid

The map projection used on Ordnance Survey Great Britain maps is known as the National Grid (Figure 11.5) and is based on the Universal Transverse Mercator system. The central meridian for the projection is located at 49°N 2°W. It is worth noting that the central meridian used by the projection is not the Greenwich meridian. The central meridian is shifted west in this local projection so that it is more centrally located within the landmass of Great Britain. This is an attempt to minimise map distortions which increase east and west of the central meridian using this projection (see Tables 11.1 and 11.2).

To help make it easier for people to use Ordnance Survey maps, the origin of the map is shifted. Eastings and northings axes are given a 'false origin' just south-west of the Scilly Isles to ensure that all coordinates in Britain are positive. The false origin is 400km west and 100km north of the 'true origin' (see Figure 11.5). The National Grid is divided into 100km squares, each of which has a two-letter code. National Grid positions can be given with this code followed by an easting and a northing. For example, from Figure 11.5 the square 'SU' denotes the 100km square that has its origin 400km east and 100km north of the origin of the grid.

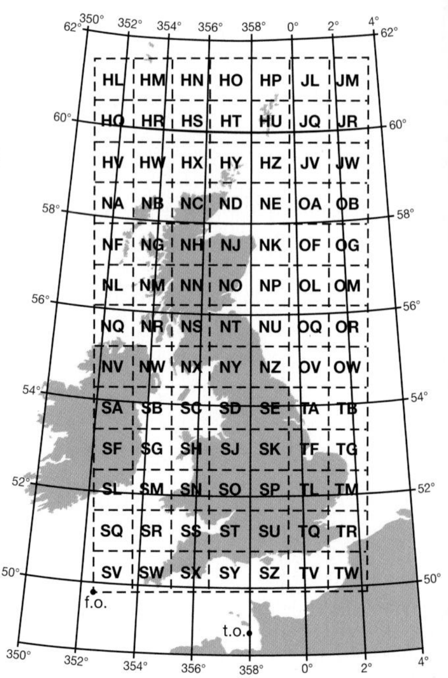

Figure 11.5: The National Grid, showing the true origin (t.o.) and false origin (f.o.). From *A Guide to Co-ordinate Systems in Great Britain*, Ordnance Survey, 2002.

Questions

- What is map projection?
- Why is it important to know how a map is projected when carrying out GIS analysis?
- What are some of the key features of the British National Grid?

Topic E: Data capture methods for GIS

Introduction to data capture methods

Data is a fundamental component of any GIS. There are many ways of collecting data for input into a GIS and the techniques have to be carefully selected. The quality of data used in a GIS project will largely determine the usefulness of any analysis carried out and the validity of any recommendations made. It is therefore very important to understand how GIS data is collected and how the methods of collection determine the characteristics of GIS data. A danger of GIS is that the images produced are often very striking and believable, and can often lead individuals to be overconfident in their use. It is important to remember that if you input inaccurate data into a GIS the results of any analysis carried out on that data will also be of limited value!

An understanding of data capture methods is also very important from a commercial point of view. This is because data collection can often account for 15–50% of the cost of establishing a GIS within an organisation. Running a business efficiently that involves the use of GIS requires a detailed understanding of the data collection process so that costly and poor decision making can be avoided.

Classification of geographic data for data collection purposes

Data falls into two major categories: primary and secondary (see Table 12.1 overleaf). Primary geographic data are captured specifically for use in GIS by direct measurement. Typical examples of primary GIS data are satellite images. Secondary data are those reused from other types of studies or obtained from other systems. A typical example of secondary data is an Ordnance Survey 1:25,000 topographic paper map. In this case the map has to be digitally scanned before it can be used in a GIS.

Primary and secondary data can be collected in either raster or vector format, preserving the advantages and disadvantages of each associated data model/structure (see Chapters 7 and 8).

Primary and secondary data can be collected in either digital or analogue format. Digital data sources are usually ready for immediate input into GIS, with only a limited amount of data preparation being required. This means that digital data sources are usually more cost-efficient. Analogue sources, which are usually paper-based and include geological, soil, mineral and climatic maps, require transformation into a digital source. This extra stage of transformation offers opportunity for errors to be introduced into the data set and could add extra cost. Digital data sets often have fewer errors associated with them than analogue data sets. However, the hardware costs connected with some digital systems can be excessive to the point that for some organisations analogue sources are the only affordable data collection solution.

Table 12.1: Classification of geographic data for data collection purposes with examples of each type. Source: Longley *et al.* (2005).

Data type	Raster	Vector
Primary	Digital satellite remote sensing	GPS measurements
	Digital aerial photographs	Survey measurements
Secondary	Scanned maps or photographs	Analogue topographic maps
	Digital elevation models from topographic map contours	Toponymy, place name databases

Stages associated with data collection

No matter what type of project is being conducted, there will be a number of stages associated with data collection (Figure 12.1). Each stage will have to be considered carefully by an organisation or individual to avoid the introduction of error.

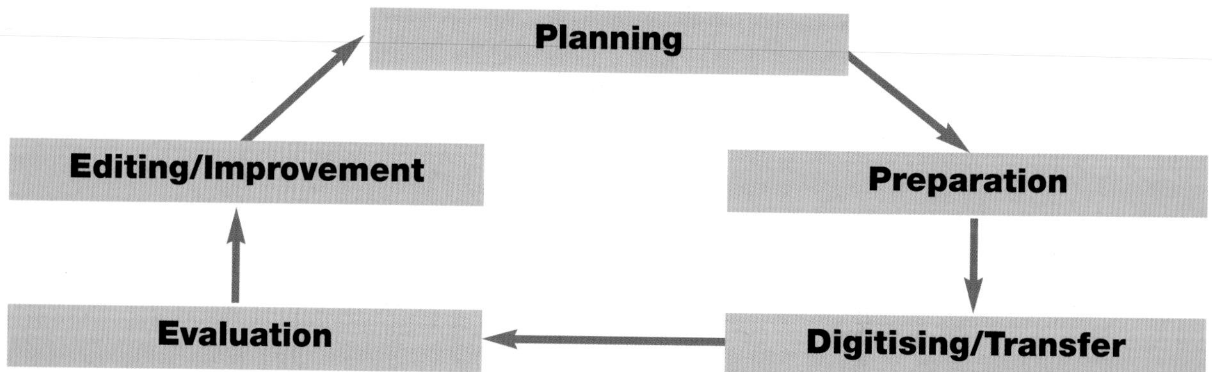

Figure 12.1: The stages involved in data collection projects. Source: Longley *et al.* (2005).

A data collection project will start with planning. This will include establishing user requirements and generating resources such as staffing, hardware and software. For example, the user will need to identify the scale of investigation and whether temporal and spatial data is required. It is also vital to establish a clear budget within which the project needs to be completed.

Preparation is very important in GIS projects and may involve setting up GIS hardware and software systems to accept data such as scanners, digitisers and spreadsheets. Data preparation may also include the purchase of scanned maps, census data and the redrafting of poorly drawn paper sources.

Digitising and transfer involves turning primary or secondary data into a digital format that can be used by a computer. This may simply involve turning an analogue source of data into a digital form. It can also involve geometrically registering an image to a properly defined projection and coordinate system. If this step is not carried out accurately, any analysis conducted on the data will be spatially inaccurate and of limited value.

After the data has been placed in the GIS it must be evaluated for error and accuracy. Any faults associated with the data must be edited and improved before confidence can be associated with the data set and meaningful analysis carried out. The importance of establishing the nature of any error connected with each stage of data collection can not be overemphasised. The methods used for data collection are outlined briefly in the next five chapters of the book and some of their advantages and disadvantages are discussed. Not all methods of data collection are examined and you are encouraged to carry out further investigations to establish a more exhaustive list.

Questions

- Why is data capture such a fundamental part of GIS?
- What are the advantages of digital methods of data collection over analogue approaches?
- Describe the main stages of GIS data collection.

13

Primary raster data capture

Primary geographic data capture

Primary data capture involves the direct measurement of objects or the deployment of techniques that were specifically designed for use within GIS. Digital data may be input directly into a GIS database, minimising the need for extra stages of digitising and transformation, and thus reducing project time and the potential for errors. Where cost and availability is not an issue, digital data is usually preferred to analogue sources. Both vector and raster methods of data capture are possible, and these are discussed in this chapter and the two that follow.

Primary raster data capture

Remote sensing techniques are the most widely used methods of primary raster data capture. 'Remote sensing is the measurement of physical, chemical and biological properties of objects on the earth without direct contact' (Longley *et al.*, 2005). In GIS, remote sensing is considered a primary data source as the user has defined how the data is to be collected for specific use within GIS.

Remote sensing largely involves the collection of data through satellite remote sensing and aerial photography. Remotely sensed data can be either digital or analogue depending on the type of sensor/camera used (see Figures 13.1 and 13.2).

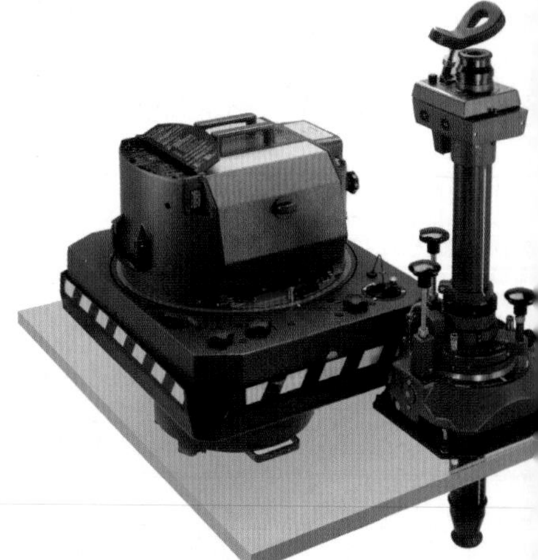

Figure 13.1: Leica RC30 analogue aerial camera. Source: Leica Geosystems. © Leica Geosystems (*www.leica-geosystems.co.uk*).

In the case of remotely sensed data, the key physical characteristic is resolution. There are three main aspects to resolution:

- Spatial resolution
- Spectral resolution
- Temporal resolution

Spatial resolution refers to the size of the object that can be seen on the ground. For example, a spatial resolution of 5m as shown in figure 13.3 reveals little local detail compared to a spatial resolution 12.5cm.

Spectral resolution relates to the parts of the electromagnetic spectrum that are measured. For example, Figure 13.2 shows an aeroplane

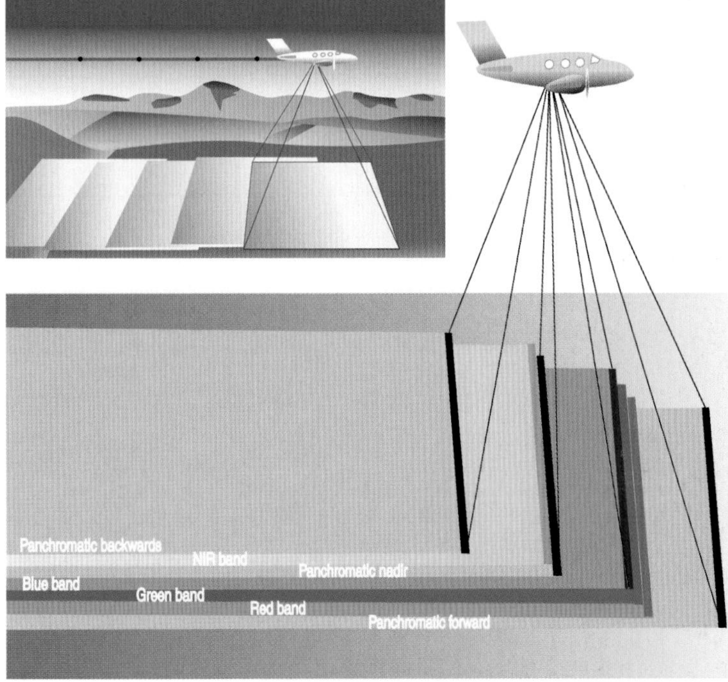

Figure 13.2: An aeroplane carries a digital sensor that allows the passive capture of the electromagnetic spectrum at different wavelengths of radiation. Source: Leica Geosystems. © Leica Geosystems (*www.leica-geosystems.co.uk*).

Figure 13.3: Changes in image features with various pixel resolutions. Source: GeoInformation Group, © South Ayrshire Council, 1999.

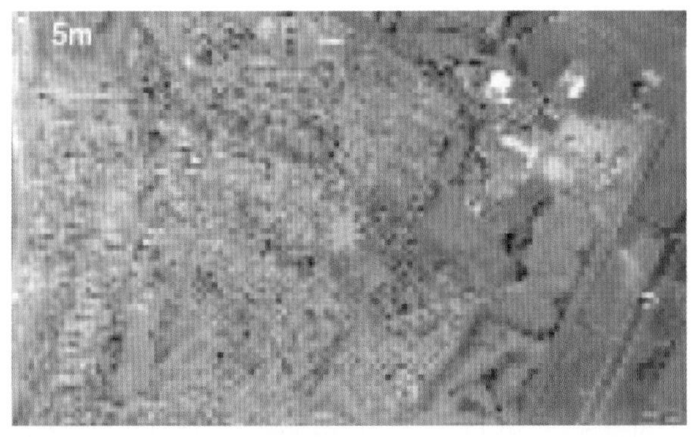

remotely sensing multiple bands of the electromagnetic spectrum simultaneously using a digital sensor. Due to the high number of bands being sampled, this device has a high spectral resolution. Data collected with a high spectral resolution is excellent for looking at a wide variety of features within one area such as water, vegetation, soil, geology and buildings. It is common for modern satellites to have a high spectral resolution. However, most aerial photography only collects data in the visible spectrum and is therefore generally considered to have a lower spectral resolution.

Temporal resolution describes the frequency at which the satellite or aeroplane collects data from the same area. The more frequently the sensor visits an area, the higher the temporal resolution associated with the data. Data with a high temporal resolution is excellent for detecting change in the earth's surface – for example, tracking the destruction of tropical forest. Figure 13.4 shows the relationship between the spatial and temporal characteristics of the most commonly used remote sensing systems and their sensors.

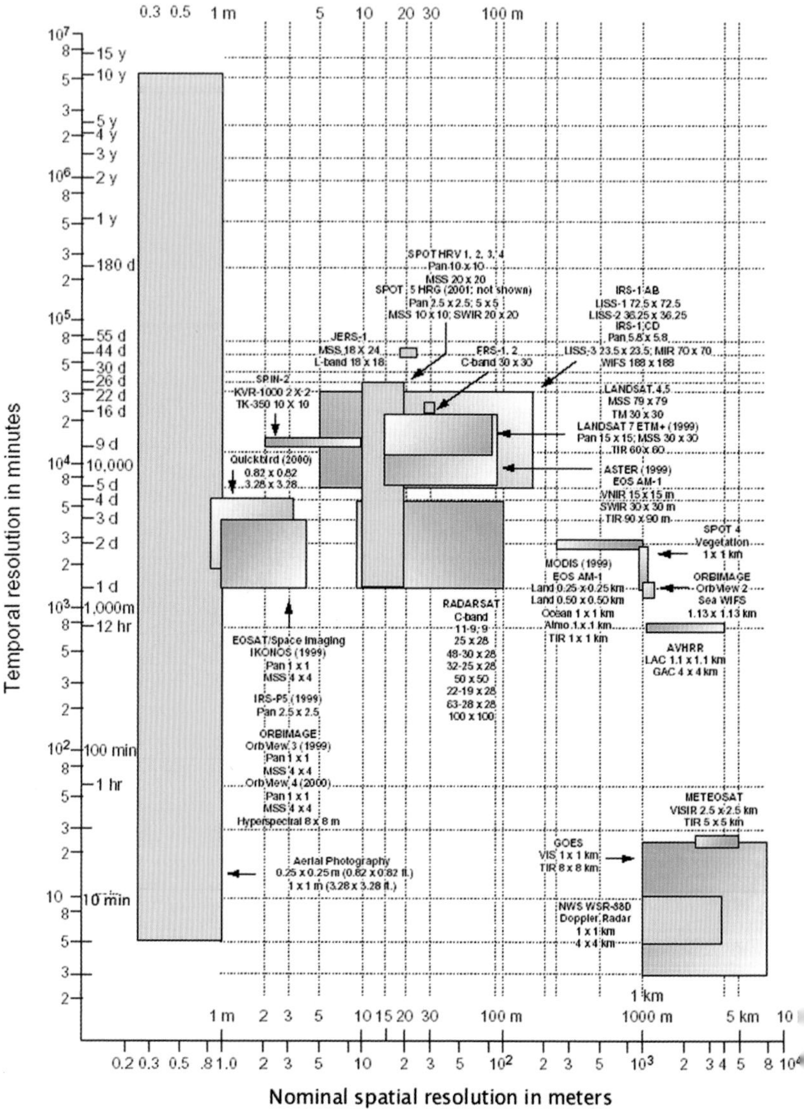

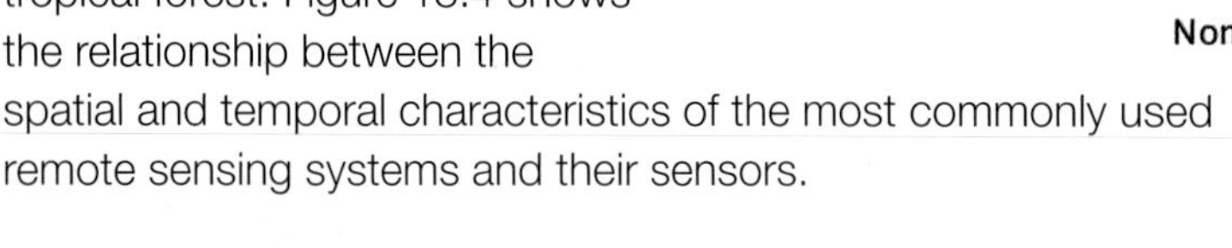

Figure 13.4: Spatial and temporal characteristics of commonly used remote sensing systems and their sources. Source: Jensen and Cowen (1999).

Questions

- What is meant by the term remote sensing?
- Describe the different formats remotely sensed data can come in.
- Describe the three types of resolution associated with remotely sensed data.

Advantages and disadvantages of RS imagery

Satellite and aerial photography technologies offer a number of advantages and disadvantages for GIS-related projects:

Advantages

1. Satellite data is excellent for large-area, small-scale mapping projects because of the consistency of the data and the availability of global coverage.
2. The regular repeat cycles of satellites, and the capability of recording data from multiple parts of the electromagnetic spectrum, make them particularly suitable for vegetation studies such as the monitoring of crop yields in developing countries that are particularly at risk from famine.
3. Aerial photography is best suited for detailed surveying and mapping – for example, mapping the urban structure of a town or city.
4. Satellite and aerial photography technologies provide mapping for otherwise inaccessible areas.

Disadvantages

1. The data volumes from both satellites and aerial photography can be extremely large, stretching the storage capabilities of even the most modern data storage systems.
2. Data from both aerial photography and satellites can be very expensive, preventing access to data for a single project or organisation.
3. Data collection via satellites and aerial photography is subject to many sources of potential error, most of which result from problems of distortion and displacement associated with the position of the sensor in relation to the ground surface. Causes of this include:
   - film and print shrinkage, which may distort the relationship between recorded objects
   - motion between the sensor and the earth's surface (see Figure 14.2 overleaf)
   - lens distortion of the landscape (see Figure 14.1)
   - the curvature of the earth, and changes in topography and relief (Figure 14.3).

We have not discussed all the potential sources of error associated with the capture of remotely sensed imagery. On the other hand, most sources of error are corrected by the majority of GIS data providers as a matter of routine. However, before purchasing GIS data it is essential to establish what corrections have been made before carrying out any GIS analysis. This approach is essential to ensuring the validity of any decisions made based on GIS.

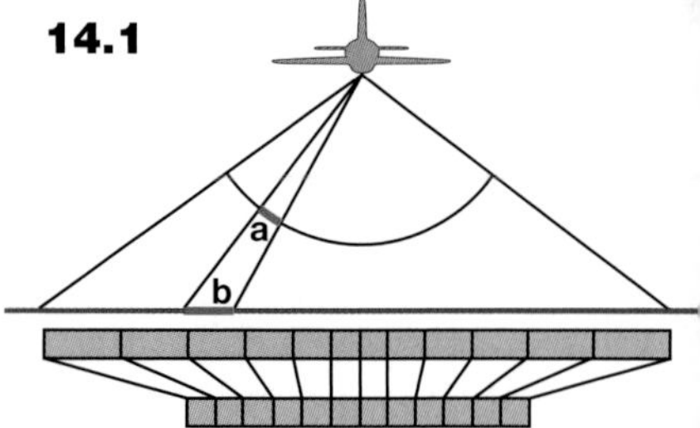

Figure 14.1: If a sensor has a wide viewing angle, pixels that are further away from the point immediately below the aircraft are increasingly distorted. If this is not corrected, the edges of the image become compressed. This is a little like looking at a series of electricity poles that appear to become closer together as they approach the vanishing point in the landscape. Adapted from Zhou (1999).

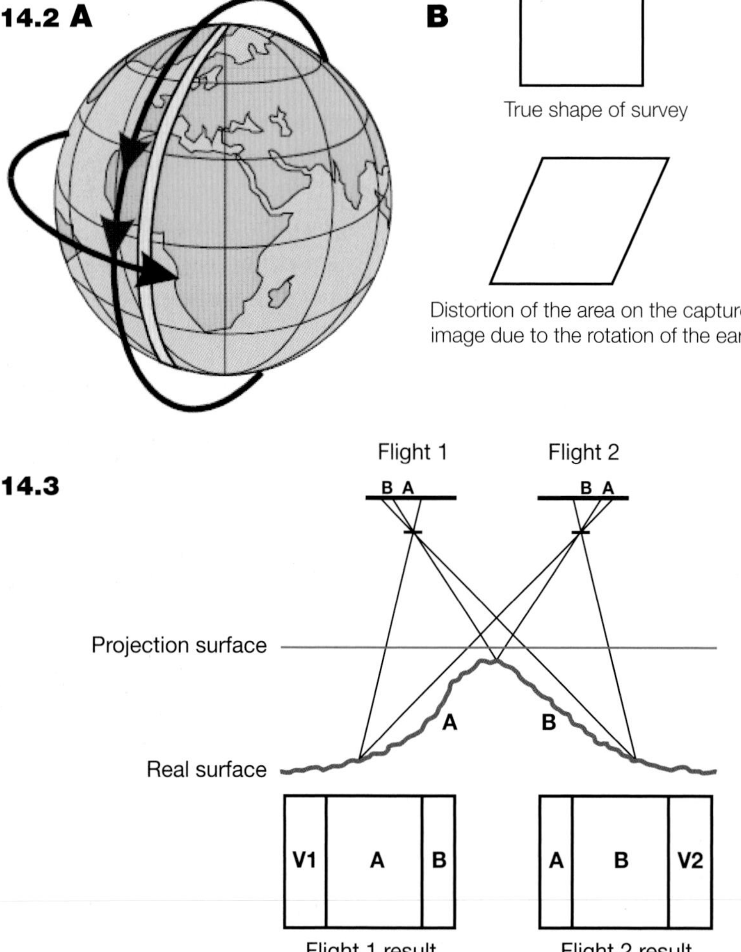

Figure 14.2: A) Satellites such as Landsat orbit approximately 700km above the earth's surface in a near-polar orbit. The earth rotates out from under the satellite, causing the image area to move progressively westward as the satellite passes from north to south. **B**) As a result of this westward movement, the captured image becomes distorted geometrically and must be corrected before features can be accurately referenced spatially. Adapted from Zhou (1999).

Figure 14.3: Successive images along two flight lines have been taken from opposite sides of a mountain ridge. In the image from flight 1, side A of the mountain occupies most of the image while side B appears to be very narrow. The opposite is true for flight 2. The extreme difference between the two images results from the distortions associated with changes in topography. This problem can be minimised by flying at higher altitudes to reduce the scale variations associated with relief. Similar distortions result from the curvature of the earth. Both relief and curvature distortions need to be corrected to ensure the accuracy of the relationship between places on the earth in terms of distance and direction. Adapted from Zhou (1999).

Questions

- What are some of the common sources of error associated with data collection using remote sensing technologies?
- What types of error associated with remotely sensed data collection do you think are the most important to manage? Explain your point of view fully.

Primary vector data capture

Vector data capture is a primary source of spatial data for GIS. Primary vector data capture breaks down into two main areas:

- Ground surveying
- Global Positioning Systems (GPS)

The distinction between ground surveying and GPS is gradually breaking down as the two technologies become increasingly integrated.

Ground surveying is one of the oldest and most accurate geographical methods of mapping. It is based on the principle that any point in the landscape can be located by measuring angles and distances from other known points (Figure 15.1).

Figure 15.1: Ground surveying using a total survey station. Source: Leica Geosystems. © Leica Geosystems (*www.leica-geosystems.co.uk*).

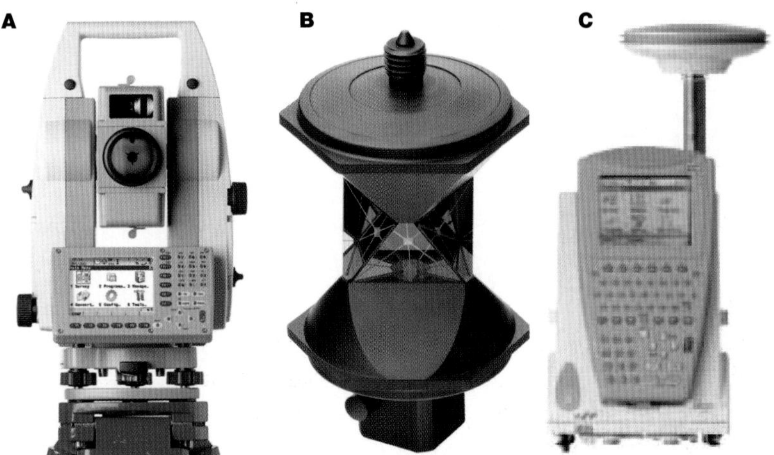

Figure 15.2: A) A modern total survey station. **B**) A 360° survey staff and reflector. **C**) A GPS unit with antenna. Source: Leica Geosystems. © Leica Geosystems (*www.leica-geosystems.co.uk*).

Surveys begin from a benchmark point, an example of which is the pile of stones frequently seen on the top of hills if you walk in the British landscape. If the coordinate system of the benchmark is known, all other points surveyed can be attached to the same coordinate system. Today most ground surveys are conducted using a total survey station (Figures 15.1 and 15.2 on previous page).

The advantage of a total survey station is that it automatically carries out the complicated trigonometric calculations required during surveying. The best systems can also create point, line and area objects in the field, making it easier to input this data into GIS. Two people are usually required to conduct a ground survey: one to operate the survey station and the other to hold the survey staff and reflector (Figure 15.2). Ground surveys are very expensive and time-consuming to conduct but offer one of the most accurate ways to capture data for GIS analysis.

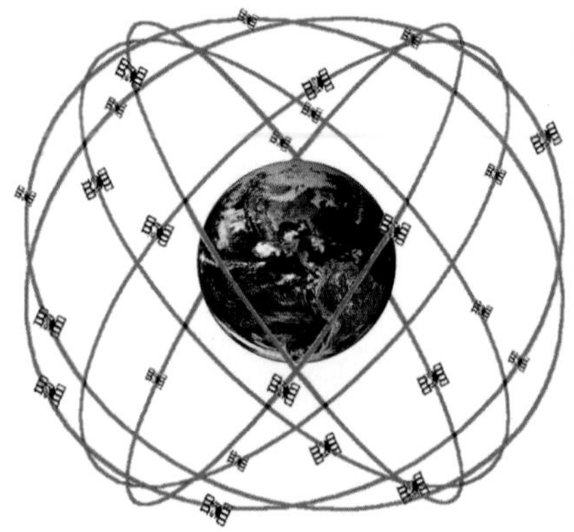

Figure 15.3: GPS satellites orbiting the earth's surface. Satellites orbit the earth at a speed of 3.9km/sec and have a circulation time of 12 hours. The orbit height is about 20,200km. Source of Earth from Space image: NASA Goddard Space Flight Center (NASA-GSFC).

The use of GPS in the capture of geographical data is becoming increasingly important. The correct name of the system is NAVSTAR (Navigation System for Timing and Ranging), but is commonly known today as GPS (see Table 15.1). The technology has rapidly become more available in recent years as operating costs have dropped significantly. GPS is now often used in conjunction with a total survey station, reducing the need for an extensive physical benchmarking system. GPS was created by the US Department of Defense and is based on the use of orbiting satellites (Figure 15.3). About 30 active satellites orbit the earth at a distance of 20,200km. GPS satellites transmit signals which enable the exact location of a GPS receiver to be determined.

A major advantage of GPS is that attribute data can be automatically linked to positional data collected in the field. With the additional development of hand-held computer technology in the form of PDAs with full colour displays, individuals are now able to capture primary vector data and link this immediately to existing mapping layers. Data linked to GPS coordinates can include descriptions of the environment in the form of written notes, digital voice recordings, digital photographs and digital video. If these technologies are then coupled with mobile communications, the capture of vector information can operate in real time. The UK Government has combined these technologies to capture the movement of convicted criminals in real time (see Figure 15.4 on page 74).

Year	Significant GPS events
1973	The decision to develop a satellite navigation system based on the TRANSIT, TIMATION and 621B systems of the US Air Force and Navy.
1974–1979	System tests.
1977	The first receiver tests are performed even before the first satellites have been stationed in orbit. Transmitters called pseudolites (pseudo-satellites) are installed on the earth's surface.
1978–1985	A total of 11 satellites are launched in this period.
1979	The decision to expand the GPS system. Thereupon the resources are considerably shortened and the programme is restructured. At first only 18 satellites are to be operated. In 1988 the number of satellites is raised to 24, as the functionality is not satisfying with only 18 satellites.
1980	Launching of the first satellite carrying sensors to detect atomic explosions. This satellite is meant to monitor the abidance of the agreement of 1963 between the USA and the Soviet Union to refrain from any nuclear tests on the earth, in a submarine or in space.
1980–1982	The financial situation of the project becomes critical as the usefulness of the system is questioned again and again by the sponsors.
1983	When a civilian airplane of the Korean Airline (Flight 007) is shot down after having got lost over Soviet territory, it is decided to allow the civilian use of the GPS system.
1986	The accident involving the Challenger space shuttle proves a drawback for the GPS programme, as the space shuttles were supposed to transport Block II GPS satellites to their orbit. Finally the operators of the programme revert to the Delta rockets that were intended for the transportation in the first place.
1990–1991	Temporal deactivation of the selective availability (SA) during the Gulf war. In this period civil receivers were used as not enough military receivers were available. On 1 July 1991 SA is activated again.
8 December 1993	The Initial Operational Capability (IOC) is announced. In the same year there is a definite decision to authorise worldwide civilian use free of charge.
March 1994	The final Block II satellite completes the satellite constellation.
17 July 1995	Full Operational Capability (FOC) is announced.
1 May 2000	The final deactivation of selective availability, thus improving the accuracy for civilian users from about 100m to 20m.
20 March 2004	Launching of the 50th GPS satellite.

Table 15.1: Key events in the development of GPS. Source: *www.kowoma.de/en/gps/history.htm*.

GPS and ground surveying is most frequently used to capture the spatial position of buildings, land and property boundaries, manholes, electricity lines and other important infrastructure. These methods are also used to obtain reference marks for use in other data capture projects. For example, GPS and land surveying data is frequently used to geo-reference and test the reliability of aerial photography and satellite imagery.

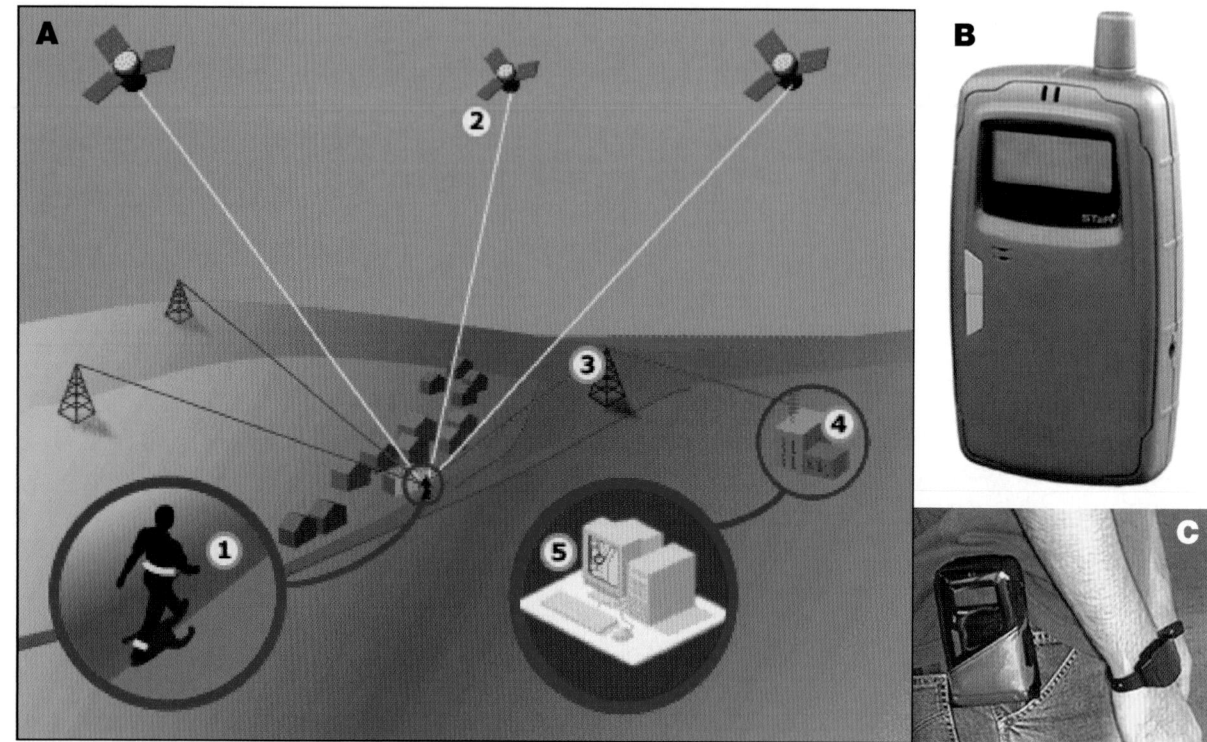

Figure 15.4: The use of GIS, GPS and mobile communications technology to capture vector data of the movements of criminals in real time. **A) 1:** Offender wears tracker device on belt, with wireless connection to ankle tag. **2:** Belt device tracks own location using GPS satellite signals. **3:** Location data transferred from belt device to telephone network. **4:** Data sent to control centre, which can be specifically alerted if offender enters exclusion zone or breaks other conditions. Radio frequency alarm also sent if tracker and ankle tag are separated. **5:** Offender's position shown as location trails on computer map. **B)** A GPS receiver worn on the offender's belt relays data to a monitoring centre. **C)** Separating the GPS device and tag from the offender's belt triggers an alarm. Source: *www.bbc.co.uk/news*.

Although GPS and ground surveying techniques are highly accurate, they are not free from error. In the case of ground surveying, the degree of error will depend on the precision and accuracy of the equipment being used and the skill of the operator. Corrections are frequently made to ground survey data on return to the office environment. The quality of GPS data can also vary depending on the device being used and the experience of the operator. Another factor that can affect the accuracy of measurement is the number of satellites in range at the time a reading is taken. As a general rule the more satellites in range, the greater the accuracy of the data being recorded.

Questions

- What is ground surveying and what equipment is often used for this approach to data collection?
- What is GPS and what technologies are needed in order to use it for GIS data collection?
- What factors affect the accuracy of GPS?

Secondary and attribute data capture

The generation of secondary data for use in a GIS involves the creation of raster or vector data from maps, photographs or any other hard-copy material. Two principal methods are used to achieve this:

- raster data is generated by scanning hard-copy material
- vector data is generated by digitising hard-copy sources.

Secondary capture of raster data

Hard-copy material is converted to a raster file format by using a scanner to create a digital file (see Figure 16.1). The scanned image is made up of pixels of a given resolution that are scaled according to colour.

Figure 16.1: An example of a large-format roll-feed image scanner. Source: GTCO Calcomp, Inc.

Scanners vary greatly in quality, and the reliability of the resulting images depends a lot on the device used. Scanned images for use as mapping in GIS must be geo-referenced, and the quality of the image can be improved through the use of specialist software to remove the presence of scratches and other image defects. This technology is relatively cheap to use, so it is employed extensively in GIS in the form of background maps to help with the visualisation of vector data sets. GIS analysts often provide three main reasons for the use of scanned imagery:

- Important documents such as property deeds, architectural drawings, Computer Aided Design (CAD) drawings and plans of communication systems are scanned to provide a backup to the original drawings, reducing wear and tear, and improving accessibility. Scanned drawings frequently act as attributes for vector data and are indexed geographically so that individuals and organisations can sort information spatially.
- Scanned images provide a background geographical context for other data sources, enhancing the visualisation of an area under investigation.
- Maps and scanned images can provide the base information from which vector data sets are developed. If scanned imagery is to be used for this purpose, the image needs to be of high quality.

Figure 16.2: Digitising equipment: **A**) digitising table; **B**) cursor. Source: GTCO Calcomp, Inc.

Secondary capture of vector data

Manual digitising is the most frequently used method of capturing secondary vector data for use in GIS. At a simple level a digitising suite consists of a digitising table and a cursor (Figure 16.2).

The digitising process works as follows. The operator attaches a hard-copy image or document to the digitising table, and then traces the required features using the cursor (Figure 16.2). The coordinate system used by the digitising table must be registered to a real-world coordinate system. The main advantage of this system of data capture is that it is cheap. However, the process is very time-consuming, and because it is driven by a human operator many errors can occur (Table 16.1), which have to be carefully checked and removed before the digitising process can be considered complete.

Table 16.1: Common errors in spatial data. Source: Heywood *et al.* (2006).

Error	**Description**
Missing entities	Missing points, lines or boundary segments
Duplication errors	Points, lines or boundary segments that have been digitised twice
Mislocated entities	Points, lines or boundaries digitised in the wrong place
Missing labels	Unidentified polygons
Duplicate labels	Two or more identification labels for the same polygon
Effects of digitising	Undershots, overshots, wrongly placed nodes, loops and spikes
Noise	Irrelevant data entered during digitising, scanning or data transfer

Apart from manual digitising, automated systems are also available but unfortunately these systems are far from perfect and require significant editing after vector data capture. Digitising is used extensively to convert raster data to a vector format.

Attribute data collection

All spatial features have physical characteristics associated with them. Attribute data is a description of these characteristics. While attribute data is often collected at the same time as spatial data, it is often more cost-efficient to separate the two tasks. This is because attribute data is regularly a lot simpler to collect and does not require the same level of skill or resources as spatial data capture. Attribute data can be captured and entered in a number of different ways and these are summarised in Table 16.2. While the techniques listed here are largely associated with attribute data capture, they can also be used to record

Table 16.2: A summary of techniques used to capture attribute data.

Data capture methods	Description	Examples of use
Keyboard entry	Operators add attribute data into a spreadsheet, which is later joined to a spatial context.	Frequently used by local government authorities to update their records.
Data loggers	Computer devices used to continually record attribute data from a fixed location.	Could be used to record changes in discharge at a point along a river.
Optical character recognition (OCR)	A system for converting written text on a page into digital characters. Frequently used when large volumes of data have been collected, avoiding the need for manual keyboard entry.	Often used to enter historical records that were not collected in a digital format.
Voice recognition software	An operator dictates the attribute data to a computer system, which then converts the recorded information into a digital format, either as a spreadsheet or as a digital recording.	Used where large volumes of data have to be processed.
Field surveys and questionnaires	Governments and organisations frequently use surveys and questionnaires to gather attribute information.	One of the most extensive attribute surveys is the collection of the government census conducted every 10 years.

spatial information. For example, a data logger can be set up to collect either spatial or attribute data.

One of the most important sources of attribute data concerning the geography of the UK is the census information that is collected every 10 years. The census in 2001 had 24 questions dealing with many aspects of how people live. Census data is collected for each household in the UK but is not available in this form to the general public. Data from the census is usually displayed for areas such as wards, postcode zones and output areas to preserve the confidentiality of the data collected.

Questions

- What is secondary data capture?
- Explain the difference between the capture of secondary data from vector and raster sources.
- What does attribute data collection involve?

17 Data supply companies and metadata

Data suppliers

An alternative to establishing a data collection project is to source the required imagery or mapping from a specialist data supply company. Many organisations choose this option as it is not only cost-effective but removes much of the difficult task involved in establishing GIS within an organisation. There are currently many data supply companies. Table 17.1 provides just a few major examples.

Table 17.1: Websites giving information about geographic data sources. Adapted from Longley *et al*. (2005).

Source	Website address	Description
Gigateway	www.gigateway.org.uk	Gigateway is a free web service aimed at increasing awareness of and access to geospatial information in the UK
Data Store	www.data-store.co.uk/	UK, European and worldwide data catalogue
NOAA	www.noaa.gov	A range of data resources related to atmospheric, oceanic and coastal processes
ESRI GIS Education Community	http://edcommunity.esri.com	Links to various data sources for use in education
MapMart	www.mapmart.com/	Extensive data imagery provider
EROS Data Center	edc.usgs.gov/	US Government data archive
Terraserver	www.terraserver-usa.com	High-resolution aerial imagery and topographic maps
Geography Network	www.GeographyNetwork.com	Global online data and map services
National Geographic Society	www.nationalgeographic.com	Worldwide maps
GeoConnections	www.geoconnections.org	Canadian Government geographic data over the web
EuroGeographics	www.eurographics.org	Coalition of European mapping organisations offering topographic map data
GEOWorld Data Directory	www.geoplace.com	List of GIS data companies
The GIS Data Depot	www.gisdatadepot.com	Extensive collection of mainly free geographic data

When data is sourced from a supply company, some careful planning is still required. The file formats that the ordered data comes in must be compatible with the GIS software that is going to be used. The user should establish clearly with the supplier other key characteristics of the data such as resolution, the projection and coordinate systems used, when the data was captured and what errors are associated with the data set. Understanding the quality of data on which judgements are to be made is a key factor in the success of GIS in decision making.

Metadata

Metadata is very important in the effective and efficient management of GIS data. Metadata in essence describes the nature of geographic data. It is a bit like the contents page of a book which tells us what it

Table 17.2: The 15 basic elements of the Dublin Core metadata standard. Source: Longley *et al.* (2005).

Standard	Description
Title	The name given to the resource by the creator or publisher.
Author or creator	The person(s) or organisation(s) primarily responsible for the intellectual content of the resource.
Subject or keywords	The topic of the resource, or keywords, phrases or classification descriptors that describe the subject or content of the resource.
Description	A textual description of the content of the resource, including abstracts in the case of document-like objects or content description in the case of visual resources.
Publisher	The body responsible for making the resource available in its present form, such as a publisher, a university department or a corporate body.
Other contributors	Person(s) or organisations(s) in addition to those specified in the creator who have made significant intellectual contributions to the resource.
Date	The date the resource was made available in its present form.
Resource type	The category of the resource, such as a homepage, working paper, technical report.
Format	The data representation of the resource, e.g. jpeg image, shapefile.
Resource identifier	The string or number used to uniquely identify the resource.
Source	The work, either print or electronic, from which the resource is delivered.
Language	The language(s) of the intellectual content of the resource.
Relation	Relationship to other resources.
Coverage	The spatial locations and temporal duration characteristic of the resource.
Rights management	The content of this element is intended to be a link to a copyright notice.

contains; the inside cover provides even more details such as who wrote and published the book, its cost and the number of print runs. Metadata is very much like this, telling us how the GIS data set in use has been put together, and enabling us to determine what use it can realistically be put to. Metadata has become very important as GIS data has become more accessible. In particular, the ability to share and access data over the internet has made it necessary to describe carefully the key features of geographic data sets. To this end GIS users have established a minimum set of descriptors that should accompany each GIS dataset (see Table 17.2).

The establishment of a metadata standard is not only useful from an analysis point of view but also aids the processes of data management and searching. For example, using the standards from Table 17.2, it is possible to index work so that it can be stored and retrieved efficiently, just as in a massive library you need a system that enables you to find the book you want quickly and without having to read the title of every volume in the building. The establishment of metadata standards has improved our ability to search for data on the internet and to know what we are getting before downloading a resource. When working with GIS data, you should try and ensure that you maintain the metadata record, especially if the data resource is to be shared in the future.

Questions

- What quality issues should you consider when ordering data from a data supply company?
- Define the term metadata and describe how it is useful in GIS data management.

Topic F: Methods of data analysis using GIS

18

Introduction to spatial analysis and GIS query

The real power of GIS comes from its ability to analyse spatial data to produce information. It is this ability to take massive data sets, such as the 2001 Census, and extract data efficiently that is at the core of GIS. In particular, GIS has the potential to ask focused questions that cut to the heart of what organisations need to run a successful business or government department. For example, an insurance company may wish to accurately determine the location of all houses that are at risk from flooding in the UK. The answers that GIS provides to such issues will affect the cost of household insurance in the UK and how much profit the company makes. Knowing how to ask questions using GIS is a key skill in the successful use of GIS techniques. When questions are asked of GIS data sets, value is added in the form of a greater understanding of how the world works. After data has been analysed using GIS, it can communicate information that is more accessible and easier to visualise and understand. However, making good use of the potential analysis capabilities of GIS is not just down to having a powerful computer, but relies heavily on the operator. Operators must think carefully about the data analysis techniques that they are using. Good answers that inform decision making only come from asking the right questions. The next five chapters consider what questions can be asked of GIS data and how the answers can be obtained using GIS analysis techniques.

Query functions

Queries are the simplest form of analysis that can be carried out using GIS. Query functions do not change the original data in any way. They are used to ask simple questions like:

- What peacekeeping operations are the United Nations currently involved in and where are they located?
- How many people live or work within 10 miles of the Houses of Parliament?
- How many schools are within five miles of the centre of Hackney, London?

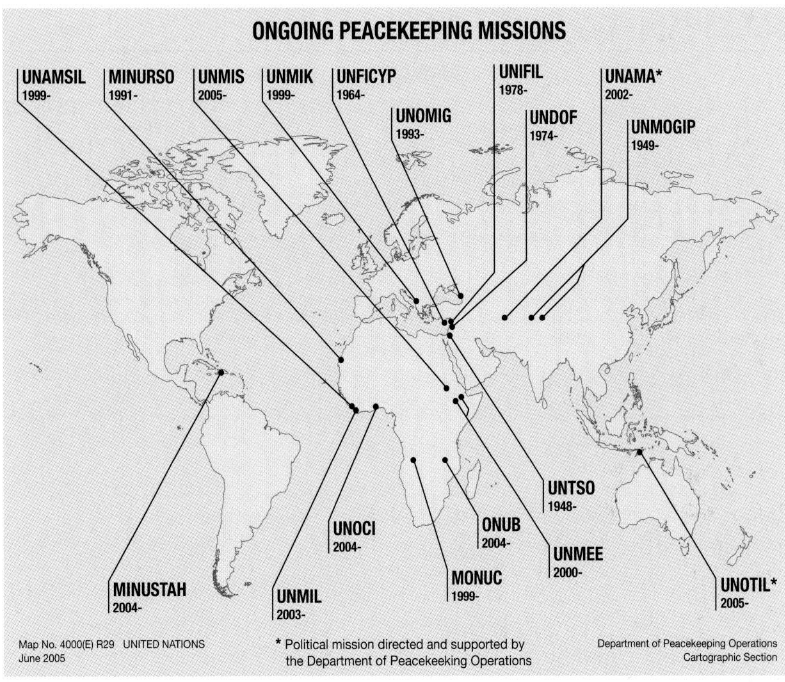

Figure 18.1: A typical example of the results of a GIS query: the locations of peacekeeping missions that the United Nations were involved in as of June 2005. Source: UN website, downloaded June 2005.

In determining an answer to the first question, Figure 18.1 shows that in 2005 the United Nations was involved in 18 peacekeeping missions around the world. A manager in the United Nations may want to further query their GIS database to establish how many personnel are involved in the peacekeeping missions and how much maintaining the programmes will cost. The answers to such types of query are shown in Table 18.1.

Table 18.1: The types of query results from a GIS database that could be used to monitor and manage UN peacekeeping operations. Source: United Nations.

UN resources associated with peacekeeping	Numbers of people involved and associated costs
Military personnel and civilian police serving in peacekeeping operations	66,851
Countries contributing military personnel and civilian police	105
International civilian personnel	4,407
Local civilian personnel	8,203
UN volunteers	1,738
Total number of personnel serving in peacekeeping operations	81,199
Total number of fatalities in peacekeeping operations since 1948	1,992
Approved budgets for the period from 1 July 2004 to 30 June 2005	About $4.47 billion

In GIS it is possible to carry out two main types of query: an attribute query and a spatial query.

Attribute query

Attributes describe the nature of map objects. They are contained in a database table and are physically linked to a map. An attribute may describe the length of a river or the size of a building. When an **attribute query** is performed, it is the database associated with the map that is examined. Attribute queries are questions about the nature of features contained within the GIS database's attribute tables.

Generally the questions can be broken down into a series of different parts. For example, how many cities in the UK have a population greater than 100,000? Results from such a query may be in the form of a table or may be displayed on a map.

Criteria for attribute queries may be based on numbers or text searches or a combination of both. In addition, the software associated with GIS usually has a query builder. These are designed to enable the user to tailor queries in a particular fashion (see Figure 18.2). For example, the query builder can specify that it only wants to identify buildings that occupy 50m². Or the query builder can identify buildings that exist within a size range of 50–100m².

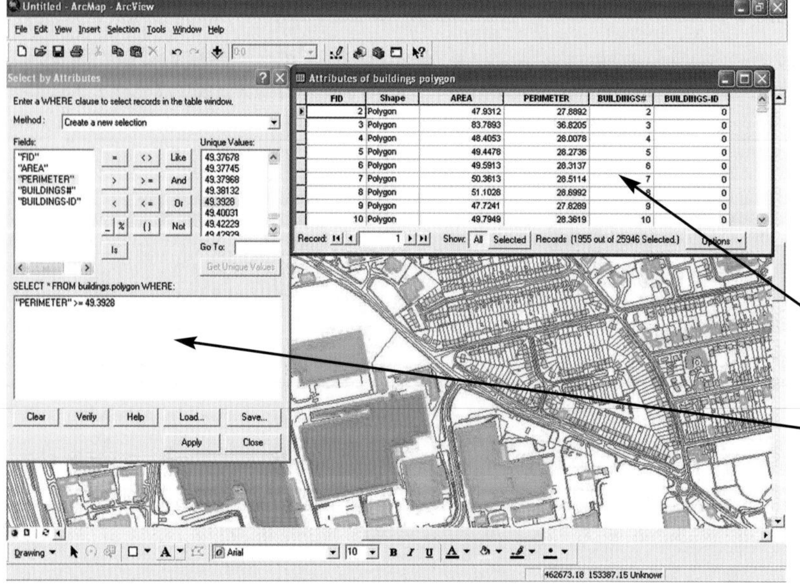

Figure 18.2: An example of an attribute query. In this example the query builder is used to identify all buildings in the Basingstoke attribute table that have an area greater than or equal to 43m². The results of those buildings meeting the conditions of the query are highlighted with a blue border on the Ordnance Survey Landline Map. OS base mapping reproduced with permission.

Attribute table

Query builder

Figure 18.2 shows an example of a query builder which can use a series of logical operations to improve the efficiency of a data search using GIS. Queries can be constructed using the following operators:

- **>** greater than (e.g. find all cities with a population greater than 1 million)
- **<** less than (e.g. find all shops less than 10km from the city centre)
- **=** equal to (e.g. find all houses that have a value equal to £150,000).

The querying possibilities represented by these operators can be quite complicated as they can be combined in a single search. For example, you may have a query that wants to find all housing that has an area *equal* to 1,500m^2 and *less than* 5km from the city centre. In carrying out these types of query it is very important to think of the order in which each operation will be performed as this will significantly affect the results given.

Spatial query

Spatial queries are carried out on the actual mapped features (see Figure 18.3). They can be related to points, lines, areas or distances.

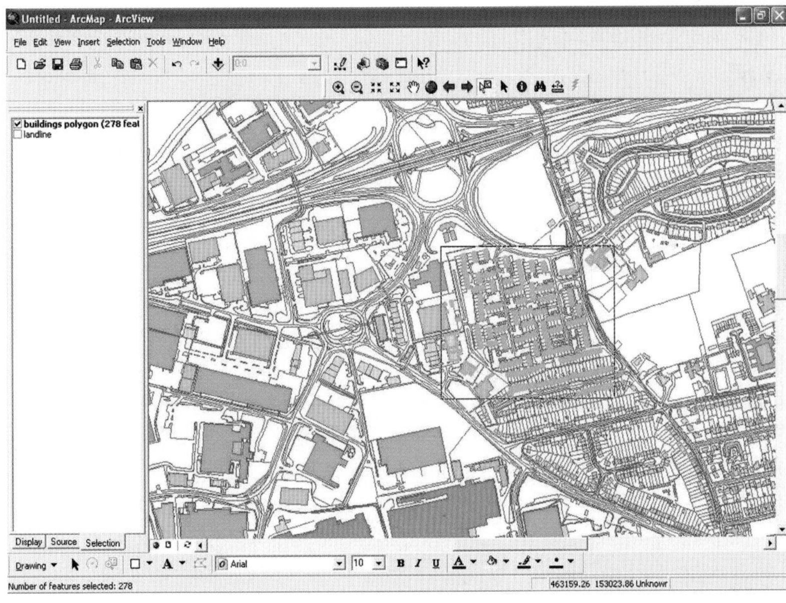

Figure 18.3: An example of a spatial query. In this example all the buildings found within a particular 500m^2 area are highlighted in blue. Tables could also be produced from this query, highlighting the number of buildings and their use. OS base mapping reproduced with permission.

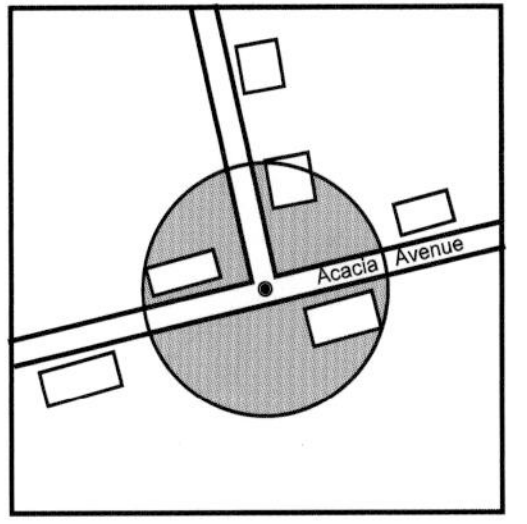

How many houses are within 50m of this junction?

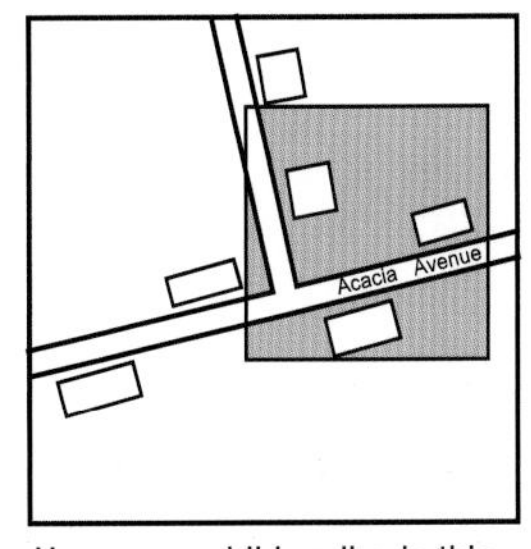

How many children live in this 100m grid square?

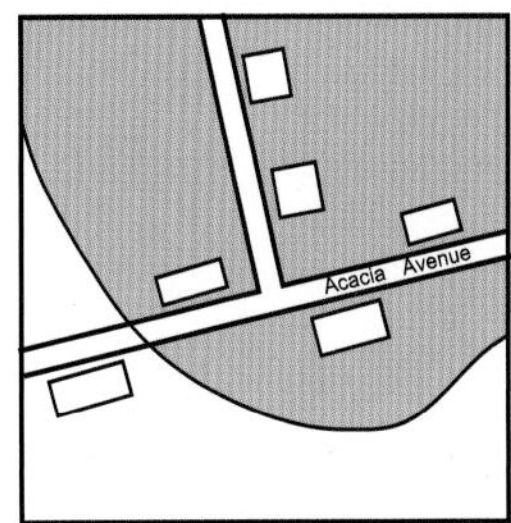

Which households fall within the floodplain?

Figure 18.4: Some basic types of spatial query. Source: ASET learning materials. OS base mapping reproduced with permission.

Typical types of spatial queries include:

- What land-use types are found within a certain radius of the city centre?
- How many pubs are found within 3km of the city centre?
- Do many adults of a certain income live within 10km of a proposed new supermarket?
- How many people commute along the M1 each year?
- How many houses are within a 10-minute drive from the local fire station?

Further examples of spatial queries are given in Figure 18.4 (see previous page). One of the main advantages of a spatial query is that the analysis process is very easy to visualise. The sophistication of query operations can be improved by combining the attribute and spatial approaches in a sequence of operations.

Questions

- What is a query used for in GIS analysis?
- What is the difference between an attribute and a spatial query in GIS analysis?

Mathematical and statistical operations

Mathematical and statistical operations can be performed on both attribute and spatial data. The mathematical and statistical operations that can be carried out using GIS can be extremely complicated, requiring a highly developed understanding of the processes involved. However, there are several techniques that can be more easily used and these are shown in Table 19.1.

Table 19.1: Some examples of statistical and mathematical operations carried out using GIS.

Mathematical calculations	Statistical calculations
+ addition	Mean
– subtraction	Mode
× multiplication	Median
/ division	Standard deviation
square root	Regression
Sin, Cos, Tan	

Analysis of the type shown in Table 19.1 usually involves the use of more than one layer of data (Figure 19.1).

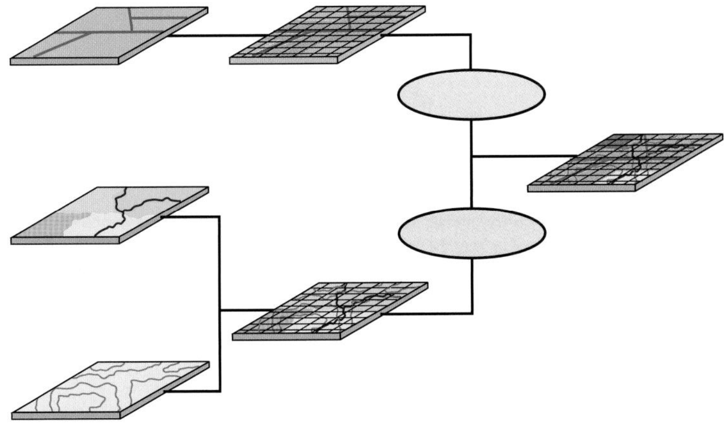

Figure 19.1: Mathematical and statistical analysis can involve the use of more than one layer of data. Layers of data may be multiplied, added or subtracted to produce new data layers that may then be used to inform decision making. Adapted from ESRI (2004b).

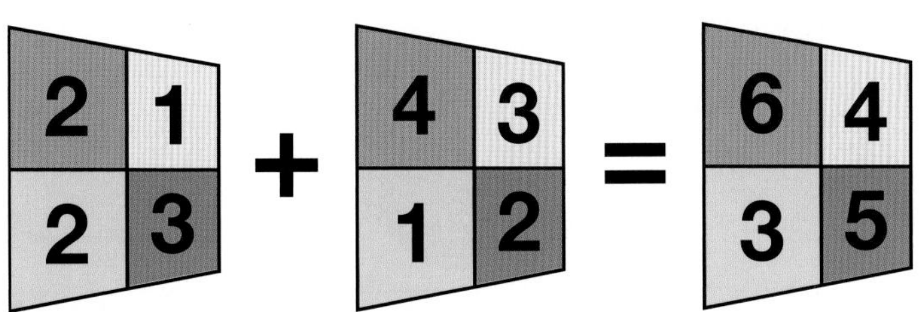

Figure 19.2: A simple example of a mathematical operation in which two layers of raster data are being added together to produce a new data layer. Adapted from ESRI (2004b).

Raster data is particularly suited to statistical and mathematical analysis as each cell has a single value (see Figure 19.2 on previous page) and the data structure is relatively simple, reducing the requirement for massive processing power.

For example, Figure 19.3 shows the Island of Stromboli in the Mediterranean. After a period of volcanic activity the north-west flank of the island suffered major landslides on 30 December 2002. As a result, tsunami waves several metres high affected the coasts of the island. Scientists wanted to establish the relationship between the size of the landslides that occurred and the resultant tsunami. To do this they carried out a series of aerial photography surveys from which a series of digital elevation models was constructed. The comparison between the data collected before the eruption and that acquired up to September 2003 allowed scientists to estimate the volume of the surfaces involved in the landslides. This was made possible by subtracting the heights established from one image from another. The differences between the images enabled scientists to determine how much the land surface had changed (Figure 19.4). This is a good example of how mathematical operations can be used to establish differences between surfaces.

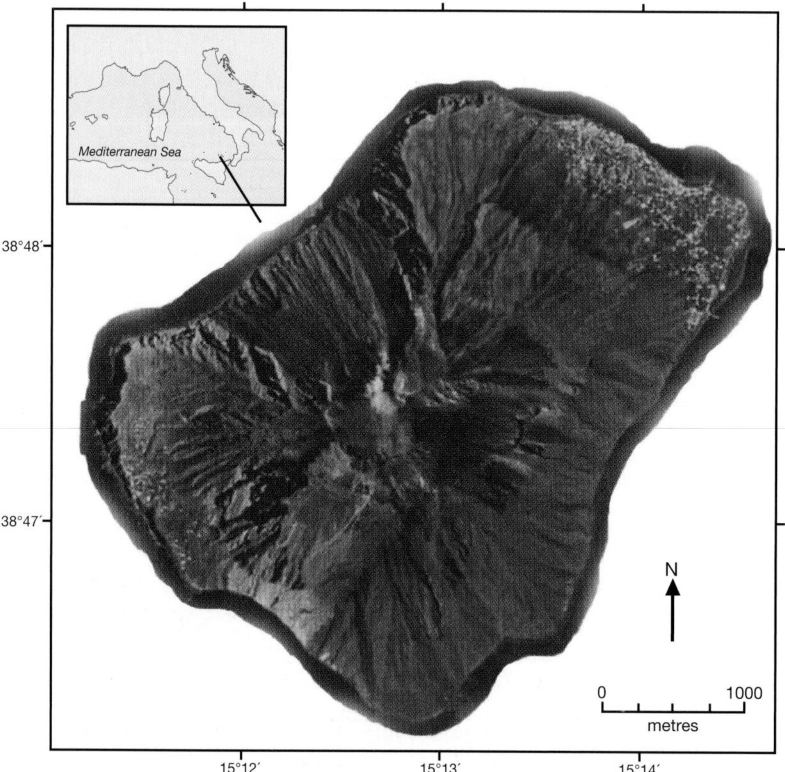

Figure 19.3: Orthophoto of Stromboli Island in the Mediterranean Sea (survey of May 2001). Note the presence of an active volcano in the centre of the photo. Source: Baldi *et al*. (2005).

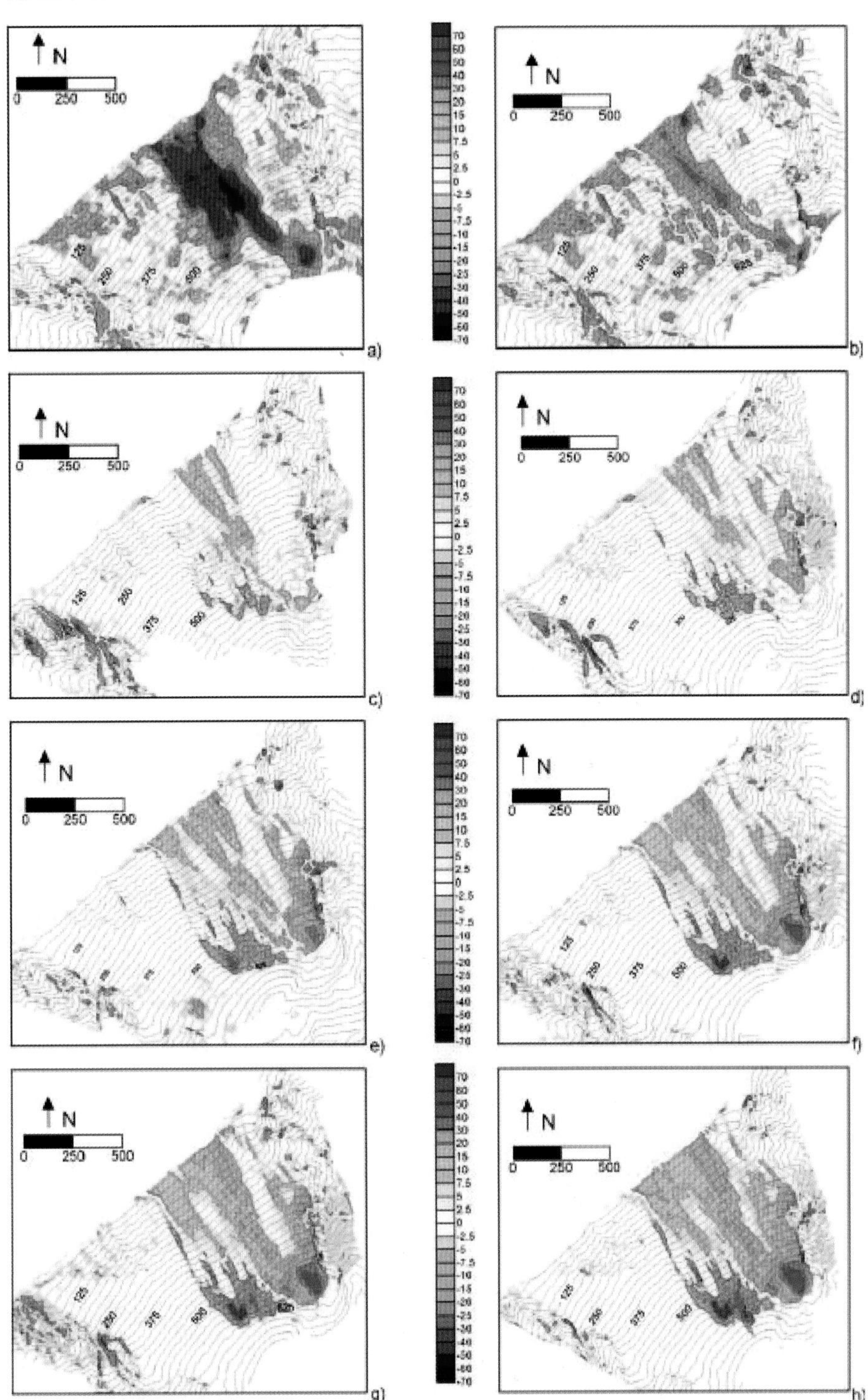

Figure 19.4: The changing shape of the north-west side of Stromboli Island. The maps shown are colour-coded from blue (erosion) to red (accumulation) to show the changing shape of this side of the mountain as a result of volcanic activity between January 2001 and September 2003. Data was surveyed at the following times:
a) 2001 and 5 January 2003;
b) 2001 and 27January 2003;
c) 27/01/03–21/02/03;
d) 27/01/03–15/03/03;
e) 27/01/03–14/04/03;
f) 27/01/03–26/05/03;
g) 27/01/03–26/07/03;
h) 27/01/03–04/09/03.
Source: Baldi *et al*. (2005).

Figure 19.5 overleaf shows how GIS statistical techniques can be used to produce an average temperature map for the UK.

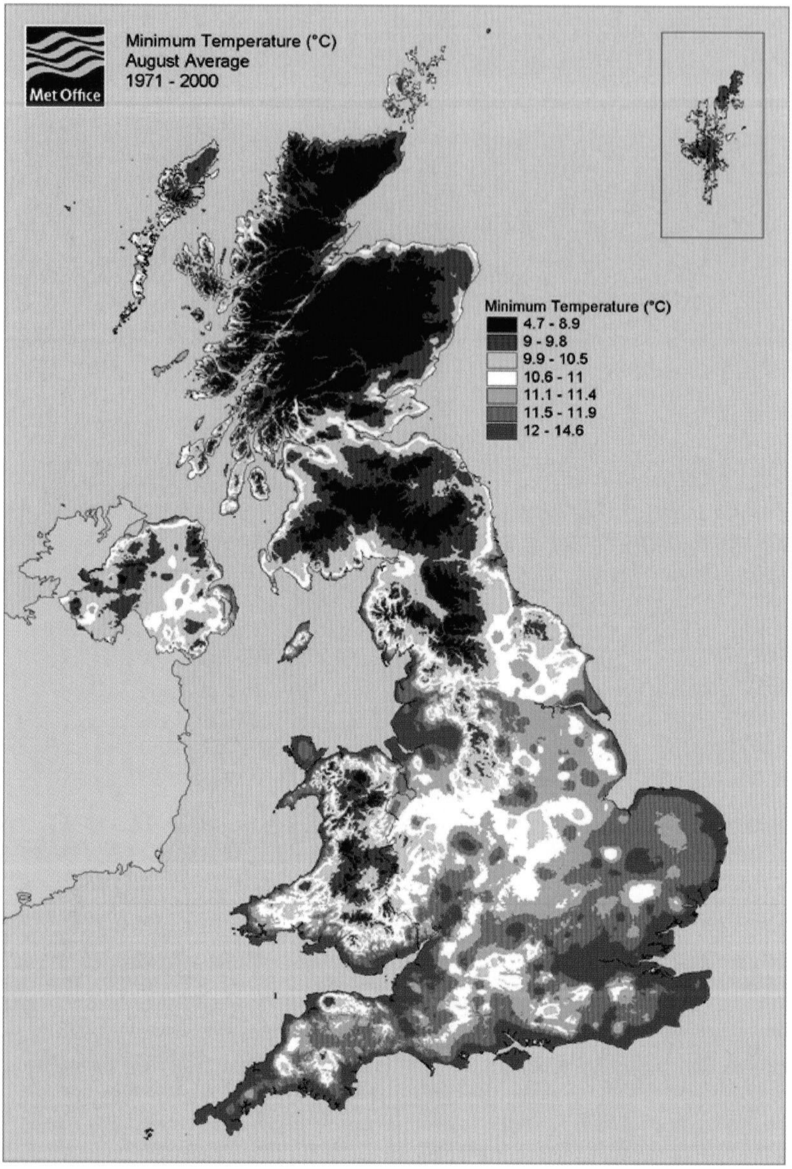

Figure 19.5: A map of UK August average temperatures between 1971 and 2000. The map was produced using GIS statistic processing techniques. Source: UK Met Office. © Crown Copyright 2008, the Met Office.

Scientists from the United Nations have used mathematical and statistical operations in GIS to estimate the likelihood of future water shortages in Africa. Their research estimates the relationship between average rainfall (Figure 19.6) and population density in Sub-Saharan Africa in order to assess the consequences of climate and demographic changes in terms of future water stress in that region. Geographic Information Systems (GIS) data on density and rainfall and climate change scenarios are combined statistically in order to identify areas which will be subject to increased pressures stemming from excessive population, given their precipitation levels (Figure 19.7).

Figure 19.6: Pattern of average yearly rainfall for Africa, 1962–1991. Source: le Blanc and Perez (2007).

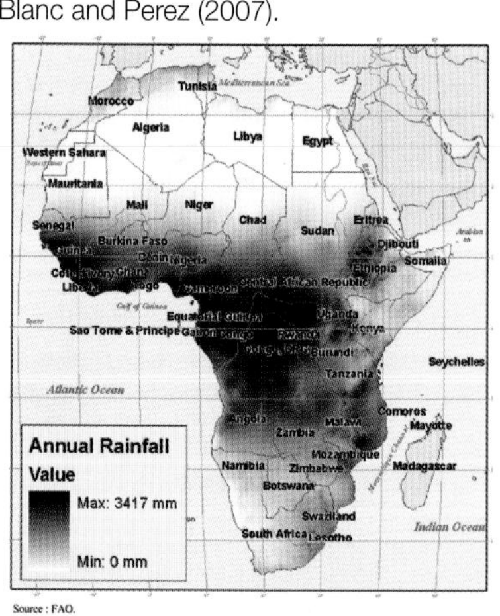

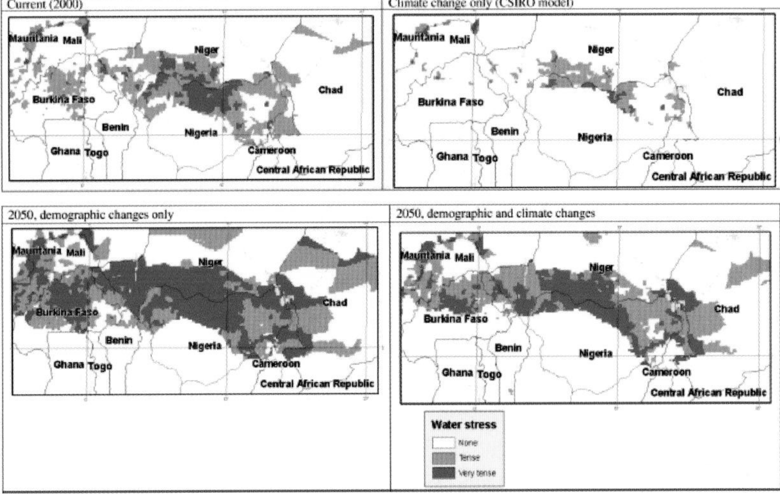

Figure 19.7: Projected estimates of areas likely to experience tense water stress and very tense water stress in the Sahel from 2000 to 2050 associated with projected population and climate change. Source: le Blanc and Perez (2007).

Questions

- Why do you think it has been suggested that raster data is particularly suited to analysis by statistical and mathematical methods?
- What mathematical or statistical techniques do you think have been used to produce the images shown in Figure 19.4?

20

Boolean operations and reclassification

Boolean operations

Another common tool used in GIS to manipulate data relates to the use of **boolean operations**. These may result in the combination of data layers or may be performed on the attribute data of a single layer. Boolean operations can be used with both vector and raster data. Boolean operations use the logical operations AND, OR, NOT, XOR to determine whether a particular statement is true or false. Each of the statements is used to find:

- The intersection of two data sets – those features that belong to both A and B data sets can be found by using the AND command.
- The union of two data sets – those features that belong either to set A or to set B can be found using the OR command.
- The difference between two data sets – those features that belong to A but not to B can be found using the NOT command.
- The exclusive data – a set of features that belong to one set or another but not to both can be found by the XOR command.

Here are some examples of the types of questions that can be asked using Boolean operations:

Where do crime and urban areas exist?	crime AND urban areas
Where do crime or urban areas occur?	crime OR urban areas
Where does crime rather than urban areas exist?	crime NOT urban areas
Where do either crime or urban areas occur?	crime XOR urban areas

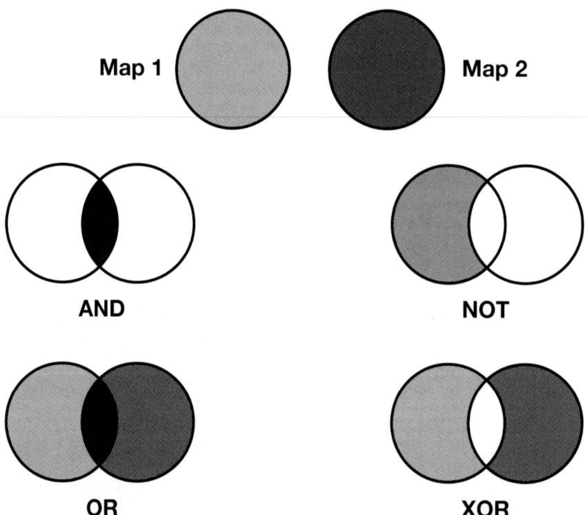

Figure 20.1: Venn diagrams showing the results of applying Boolean operations. Source: ASET (2005).

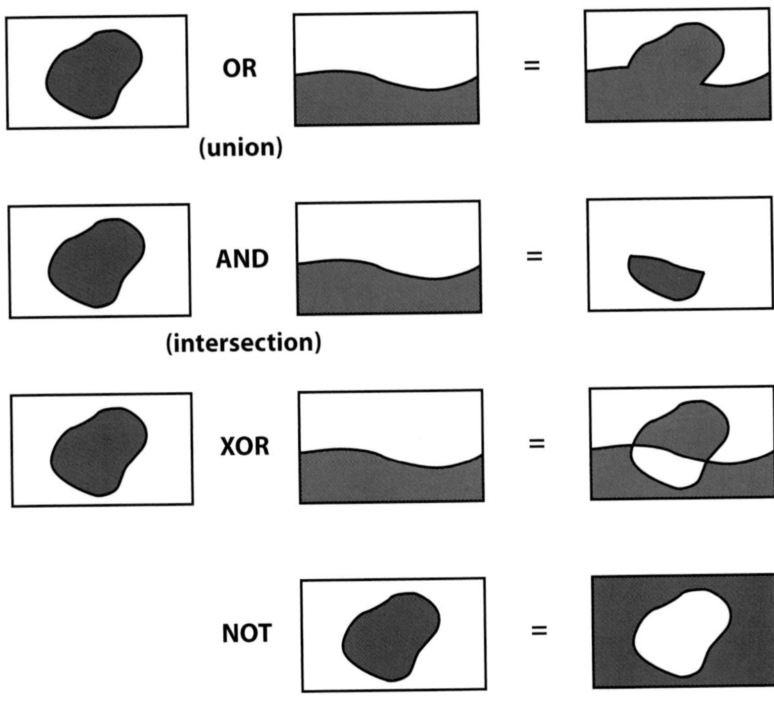

Figure 20.2: The application of Boolean logic to a simplified map. Source: Morad and Connolly (2001).

Using these types of questions, a GIS analyst might be trying to find out whether there is any relationship between the existence of urban areas and the level of criminal activity.

Figure 20.1 opposite shows the result of Boolean logical operations as applied to a series of Venn diagrams. Figure 20.2 shows how Boolean operations would apply to two simplified mapping layers.

Figure 20.3 shows the application of Boolean logic to find the number of train stations that exist in the Peak District National Park, England. The search was completed using a simple AND operation:

Where do the Peak District National Park AND train stations occur?

This search quickly established that there are only five train stations in the Peak District National Park out of the 2,645 stations that occur nationally.

Figure 20.3: The use of Boolean logic to find the number of train stations located in the Peak District National Park, England. Note how the map highlights the location of the train stations in light blue while also displaying their names in the attributes table. Created in ArcView using ESRI Data and Maps.

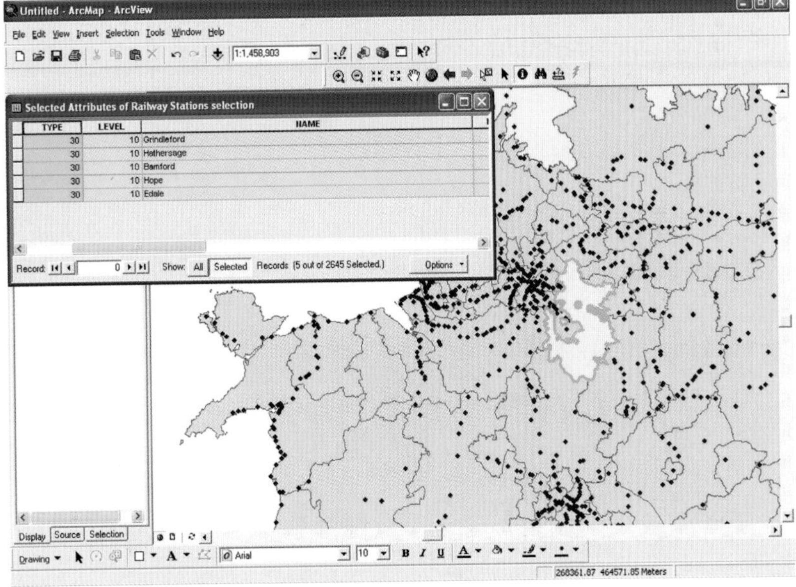

Reclassification functions

Reclassification is a method frequently used in GIS. Consider the problem of trying to identify all the areas along a coast that would flood if there was a 5m rise in sea level associated with global warming. Reclassification techniques could help identify the answer. Figure 20.4 shows a height model for the south-eastern United States. Each green-coloured cell in the image holds a unique value to represent height. Therefore the image could have potentially thousands of height values depending on its resolution. To help identify clearly the land area that would be affected by a 5m rise in sea level, all the cell values in the image that are less than or equal to 5m can be given a single new value. The new value can then be associated with a new colour – in this instance red. The resulting reclassification clearly shows the areas of land that could be flooded as a result of future global warming (Figure 20.4).

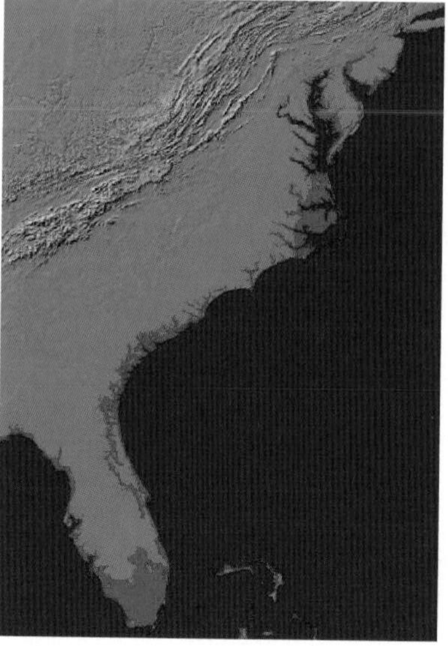

Figure 20.4: An example of an image that could be produced using reclassification. The image shows the effects of a potential rise in sea level caused by the melting of Greenland's ice sheets. Red indicates where land would be submerged as a result of an estimated 5m sea-level rise. The area shown includes Florida and other parts of the south-eastern United States. Source: Tralli *et al.* (2005).

Other frequently used reclassification methods include the processes of **dissolve** and **merge**. The merging of data is often necessary to display data collected at a small scale with maps that cover larger areas. For example, census data which is collected at the household level is merged and averaged out over larger areas to ensure confidentiality. Figure 20.5 shows lower super output areas and county boundaries in the UK. The scale of the lower super output areas is too small for visualising patterns at the national scale. As a result, data from lower super output areas is often merged to produce an average for a county, which is a much more useful scale for recognising national patterns. Census data is often merged to show national variation by county in population size, car ownership, household size, incidence of crime, standards of housing, and other social and economic indicators.

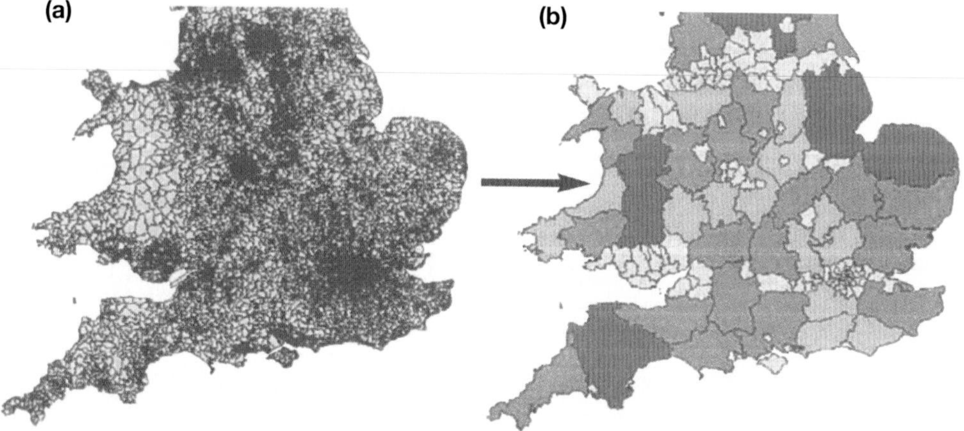

Figure 20.5: A) Lower super output areas in the UK. **B**) County boundaries in the UK. The data held at lower super output area scale has been merged and displayed at county level. This type of operation is called data merge of aggregation. Created in ArcView from digital mapping supplied by ONS.

Dissolve operations are often used to simplify the number of boundaries that appear on a map. For example, Figure 20.6 shows two simplified maps A and B. The colours in each of the maps represent different soil types. Map A shows that the soil survey took place in four different areas as represented by the four rectangles. In order to enhance the use of the map, the boundaries between soils of the same type have been removed. This produces a simpler map B. Such techniques are often used by major map producers to make maps more accessible to the non-specialist user.

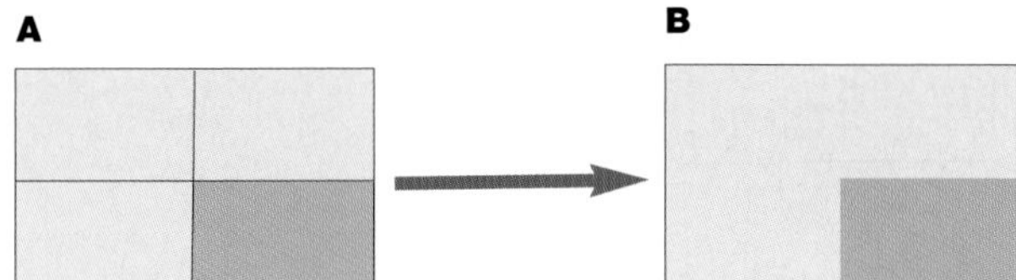

Figure 20.6: The dissolving of boundaries in **A** to produce a simpler image in **B**.

Questions

- What are Boolean operations in GIS?
- Design two geographical questions that could be asked using Boolean operations.
- What types of geographical problems could be investigated using reclassification methods?

21

Overlay operations

Overlay operations are an essential part of GIS. The process of overlay offers the potential for combining different layers of imagery to create new maps.

Figure 21.1 is an example of a raster overlay operation. Here images that relate to % unemployment, deprivation, % elderly population and distance to existing GP practices have been combined to suggest possible locations for new 'super surgeries'. When raster overlay operations are carried out, cells in one layer will correspond directly with cells in another layer (see Figure 21.2).

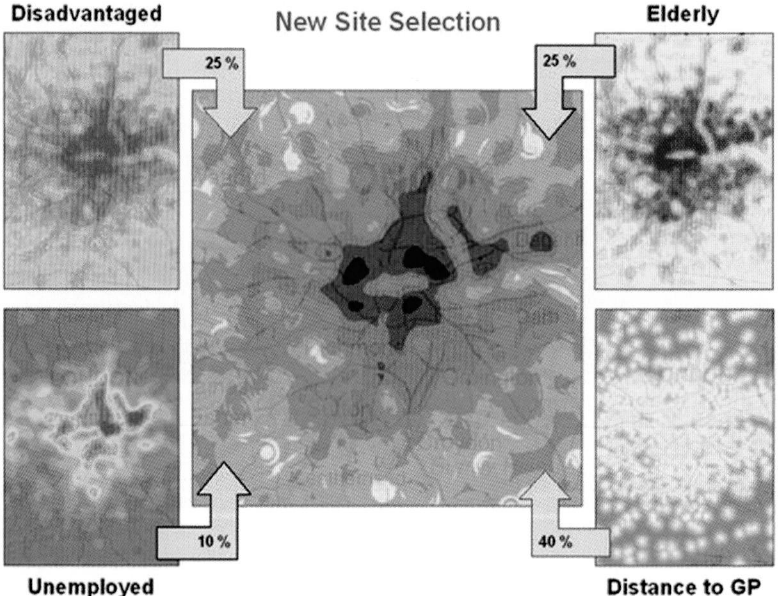

Figure 21.1: The four images in this dataset have been combined to suggest possible locations for new 'super surgeries'. Source: ESRI (UK).

Figure 21.2: An example of a raster overlay operation. When raster overlays are conducted, the value of a cell in one layer is directly combined with the corresponding cell in the other layer. How the cells are combined will depend on the mathematical or statistical methods chosen. Source: Adapted from ESRI (2004b).

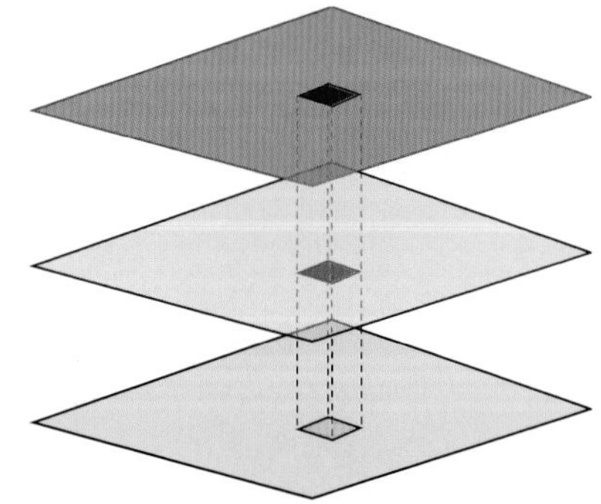

In the case of vector data there are three main types of overlay operation:

- Point-in-polygon
- Line-in-polygon
- Polygon-on-polygon overlay

A **point-in-polygon** overlay represents issues of containment. Containment often deals with questions such as how many houses are located within the city boundaries of Manchester, England. Figure 21.3 shows a point-in-polygon overlay. The points in this instance represent large towns. The polygons represent the county boundaries to be found in Wales and neighbouring parts of England. When the two layers are superimposed, it is possible to count the number of large towns in each county.

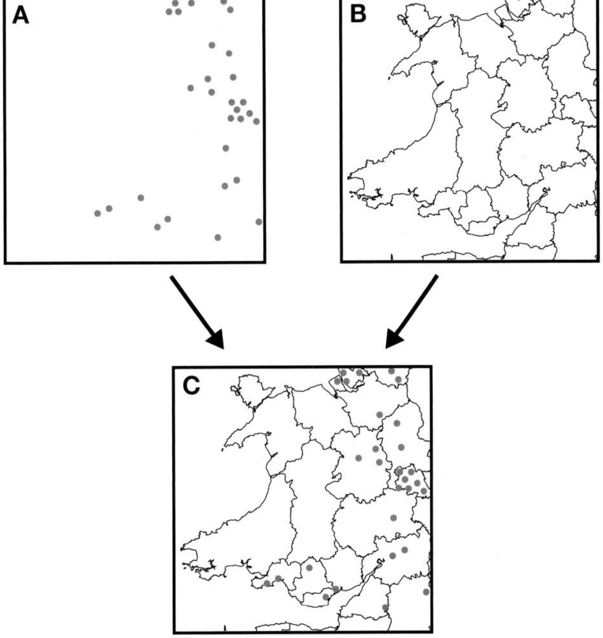

Figure 21.3: A point-in-polygon overlay between (**A**) large towns and (**B**) counties results in the combined image **C**.

A **line-in-polygon** overlay also considers issues of containment. An example of this type of process is shown in Figure 21.4.

Polygon-on-polygon overlay operations are frequently used to find

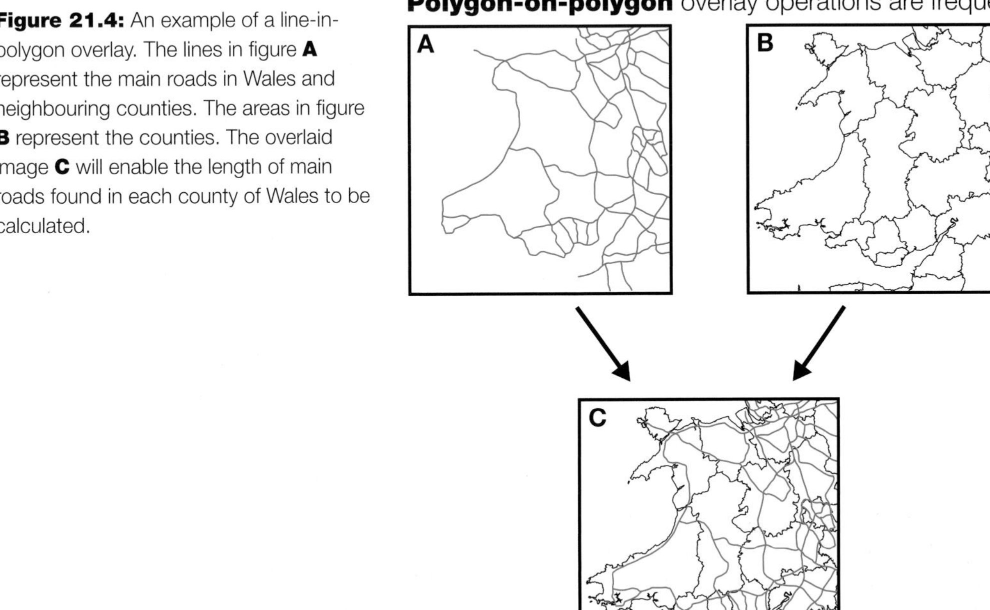

Figure 21.4: An example of a line-in-polygon overlay. The lines in figure **A** represent the main roads in Wales and neighbouring counties. The areas in figure **B** represent the counties. The overlaid image **C** will enable the length of main roads found in each county of Wales to be calculated.

Polygon-on-polygon overlay operations are frequently used to find sites for proposed developments. With multiple layers of data, the features best suited to a development can be identified from each layer and then combined to find a best site. Boolean logic is commonly applied to the process of overlaying different layers of information. Such techniques have been employed in trying to locate sites for the handling of nuclear waste. Figure 21.5 shows a simplified diagram which attempts to locate future sites for urban development while trying to avoid the best agricultural land.

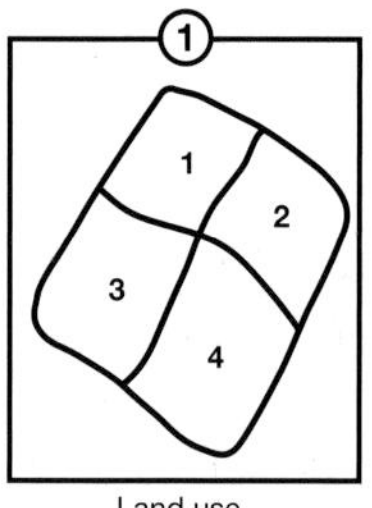

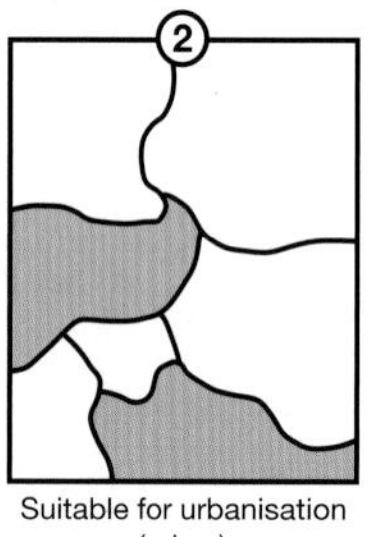

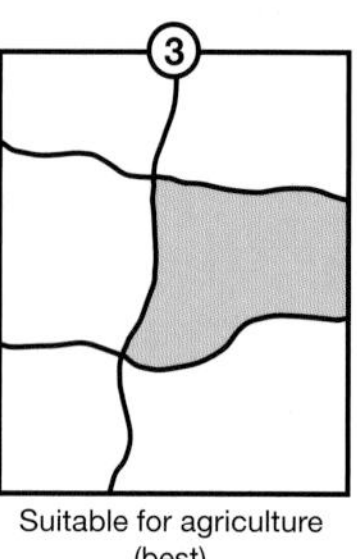

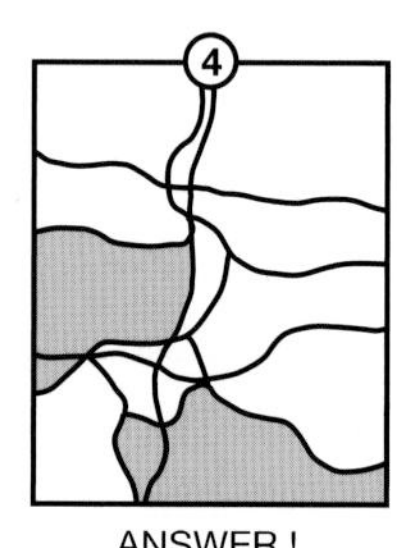

Figure 21.5: An example of a polygon-on-polygon overlay used to identify the best potential sites for urban development. Source: ASET (2005).

Questions

- What is the function of overlay operations in GIS?
- What types of vector overlay operations can be used in GIS? What types of geographical questions can be asked using vector overlay operations?

22 Buffer operations

Buffer operations create units of distance around points (see Figure 22.1), lines and polygons. This function is used widely in GIS to address many practical problems.

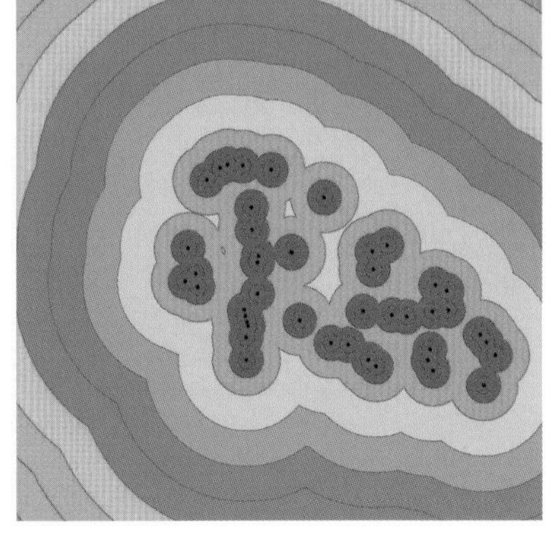

Figure 22.1: An example of buffer zones around a series of points. The points in this instance are water wells and each of the different coloured buffers represents an increase in distance of 1km from the wells.

For example, buffers are often created around buildings or towns during emergency situations to identify zones of exclusion or safety that can be managed by the police and other public safety services (e.g. Figure 22.2).

Buffers can also be used to establish accessibility of resources such as hospitals, schools and shops to different groups. Governments and other organisations are using such techniques to identity areas where service provision is not sufficient to meet the needs of local populations.

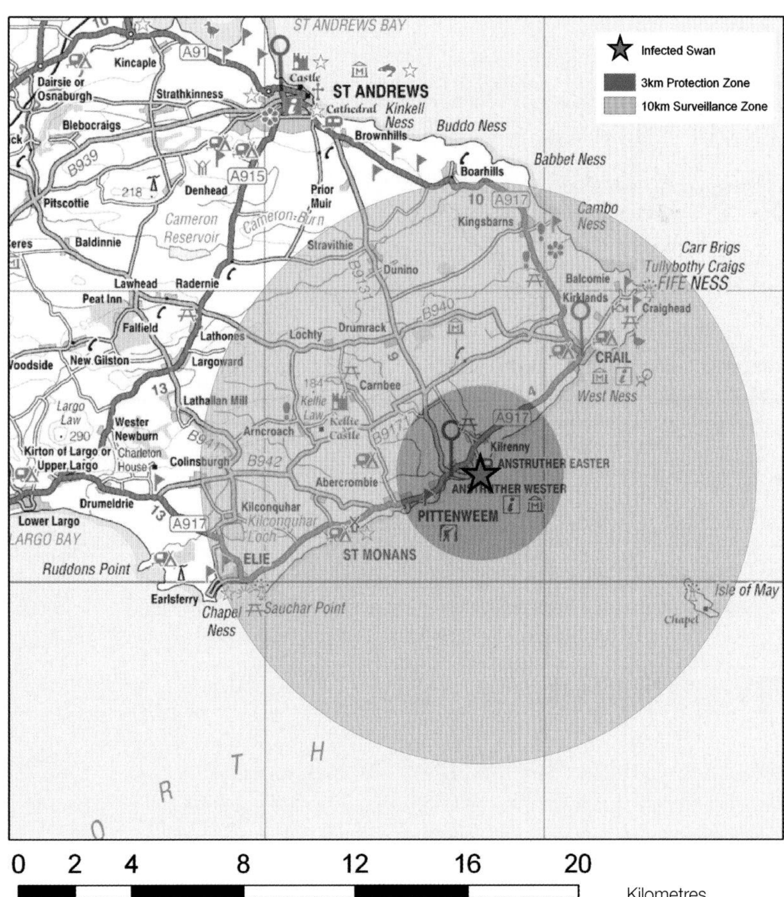

Figure 22.2: A buffer analysis used to show emergency planners a 3km protection zone and an 10km surveillance zone around a suspected case of avian flu. Source: ESRI (UK). OS base mapping reproduced with permission.

For example, malaria is one of the biggest single causes of death in less economically developed countries. Figure 22.3 shows the number of cases of malaria that occur in an area of South Africa. Figure 22.4 shows the location of medical facilities in the same area with buffers at 5km intervals drawn around the medical centres.

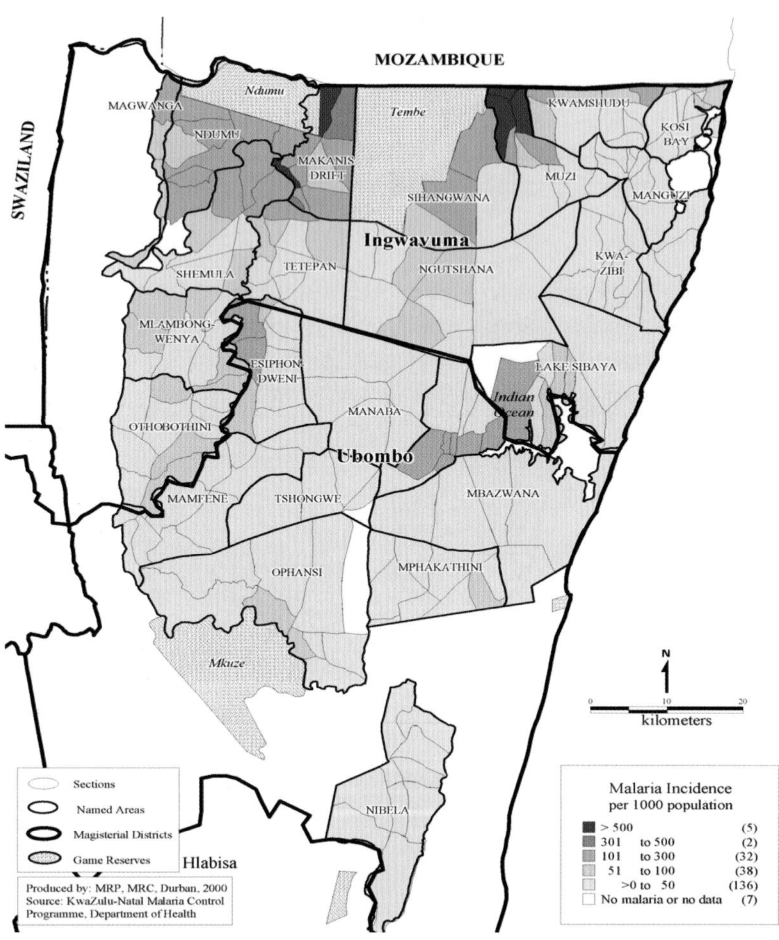

Figure 22.3: Incidence of malaria cases by malaria sections in the Ingwavuma and Ubombo Districts of KwaZulu-Natal Province, South Africa, 1998/99. Source: Martin *et al.* (2002).

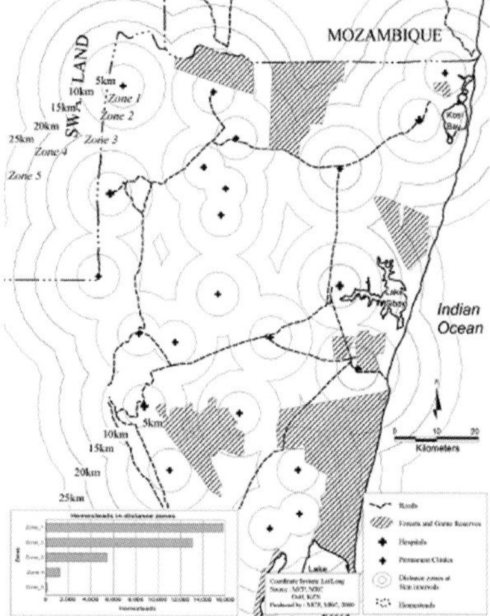

Figure 22.4: Location of homesteads with respect to distance from health facilities in KwaZulu-Natal Province, South Africa. The buffers are shown around centres of local health provision. The buffers are in units of 5 km. Source: Martin *et al.* (2002).

A comparison of these two maps will allow government officials to determine whether the medical facilities that do exist in this area are situated in the right locations for managing malaria effectively.

Questions

- What is meant by the term buffer operation in GIS?
- What types of geographical issues can buffer operations be used to investigate?

Topic G: Advanced techniques in GIS analysis

23 Network analysis

There are a range of GIS analysis techniques that require a highly developed understanding of the topic if they are to be applied accurately. Also, these techniques are often not standard in most GIS packages and have to be purchased as add-ons before analysis can be carried out. However, advanced spatial analysis is becoming more common among organisations and government departments, so an awareness of these techniques is fundamental to understanding the full capability of GIS. The first of them to be considered here is **network analysis**.

Networks exist all around us in the form of linear features that connect items together. The lines could be roads, rivers, electricity cables, phone lines, gas or water pipes, telephone lines or any other type of linear feature. When more than one of these lines are joined together they become a network. Network analysis is particularly important to utility companies that deliver services such as electricity and gas. Electricity companies use network analysis to find the shortest distance between two places. Finding the most efficient route between a power station and a new housing development could make the company a significant financial saving by reducing labour and material costs. The other major functions associated with network analysis include:

- Drive-time analysis – how long will it take to travel from London to Glasgow?
- Point-to-point routing – what is the best route to take between London and Glasgow?
- Route directions – attribute descriptions can be provided indicating which roads to take and when to turn left or right.
- Service area definition – providing descriptions of areas where utilities need to managed.
- Shortest path – finding the shortest route between two locations.
- Optimum route – this suggests not only the shortest route, but also the most cost-efficient one in terms of laying pipelines etc.
- Closest facility - where is the closest hospital given the location of an emergency incident (see Figure 23.1 overleaf)?

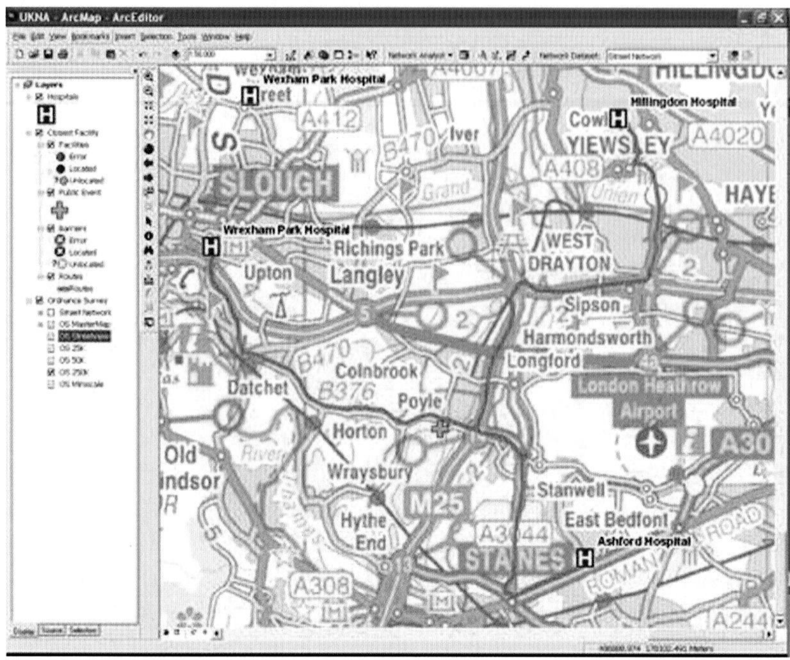

Figure 23.1: An example of network analysis being used to identify the closest hospital, given the location of a traffic accident. Source: ESRI (UK). OS base mapping reproduced with permission.

Network analysis in GIS is commonly employed on the internet to help with route planning. For example, the Automobile Association (AA) has a website (*www.theaa.com*) that enables motorists to plan journeys and map routes. Figure 23.2 provides an example of how the system works.

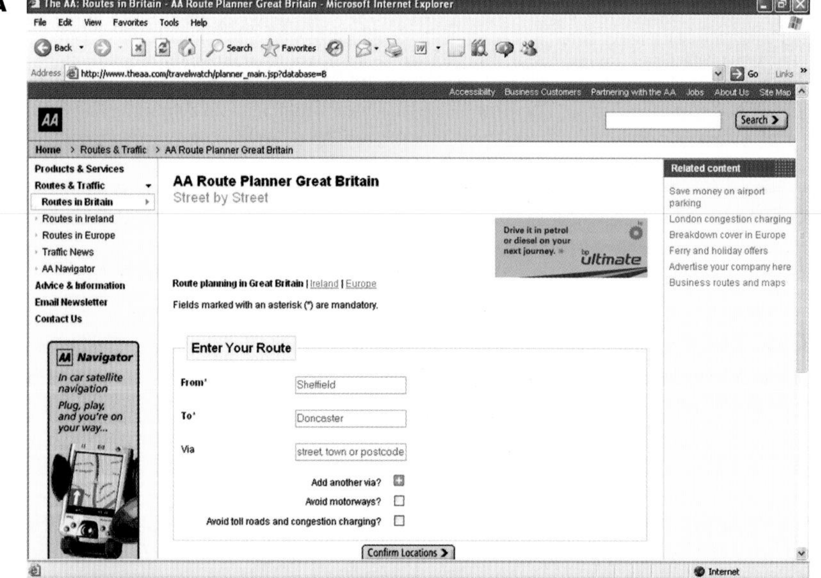

Figure 23.2: A) The town, street or postcode is entered for the source and destination locations – in this instance Sheffield and Doncaster. **B**) A map is created showing the route between Sheffield and Doncaster. **C**) A report is produced listing directions, road names and mileages along the route from Sheffield to Doncaster. OS base mapping reproduced with permission.

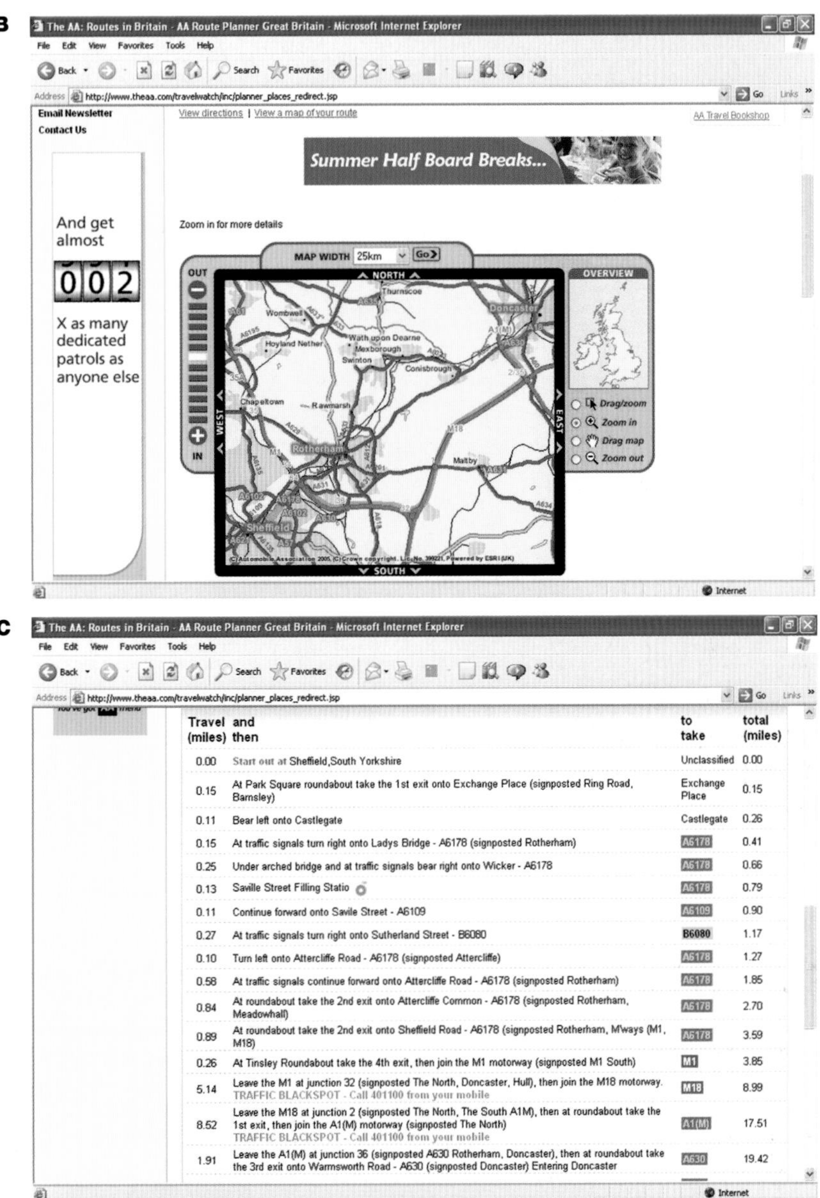

Travel (miles)	and then	to take	total (miles)
0.00	Start out at Sheffield,South Yorkshire	Unclassified	0.00
0.15	At Park Square roundabout take the 1st exit onto Exchange Place (signposted Ring Road, Barnsley)	Exchange Place	0.15
0.11	Bear left onto Castlegate	Castlegate	0.26
0.15	At traffic signals turn right onto Ladys Bridge - A6178 (signposted Rotherham)	A6178	0.41
0.25	Under arched bridge and at traffic signals bear right onto Wicker - A6178	A6178	0.66
0.13	Saville Street Filling Statio	A6178	0.79
0.11	Continue forward onto Savile Street - A6109	A6109	0.90
0.27	At traffic signals turn right onto Sutherland Street - B6080	B6080	1.17
0.10	Turn left onto Attercliffe Road - A6178 (signposted Attercliffe)	A6178	1.27
0.58	At traffic signals continue forward onto Attercliffe Road - A6178 (signposted Rotherham)	A6178	1.85
0.84	At roundabout take the 2nd exit onto Attercliffe Common - A6178 (signposted Rotherham, Meadowhall)	A6178	2.70
0.89	At roundabout take the 2nd exit onto Sheffield Road - A6178 (signposted Rotherham, M'ways (M1, M18)	A6178	3.59
0.26	At Tinsley Roundabout take the 4th exit, then join the M1 motorway (signposted M1 South)	M1	3.85
5.14	Leave the M1 at junction 32 (signposted The North, Doncaster, Hull), then join the M18 motorway. TRAFFIC BLACKSPOT - Call 401100 from your mobile	M18	8.99
8.52	Leave the M18 at junction 2 (signposted The North, The South A1M), then at roundabout take the 1st exit, then join the A1(M) motorway (signposted The North) TRAFFIC BLACKSPOT - Call 401100 from your mobile	A1(M)	17.51
1.91	Leave the A1(M) at junction 36 (signposted A630 Rotherham, Doncaster), then at roundabout take the 3rd exit onto Warmsworth Road - A630 (signposted Doncaster) Entering Doncaster	A630	19.42

Networks, just like any other data type used within GIS, can have vast amounts of attribute data linked to the displayed mapping layer. Attribute data can include photographs, documents, schematic drawings and flow directions (see Figure 23.3). This capability, linked to the types of questions that network analysis can answer, makes network analysis a very powerful and important technique in GIS.

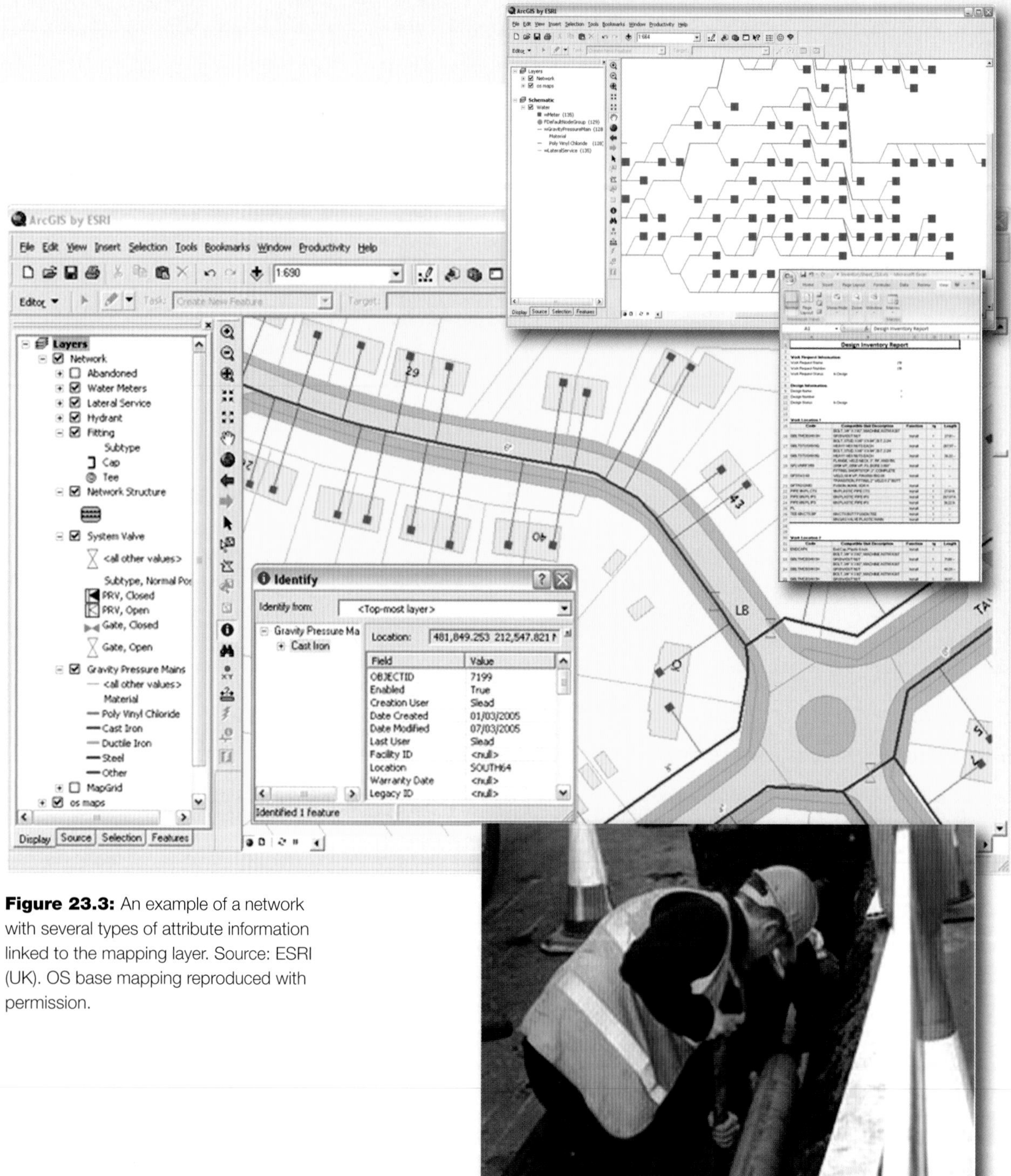

Figure 23.3: An example of a network with several types of attribute information linked to the mapping layer. Source: ESRI (UK). OS base mapping reproduced with permission.

Questions

- What industries would benefit from network analysis within their organisations and why?
- Why is the linking of attribute data to network analysis important?

24

Spatial interpolation and density estimation

Spatial interpolation

Spatial interpolation is used to turn a series of point observations into a continuous surface. Point data sets are limited in their ability to represent surface elevation, rainfall, temperature and other variables that have a large potential surface variability. Polygons and lines are also sometimes limited in their ability to represent continuous surfaces because the boundaries between features are too sharp and unrealistic (see Figure 24.1).

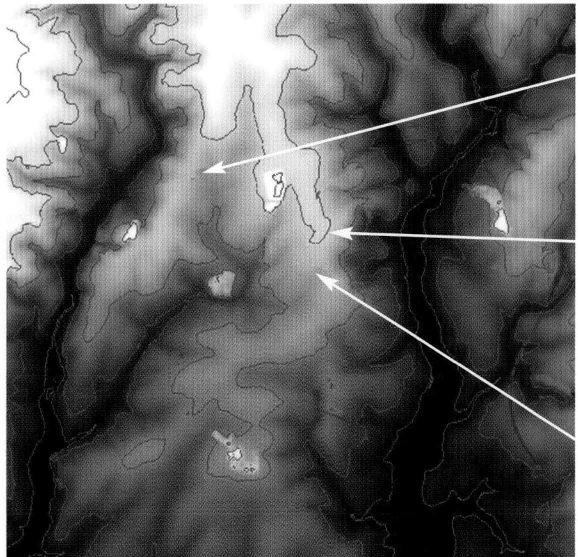

Figure 24.1: Vector and continuous (raster) height models of the area of Bishop's Stortford, East Hertfordshire, England. The green lines are at 15m contour intervals representing changes in height across the landscape. The black-and-white image is a raster-model continuous surface. The lighter, whiter colours represent increases in height. The raster model is made up of cells, with each cell recording an individual height value. The higher sampling rate of the raster continuous surface is a more accurate representation of the height variations occurring in the landscape. Created in ArcView from original image supplied by Digital Worlds.

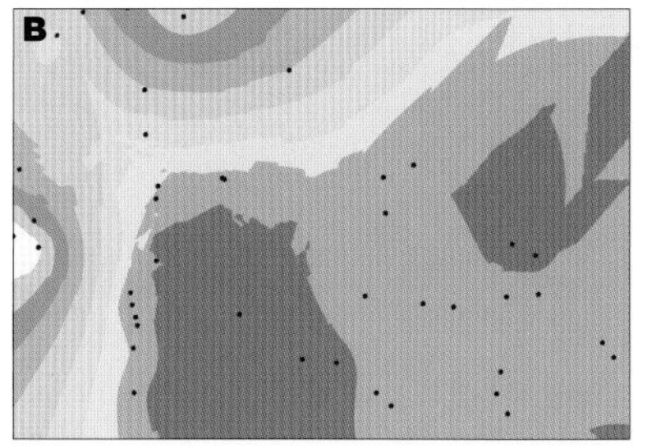

Figure 24.2: A shows a series of points that record height. **B** is the interpolated surface from **A**. Which image is best used for visualising changes in altitude?

The process of spatial interpolation is useful for a number of reasons:

- Interpolation estimates the characteristics of areas where no data has been collected.
- It is often easier to recognise the spatial patterns associated with an interpolated surface than to try to understand the meaning of a series of points (see Figure 24.2).
- Interpolation is a cost-effective way of generating a continuous surface.

Interpolation is most frequently used to generate height models from a limited number of ground observations. These height models are then often used to generate contour lines for topographic mapping.

Interpolation is generally only used for estimating surfaces for features that occur continuously within the environment, such as rainfall and temperature. For example, there would be no point in trying to interpolate a housing surface, as houses are discrete and do not occur everywhere in the landscape.

Density estimation

A technique related to interpolation is **density mapping**. However, density mapping is performed on discrete features in the landscape such as cities, populations, diseases, animals and crime incidents. For example, Figure 24.3 includes a density map for the number of train stations in the UK.

Figure 24.3: **A**) The point locations of train stations in England and Wales. **B**) A surface density estimation of train stations in England and Wales, calculated from **A**. Created in ArcView using ESRI Data and Maps.

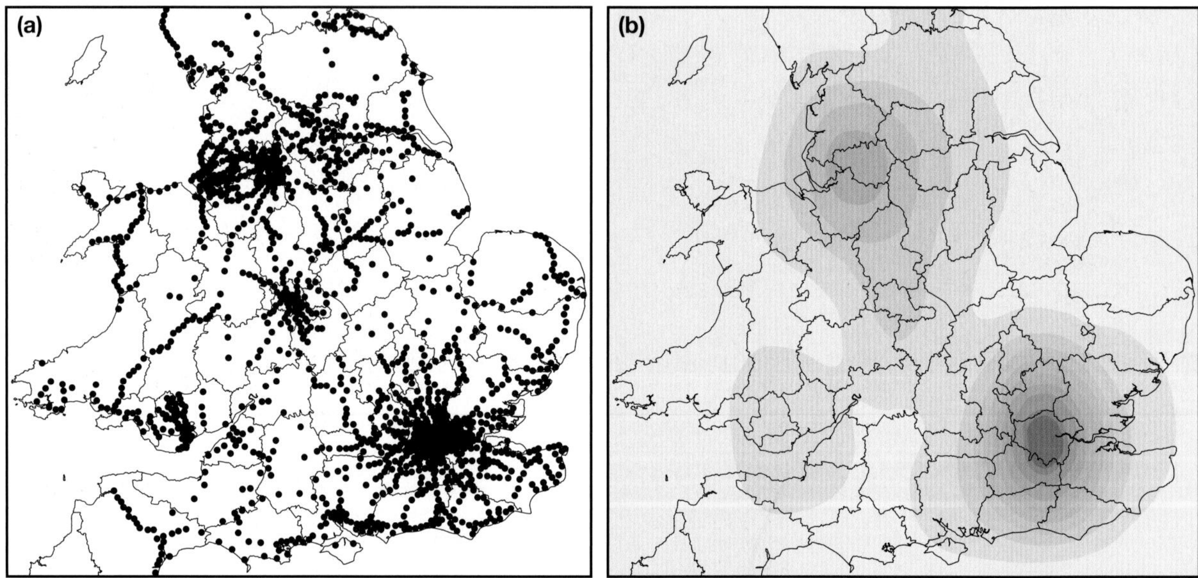

Density estimations are also used in policing to identify so-called crime hotspots. The hotspots show areas where certain types of crime have occurred the most – or put another way, areas of highest crime density. Figure 24.4 shows a hotspot map for burglaries in Harlesden. Police can use this information to target resources in particular areas so as to discourage criminal activity.

Figure 24.4: A crime density map showing the average number of burglaries committed in Harlesden. The red and blue represent high and low levels of crime. This map was generated using 12 months of crime statistics. Source: ESRI (UK).

Questions

- What is the difference between continuous and discrete data?
- What is the difference between spatial interpolation and density estimation?
- Identify examples of geographical questions that could be derived from interpolation and density estimation techniques.

25 Three-dimensional analysis and landscape visualisation

Most of the discussion so far has dealt with GIS analysis within two dimensions. However, GIS also has the capability to perform analysis in **three dimensions** (3D), adding in the extra dimension of height (see Figure 25.1). These 3D landscapes can be used not only for analysis but also for visualising the environment. Some of the techniques most commonly used in GIS are outlined below.

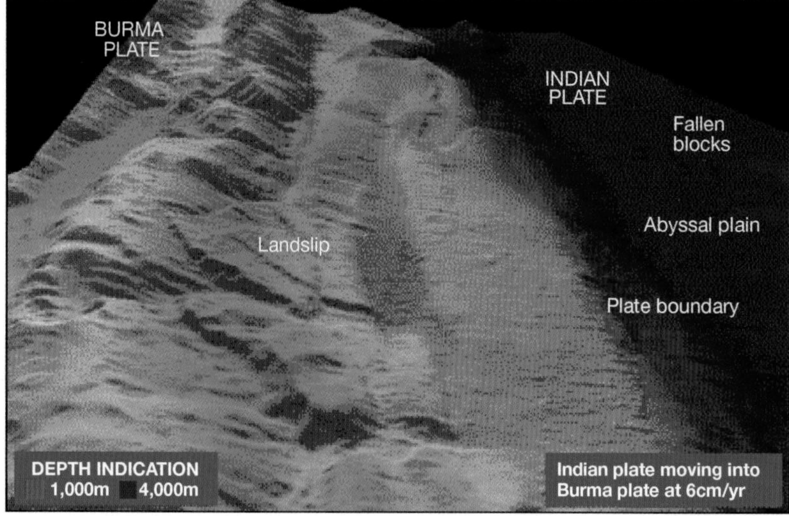

Figure 25.1: A 3D model of the boundaries between the Burma and Indian tectonic plates, the movement of which caused the Indian Ocean tsunami in December 2004. Scientists have been examining images like this in order to gain a better understanding of the causes of the tsunami, which killed over 250,000 people. Data were gathered by HMS Scott, a UK Royal Navy Survey vessel, during maritime scientific research co-ordinated by the Joint Environment Directorate of Defence Intelligence. The Royal Navy, British Geological Survey, National Oceanographic Centre (Southampton), United Kingdom Hydrographic Office and the Government of Indonesia co-operated on this project. Source: Royal Navy (2005).

Three-dimensional models of the landscape, frequently referred to in GIS as digital elevation models (DEMs), are a powerful data set from which many types of analysis can be made. However, DEMs are most frequently used to calculate:

- contour values for topographic mapping (Figure 25.2 overleaf)
- estimates of slope (Figure 25.3 overleaf)
- estimates of aspect (Figure 25.4 overleaf)
- hillshade models of an environment (Figure 25.5 on page 110)

and construct visualisation models of landscapes.

DEMs are most commonly used to produce contours for topographic mapping. Estimates of slope and aspect are used in selecting the best sites for different human activities. For example, if a new shopping development were to be built, areas with steep slopes would need to

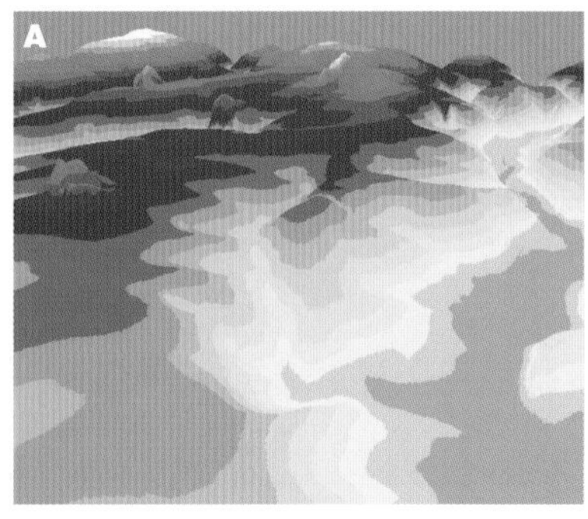

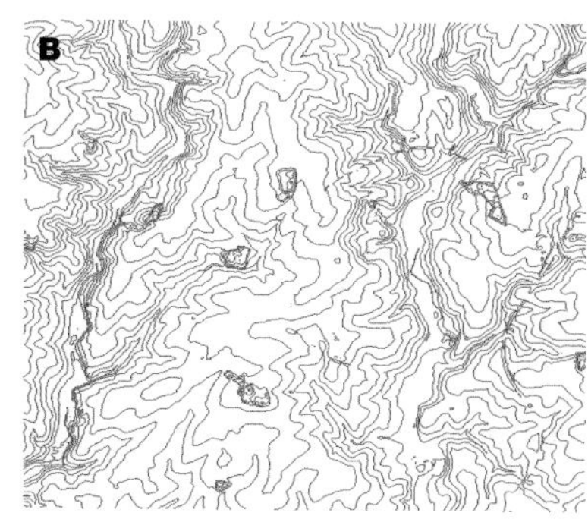

Figure 25.2: An example of a DEM (**A**) used to estimate contour values (**B**) that would then most probably be added to a topographic map. Adapted from ESRI (2004e).

be avoided to reduce building costs and enable easy access. Likewise, farmers might want to choose an area with a sunny aspect that exposed their crops to the maximum direct sunlight to increase yields. These types of analysis techniques are commonly employed by civil engineers, business developers and agricultural workers.

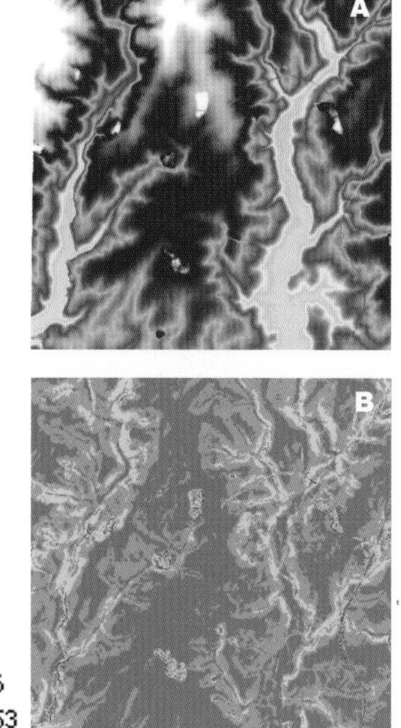

Figure 25.3: An elevation model (**A**) is used to calculate slope values (**B**) for the area of the map.

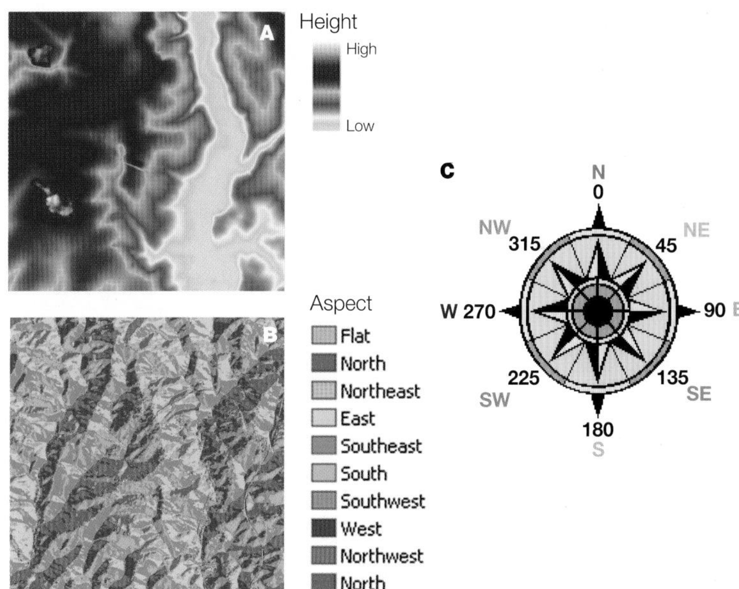

Figure 25.4: An elevation model (**A**) is used to produce a map (**B**) which shows aspect. Aspect is a measure of the direction that a slope faces and is either given as a compass bearing or in units of degrees (**C**). Adapted from ESRI (2004e).

Hillshade models are calculated from DEMs to show the movement of shadow across a landscape. If the number of direct sunshine hours is important in the positioning of a house, this type of analysis is very useful. Hillshading is a technique frequently used in GIS to enhance the look of an image. Adding hillshade into an image adds depth, making landscapes look more realistic (Figure 25.5).

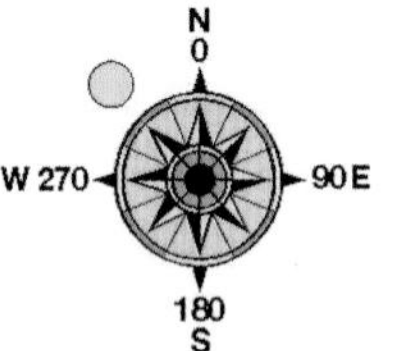

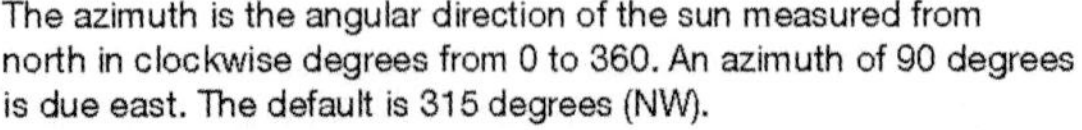

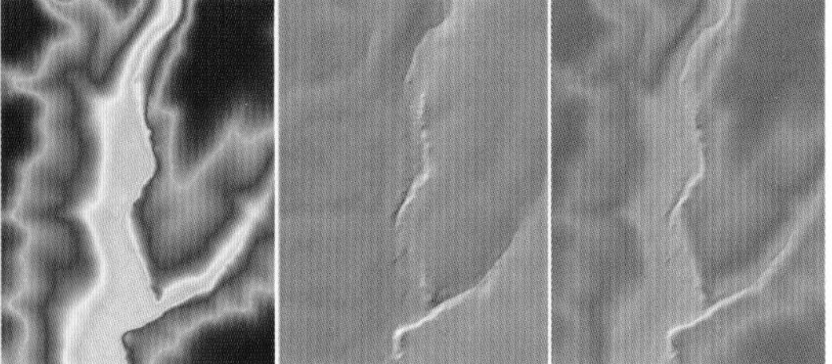

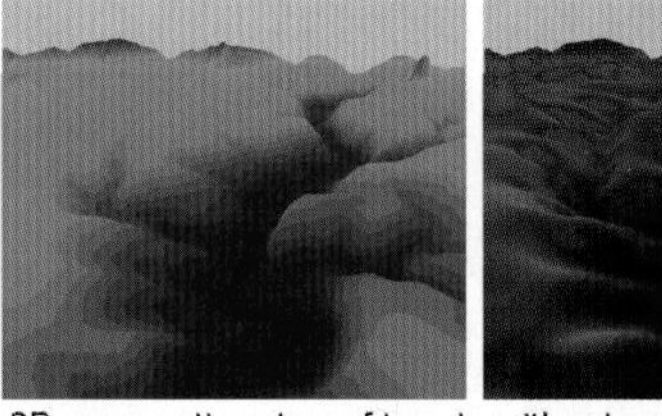

Figure 25.5: Elevation data can be used to produce maps of hillshade. Hillshade models indicate which parts of the landscape are in shadow at different times of the day. Adapted from ESRI (2004e).

DEMs are regularly used as a base layer for the overlay of other imagery in landscape visualisation. For example, Figure 25.6 shows a

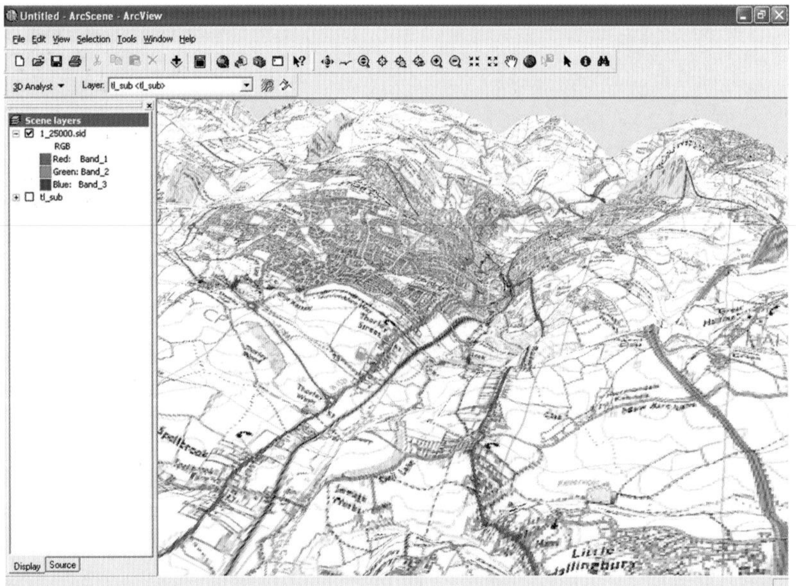

Figure 25.6: A 3D model of Bishop's Stortford, Hertfordshire, England. In order to be able to see clearly the height variations that exist in Bishop's Stortford, the heights in this image have been exaggerated by a factor of 15. OS base mapping reproduced with permission.

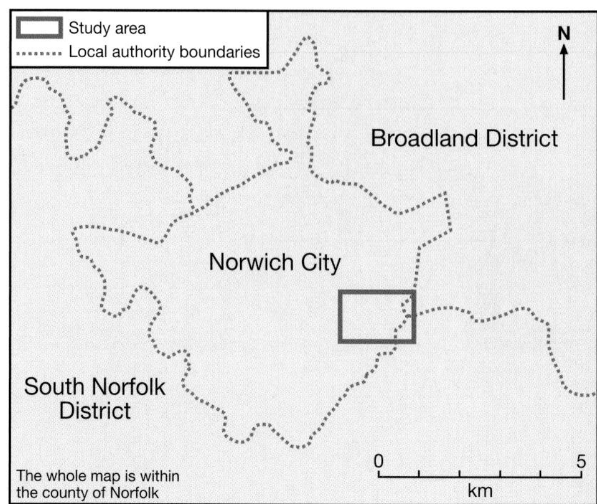

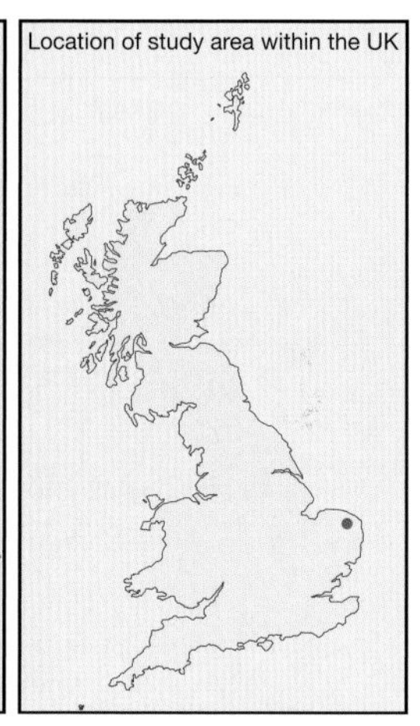

Figure 25.7: The location of Norwich City in relation to other neighbouring local authorities. Source: Appleton and Lovett (2005).

DEM of Bishop's Stortford, England with a 1:25,000-scale Ordnance Survey topographic map draped over it. Any type of imagery can be draped over a DEM, including aerial photography, satellite imagery or any other type of raster or vector data.

It is becoming more common to use GIS visualisation techniques in the planning process, especially to help members of the public understand the nature of proposed new developments. This can aid developers with their planning applications by helping the general public to understand what a development will look like in their existing environmental setting. In Figures 25.7 and 25.8, for example, Norwich City Council and researchers from the University of East Anglia have used visualisation techniques to help local residents understand how a proposed new riverside path for cyclists and pedestrians would look. Figure 25.8

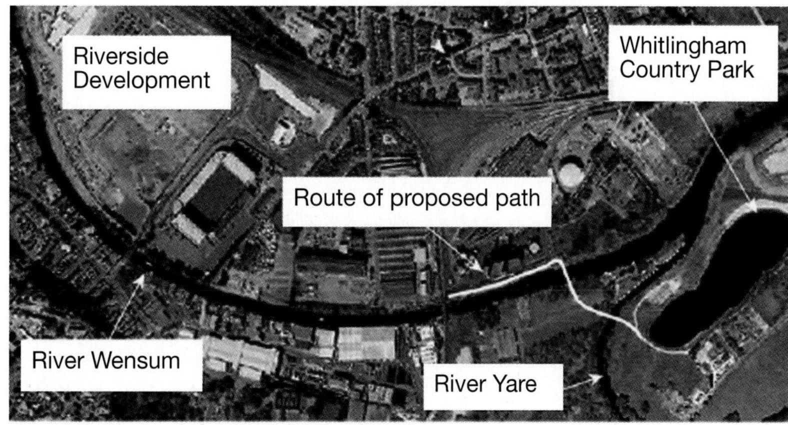

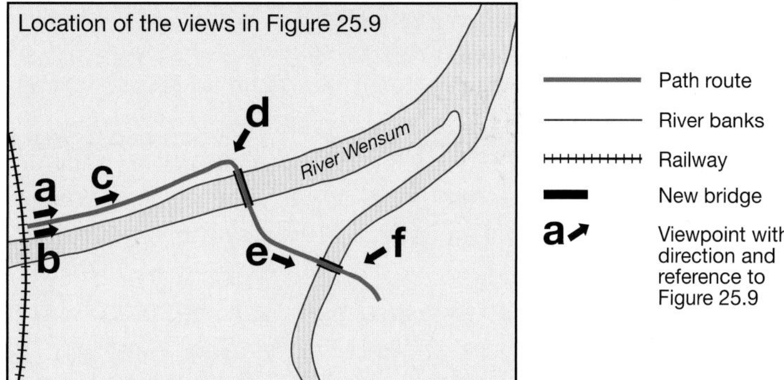

Figure 25.8: Overview of the area showing nearby features, path route and viewpoints associated with the Norwich City development. Source: Appleton and Lovett (2005).

shows the immediate surroundings for the development and the proposed route the new path will take.

Figure 25.9: Visualisations produced from each of the six viewpoints shown in Figure 25.8. Source: Appleton and Lovett (2005).

Figure 25.9 shows visualisations of different viewpoints along the proposed cycle route. The development of such images gives the public a much greater opportunity to interact with the planning process. This greater potential participation comes from the fact that the visualisations are much easier to understand. The public requires no technical background in landscape drawing or architecture to understand the look and function of the proposed development. In this way, public accessibility to the processes of planning and development is made easier by GIS visualisation techniques.

Questions

- Explain how a DEM is different from traditional raster or vector data.
- Give examples of the types of geographical investigations that could be carried out using DEM data.
- How can visualisation techniques associated with GIS help improve communication with the general public in the planning process?

26 Temporal and tracking analysis

It is also possible to link the dimension of time to GIS analysis. The data associated with time in geography and GIS is often referred to as **temporal data**. The temporal capabilities of GIS are often used to track moving objects on some sort of background mapping. For example, Figure 26.1 shows a series of vehicles on a background map. The map is updated in real time to show the location of each of the company's fleet of taxis. The dispatcher can therefore direct the most appropriate car to answer a request from a customer. Many of the emergency services also use tracking analysis to show the location of their vehicles. If there is an emergency, operational commanders know exactly where all their resources are and can redeploy them. A similar type of monitoring is carried out on security vehicles transporting money between banks.

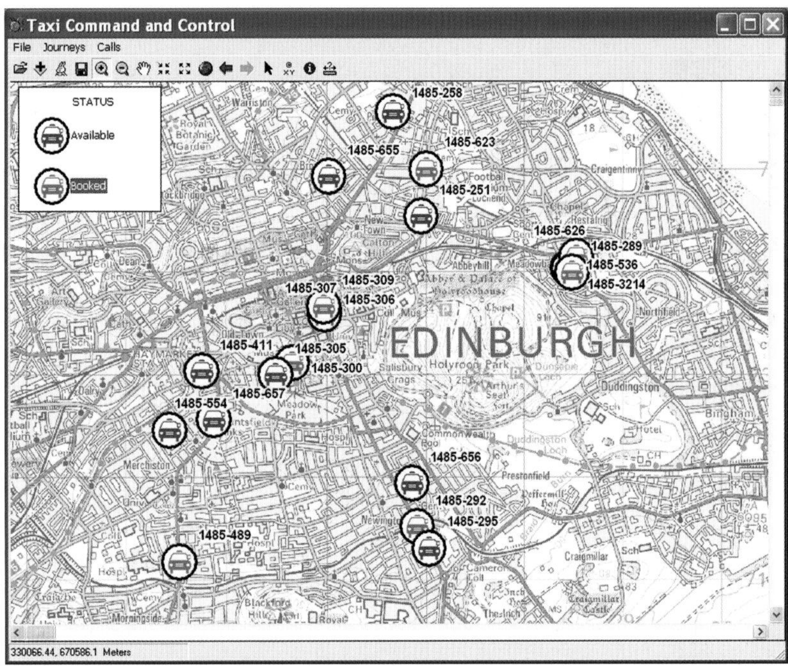

Figure 26.1: Taxis are monitored in real time so that a dispatcher can allocate vehicles to customers in the most efficient way. Source: ESRI (UK). OS base mapping reproduced with permission.

Tracking can also be employed to follow the paths of hurricanes, which, if linked to other GIS data, can be used to issue warnings and determine whether cities need to be evacuated (Figure 26.2).

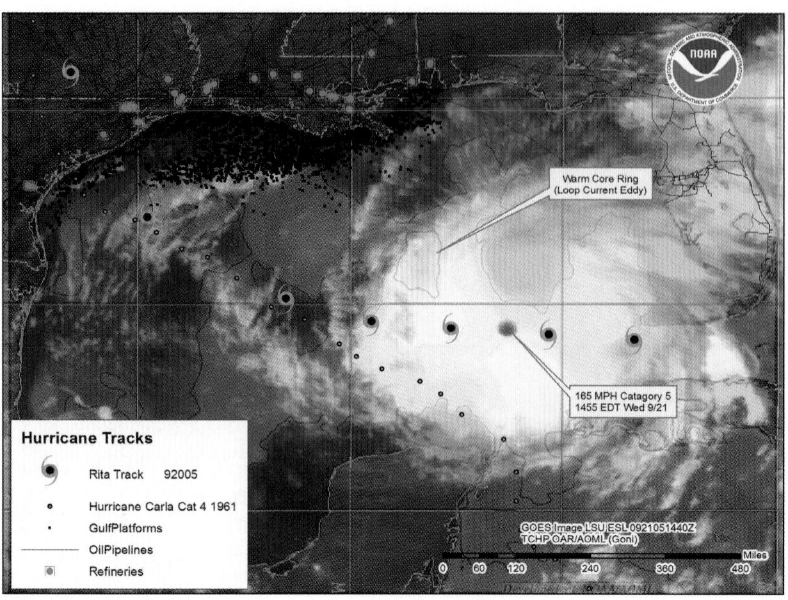

Figure 26.2: The track of Hurricane Rita is monitored in relation to the locations of energy infrastructure. Tracking analysis can be linked to other GIS functions to model the likely damage and impacts of the hurricane's movements. Source: *www.noaa.gov*.

Such data as is shown in Figures 26.1 and 26.2 can also be played back later to look for patterns or to determine if resources have been used efficiently. GIS can also produce time charts of specific events (see Figure 26.3).

Figure 26.3: A temporal (time) graph produced using GIS to indicate variations in the timing of street robbery events. The graph suggests that the safest hour to be out on the streets is between 4 and 5 am, as there were four days which had no street robberies during this time.

Scientists from the University of Maryland in the United States have been using GIS to model the spread of fire over time in Northern Eurasia. Fire in this region impacts on various aspects of the environment and affects human well-being through the inhalation of smoke. Fire spread reconstruction with GIS provides a means of understanding how fire spreads in both space and time. The scientists' reconstructions attempt to identify the points of ignition for individual fire events in both spatial and temporal dimensions for fire danger and fire threat prediction (Figure 26.4).

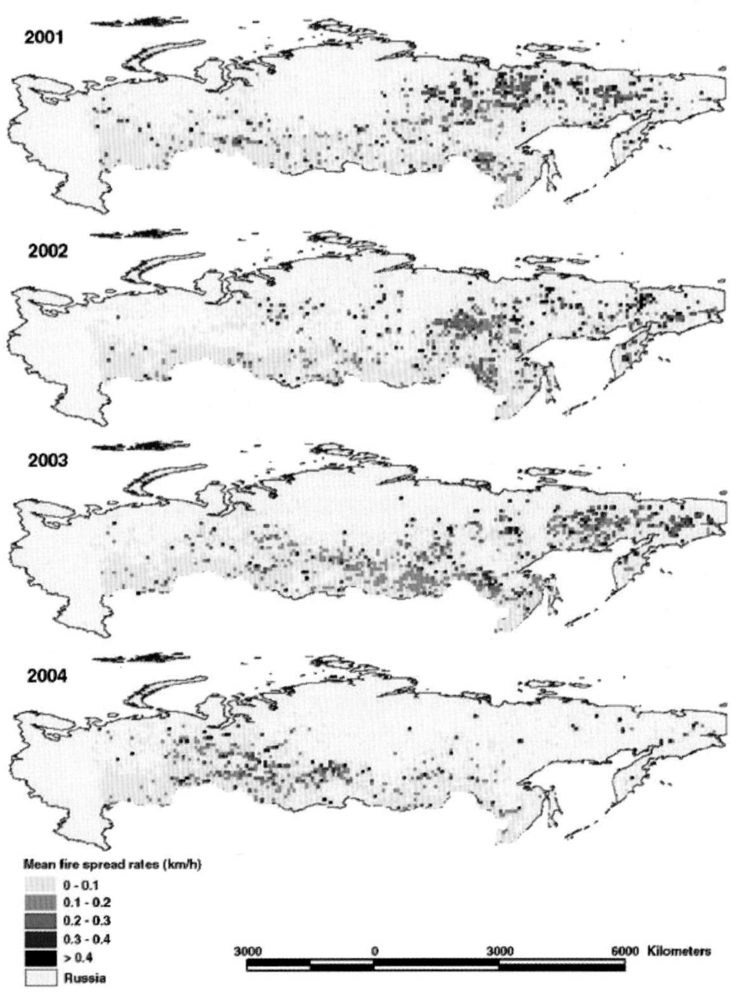

Figure 26.4: Average fire spread rates in 2001–2004 by 0.5° grid cells calculated using GIS temporal analysis. Source: Loboda and Csiszar (2007).

Questions

- What is temporal data and how can it be used to aid geographical research?
- Examine Figure 26.3. What are the limitations and advantages of presenting data in this format?

Topic H: GIS output

Data output from GIS

After all the data has been collected and processed, there are six main ways in which data can be outputted from a GIS:

- **maps**
- **graphs and diagrams**
- **tables**
- **reports**
- **images**
- **video.**

Not all GIS software packages will be able to output all types of information but most will have the capability to produce some of the data types listed above. Of all the output types from GIS, maps are arguably the most important as they are the cornerstone of most GIS operations.

Map output from GIS

The construction of maps is a creative process, whereby the end design of a map hopefully complements the function of the map. The main purpose of maps is to share information between individuals and organisations in a way that meets the needs of users. To this end, the layout of a map should also be engaging and interesting. While there is an almost infinite number of map styles available, all map design should try to include the following elements:

- **The map body** – the main focus of the map; it should be given enough space so that its contents are clear.
- **Title** – should inform the user about the content of the maps
- **Legend/key** – explains what the symbols on the map represent.
- **Scale** – gives an indication of the distances covered by the map. It also enables the user to identify distances between places on the map.
- **Direction** – gives the user information about how the map is oriented.
- **Grid** – relates points on a map to their true location on earth.
- **Map metadata** – should tell the user who made the map and the origin of the data used to construct the map; it should also give the date the map was constructed and the projection system used.

Figure 27.1 opposite is a sample of a map of the UK that contains all the elements listed above. Maps can also include insets, which are used to show a section of the main map body in more detail. However, whatever methods are chosen, a visual balance needs to be maintained between each of the components of the map.

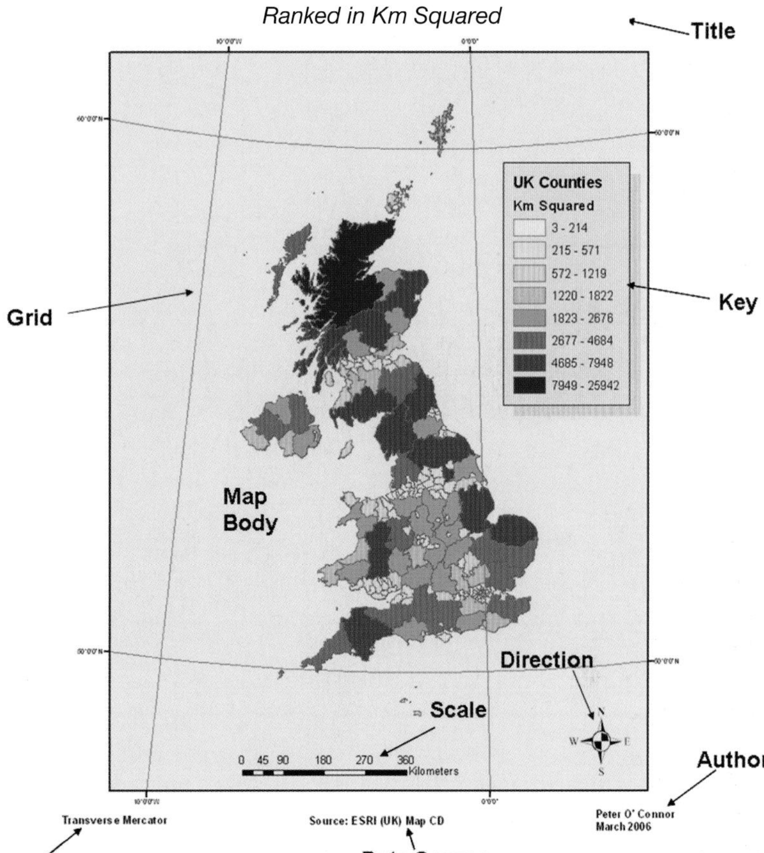

Figure 27.1: An example of a map output from GIS containing all of the major elements required for good map design.

Graphs, diagrams and tables

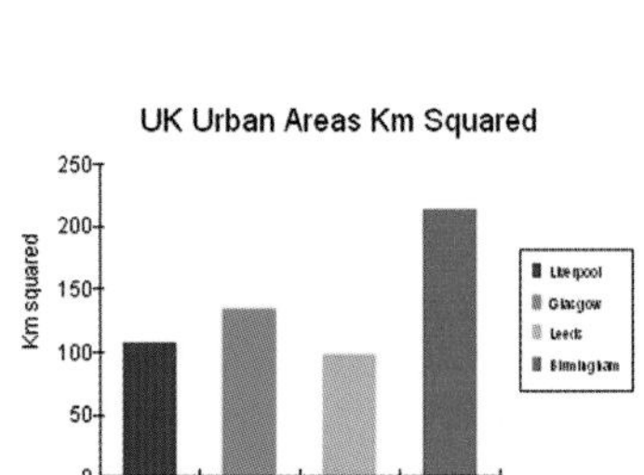

Figure 27.2: A typical graph produced using a GIS.

Most GIS software has the capability to produce tables and graphs from the attributes contained in the systems databases. GIS will produce all the common graph types such as bar charts, pie charts and scatter graphs. Figure 27.2 shows a graph that was produced from the attributes table associated with Figure 27.1. Diagrams are often provided as inserts with maps for final output, to highlight key statistics or patterns that would otherwise be difficult to recognise from the map body alone. Diagrams may also be linked to points on a map to expand the level of detail associated with the final GIS output. Figure 27.3 contains examples of the different types of diagrams that

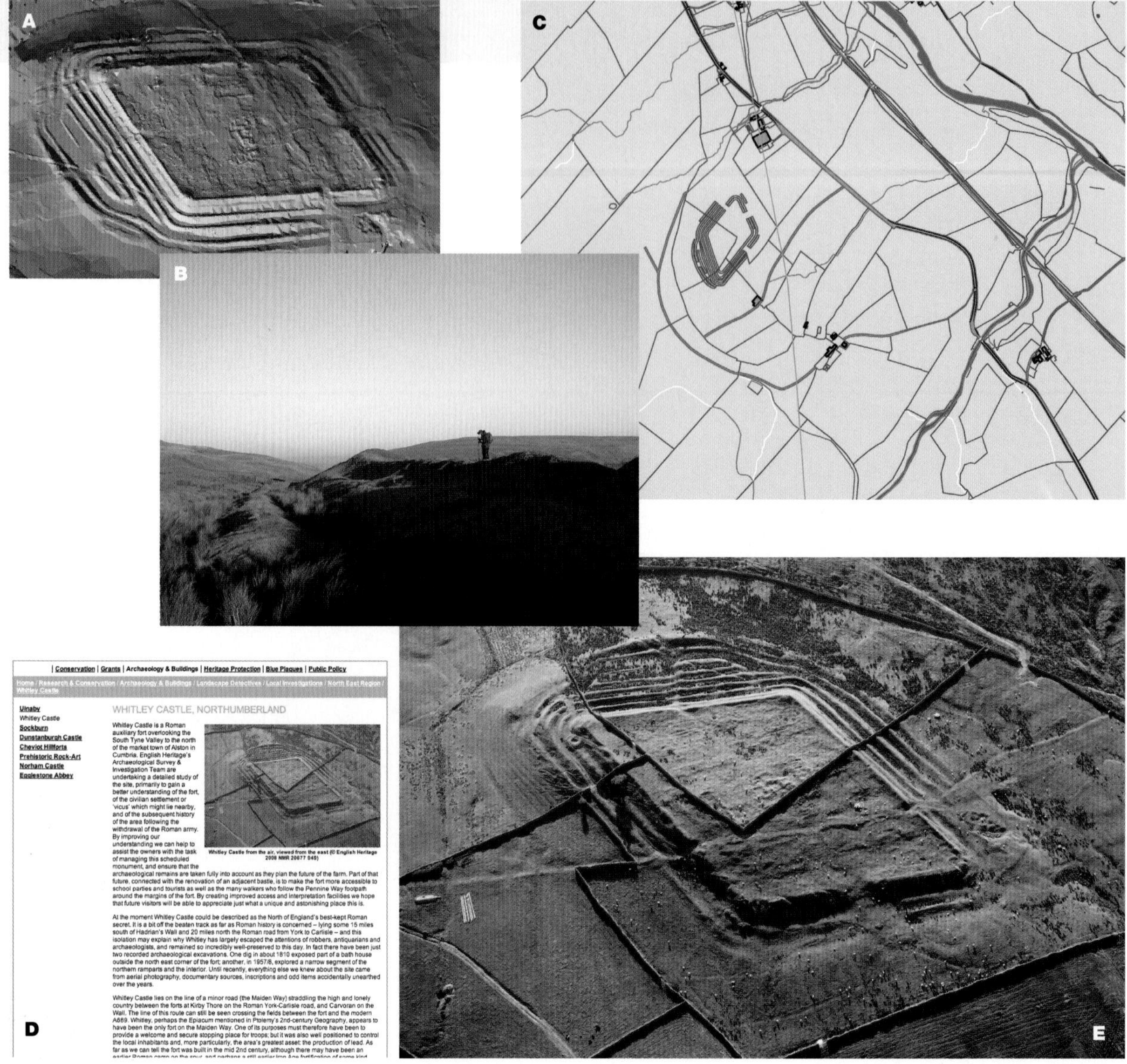

Figure 27.3: An example of the type of output that can be produced from GIS. The map (**C**), digital elevation model (**A**), photography (**B**, **E**) and report (**D**) relate to Whitley Castle, which is a Roman auxiliary fort overlooking the South Tyne Valley to the north of the market town of Alston in Cumbria. It is important for users of GIS to be able to select different output options so that the correct tools can be chosen to carry out different types of task. Source (B) and (D): © English Heritage 2008 NMR 20677 049; (A), (C) and (E): © English Heritage.

can be linked to a GIS mapping layer for output. It is this ability to link different types of data to a mapping layer that gives GIS such a huge range of flexibility in the types of tasks it can tackle.

Reports

GIS has the capability to output attribute data in the form of reports. Reports may contain the types of information and data outlined in Figure 27.4 opposite. These often accompany map output so that the user can look in more detail at the data that was used to create the maps and images. Reports are also used when additional information is required but the main body of the mapping page is already full.

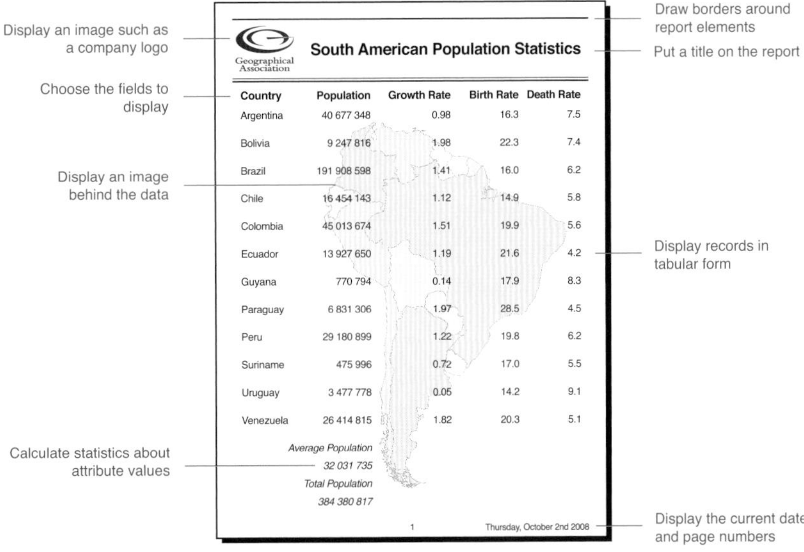

Geographical Association

South American Population Statistics

Country	Population	Growth Rate	Birth Rate	Death Rate
Argentina	40 677 348	0.98	16.3	7.5
Bolivia	9 247 816	1.98	22.3	7.4
Brazil	191 908 598	1.41	16.0	6.2
Chile	16 454 143	1.12	14.9	5.8
Colombia	45 013 674	1.51	19.9	5.6
Ecuador	13 927 650	1.19	21.6	4.2
Guyana	770 794	0.14	17.9	8.3
Paraguay	6 831 306	1.97	28.5	4.5
Peru	29 180 899	1.22	19.8	6.2
Suriname	475 996	0.72	17.0	5.5
Uruguay	3 477 778	0.05	14.2	9.1
Venezuela	26 414 815	1.82	20.3	5.1

Average Population
32 031 735
Total Population
384 380 817

1 Thursday, October 2nd 2008

Figure 27.4: An example of the type of report that can be produced using GIS.

Images and video

Images are a common source of output from GIS that can communicate often complex information very efficiently. Increasingly images are being used to aid the visualisation of landscapes in three dimensions (see Figure 27.5). Images in GIS are also used as a context for further exploration of the nature of place as represented on a map. For example, the nature of a building displayed on a map as a simple rectangular shape can be better understood if it also has an image

Figure 27.5: A 3D image of London which can aid the visualisation of landscapes to help inform the public and professionals like about the future of the city. Source: Hudson-Smith (2008). OS base mapping reproduced with permission.

attached. Such linkages of images to maps have been used to help emergency services in disaster management and assessment. Images also give places on a map a sense of age and condition, and can communicate other important social and cultural information.

GIS is becoming increasingly capable of outputting video. Animations have been developed to indicate processes and patterns over time. This type of output is most frequently used for examining temporal data. Yet more approaches to the display of GIS output are being constantly evolved (see Figures 27.6 below and 27.7 opposite).

Figure 27.6: The complete set-up of a six-panel display for visualising GIS output. Source: Liang *et al.* (2007).

Questions

- What are the key elements of map design?
- Why do you think it is necessary for GIS to output data in different forms?

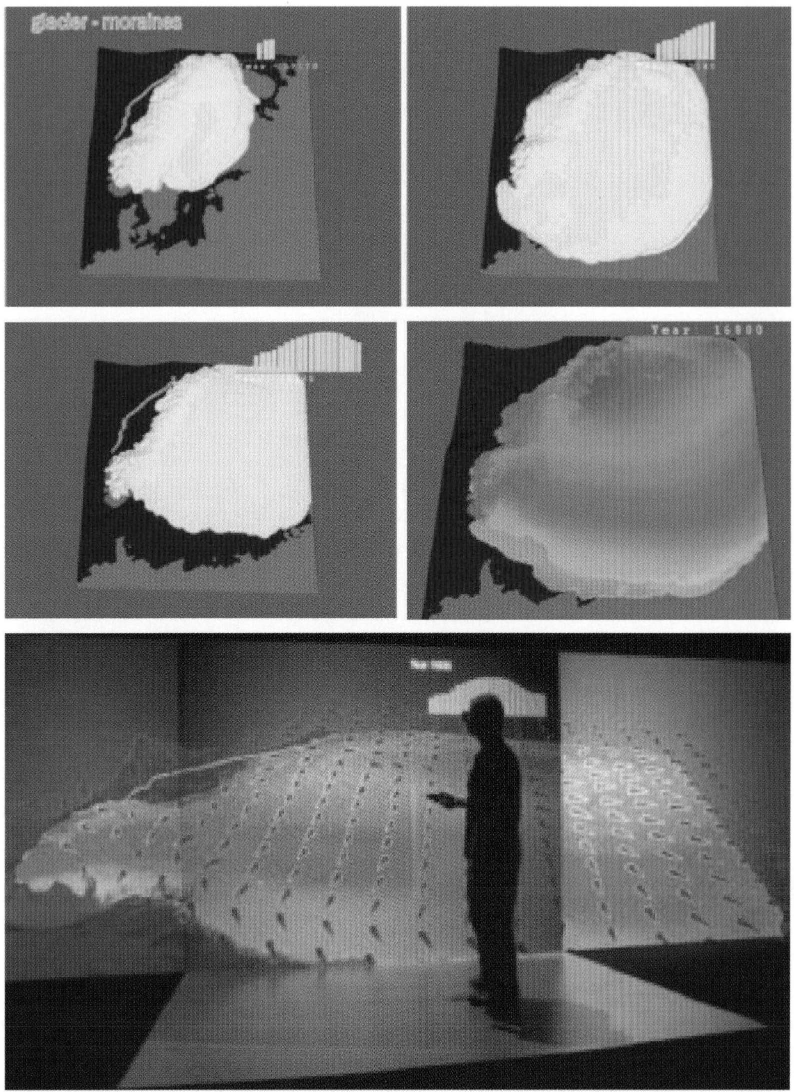

Figure 27.7: Emerging areas in GIS and glacial geomorphology include ice-sheet models linked to GIS in which the user is able to experience model results through immersive visualisation. In this case output during different time slices from an ice-sheet model is evaluated against a major moraine along the western margin of the Scandinavian Ice Sheet during the last major glaciation (top diagrams). Each time slice (1,000 years) is checked against the moraine using a statistical method developed in GIS, and a bar graph is used to indicate the time slice in which good correspondence occurs. Other GIS techniques compare ice flow orientation against suites of glacial lineations (bottom right) to indicate the potential times in which simulated ice-flow orientation best corresponds with field evidence. The visualisations illustrate various glaciological conditions such as surface or subsurface temperature (bottom left) and ice-flow orientation (bottom right). Source: Napieralski *et al*. (2007).

GIS in the workplace and home

28

The use of GIS is now well integrated into society, cutting across many areas of human activity. It is now possible for anybody in the world who has access to the internet to use some form of GIS. This degree of accessibility has come about through advances in technology and the widespread adoption of GIS by business and government organisations. Quickly disappearing are the days when GIS involved simply loading a piece of software onto a single computer.

Modern GIS setups

Today organisations and governments have to provide access to GIS for user groups ranging in size from small numbers of specialists to millions of casual users in the home (see Figure 28.1).

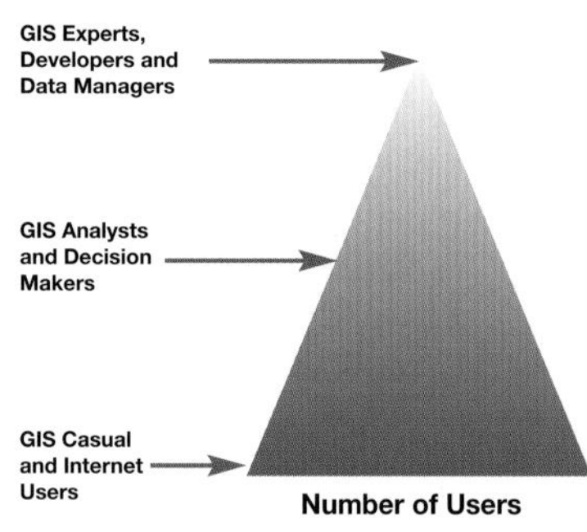

Figure 28.1: A pyramid of GIS use. The more specialised the GIS function, the fewer people will use that part of the technology. Source: ESRI (UK).

Figure 28.2 provides an indication of how a modern GIS might be set up within an organisation. It includes a centralised geodatabase which can be accessed by users across a network within the organisation via desktop GIS. Desktop GIS users may include analysts who have access to the full capabilities of the technology. The maps they produce may then be distributed to a wider audience across the world wide web using specialist GIS internet software. It is worth noting that the capability of GIS tends to decrease

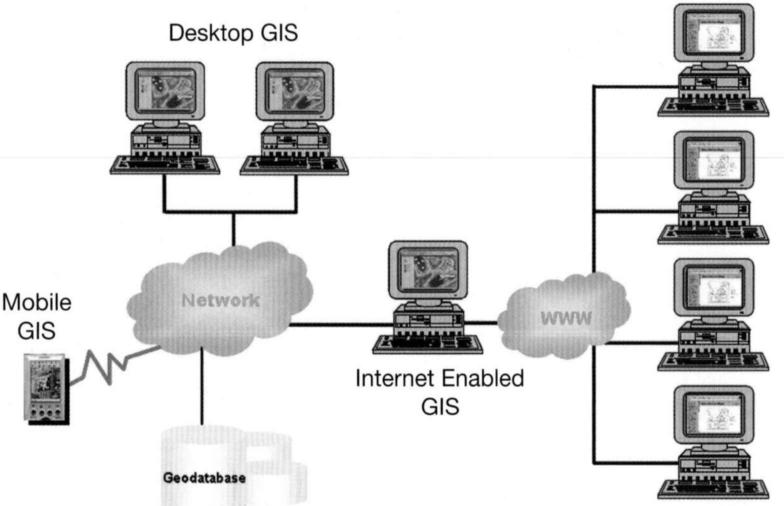

Figure 28.2: An example of a modern GIS setup within an organisation. Source: ESRI (UK).

as the number of people accessing the system increases. For example, while the GIS analyst would be able to carry out operations such as overlay and reclassification, the internet user would only have access to basic functions such as spatial and attribute queries. It is necessary to restrict the functionality of GIS to such users in order to protect the quality of the original data. Although less common, mobile and wireless capabilities can now be included in GIS setups. It is possible, for example, for users to take mobile computer devices into the field, record spatial data and send it back in real time to a geodatabase using mobile phone technology.

The cost of establishing such commercial systems is not cheap. Organisations may pay anything from £10,000 to £10 million to establish a system like the one shown in Figure 28.2. The costs vary widely as price is heavily linked to the number of users requiring access to the system within the organisation.

Delivering GIS into the home over the internet

There are now numerous examples of GIS technology that can be accessed away from the host organisation via the internet. Developers tend to use the term GIS portals for GIS that is accessible over the internet. Figure 28.3 shows an example from the Ordnance Survey's GIS portal that enables users to print maps at a range of different scales for any part of the United Kingdom. Queries can be performed using either place names or postcodes.

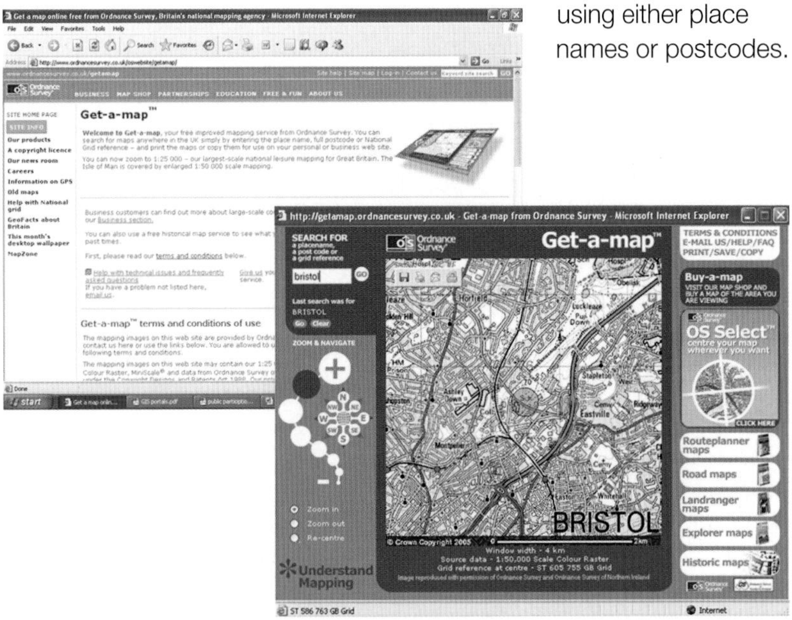

Figure 28.3: An example from the Ordnance Survey's GIS internet website, which provides access to a range of map databases for the entire United Kingdom. Source: getamap.ordnancesurvey.co.uk. OS base mapping reproduced with permission.

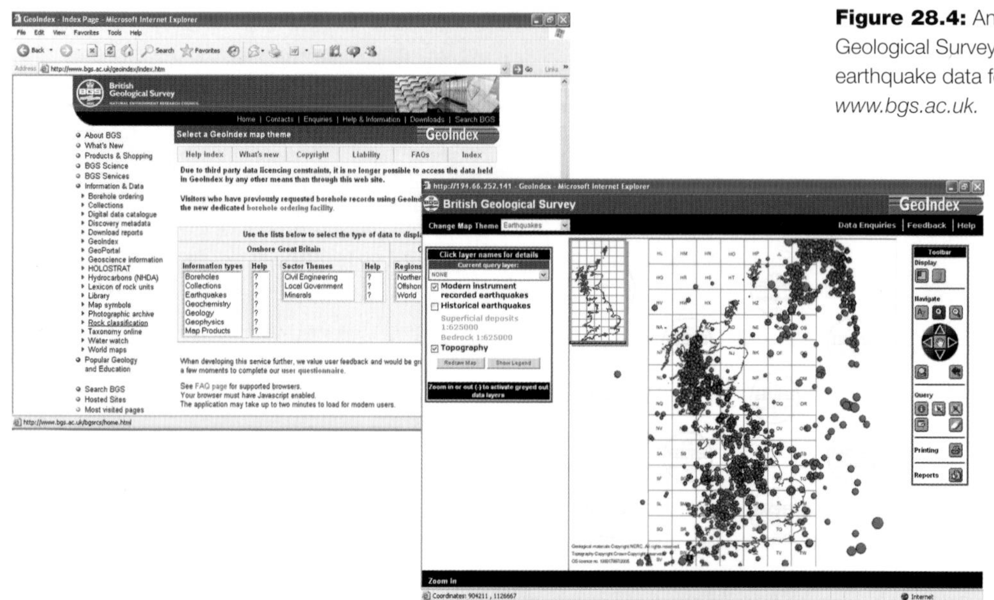

Figure 28.4: An example of the British Geological Survey's GIS portal showing earthquake data for the UK. Source: *www.bgs.ac.uk.*

GIS over the internet is not only a source for base maps. For example, the British Geological Survey provides access to a whole range of geological and environmental resources via its GIS portal (Figure 28.4). Users can readily access borehole records, earthquake data, geology maps and geophysical information.

Sophisticated GIS visualisation techniques using 'virtual globes' are also becoming accessible via the internet. These include Google Earth, ArcGIS Explorer, Microsoft Virtual Earth and NASA World Wind. Google Earth (*earth.google.com*) provides raster and vector data coverage at different resolutions for the entire globe. Once the viewer has been

Figure 28.5: 3D images of (**A**) Snowdon, Wales, and (**B**) Manhattan Island, New York, created from Google Earth.

Figure 28.6: Images of (**A**) the pyramids outside Cairo, Egypt, and (**B**) Buckingham Palace, London, England, created from Google Earth.

downloaded from the Google Earth website, imagery can be streamed via the internet. Google Earth has the ability to view data in both two and three dimensions (see Figures 28.5 on previous page and 28.6 above). However, while the site is very impressive, it does not have the full capability of most commercially available GIS software, in comparison to which it is largely a data viewer. In contrast, ArcGIS Explorer is a 'virtual globe' made expressly for GIS users, integrating seamlessly with GIS data.

The growth of GIS portals is beginning to affect how organisations behave and deliver their services to customers. In this regard GIS over the internet is not just another tool to view information but an emerging strategy in the management of public and private service provision. Furthermore, the range of technologies that can be used to deliver GIS access is changing rapidly. In the future GIS will also be accessible via interactive digital television, call centres and mobile devices such as smart phones or personal data assistants (PDAs).

Questions

- In what ways is GIS likely to be used differently by the casual user compared to a GIS specialist?
- Use the internet to investigate some of the GIS portals discussed in this chapter and identify what types of GIS analysis they can carry out.

Government GIS service delivery over the internet

In 1999 the UK Government published a White Paper called 'Modernizing Government'. The paper stated that all government services should be available electronically by 2008. Later this date was brought forward to 2005. The proposal was a result of the Government coming under increasing pressure to improve public service management both at national and local scales. Public services include, among other things, hospitals, schools, road maintenance, care for the environment, planning and social care.

Figure 29.1: The role played by internet GIS in linking together national and local government service provision with the general public.

The delivery of GIS over the internet was seen as an important component of improving government services. In particular, the use of GIS over the internet (GIS portals) was perceived as a way of linking together the ever-expanding range of publicly-funded organisations and service users (Figure 29.1).

For example, if an area of a town is vandalised it is the police's job to identify the person who committed the crime and the local council's responsibility to clean the area up. However, communication between the two organisations is not automatic. The area may be cleaned up by the council without ever having been investigated by the police. Alternatively, the council may never even be contacted, leaving the area vandalised and often leading to further crime. GIS has been seen as a way of joining these two organisations together by the sharing of common data resources. If both the police and the local council recorded incidents to a shared GIS, each group could be assured of knowing what incidents had taken place in their areas, enabling them to take quick and effective action. In this way GIS will encourage partnership and the sharing of information between different government-funded organisations. Sharing of information provides policy makers with the tools for making good or at least better decisions.

Figure 29.2 opposite shows the Multi Agency Internet Geographic Information Service (MAIGIS) website for the Midlands area of England. The site, which was live from 2005-2008, provided GIS information for health, social and environmental indicators. The objectives of the website were:

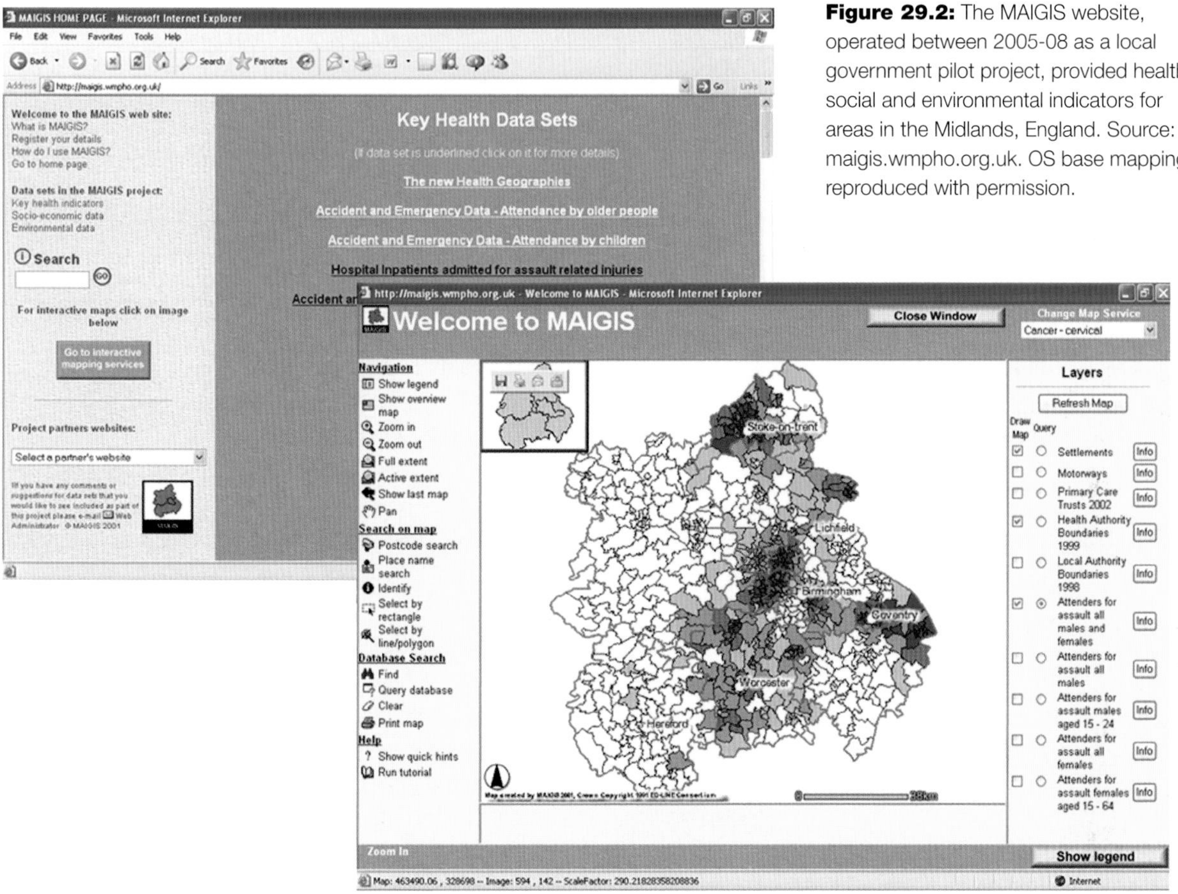

Figure 29.2: The MAIGIS website, operated between 2005-08 as a local government pilot project, provided health, social and environmental indicators for areas in the Midlands, England. Source: maigis.wmpho.org.uk. OS base mapping reproduced with permission.

- to encourage sharing of information by government organisations in the region, thus avoiding duplication of effort and facilitating a more holistic policy response to health and social issues
- to enable easy access to regional information for professionals and the general public
- to identify relevant health and health-related data that could be used to improve the quality of life of individuals living in the Midlands
- to establish a website with an interactive mapping capability to identify areas for priority investment and action
- to use technological developments to enable spatial querying of data to aid decision-making.

The idea of a holistic approach to problem-solving is a key feature of the MAIGIS site and internet GIS. For example, if a local authority wanted to improve the health of its residents, it would need to bring together several different departments to work on the problem as poor health has many potential causes (see Figure 29.3).

Figure 29.3: Health experts have long recognised the link between low income, poor housing and poor health. Poor men are 68% more likely to die in middle age than their richer counterparts, with poor women having a 55% greater risk of dying young. Photo: David Barrington.

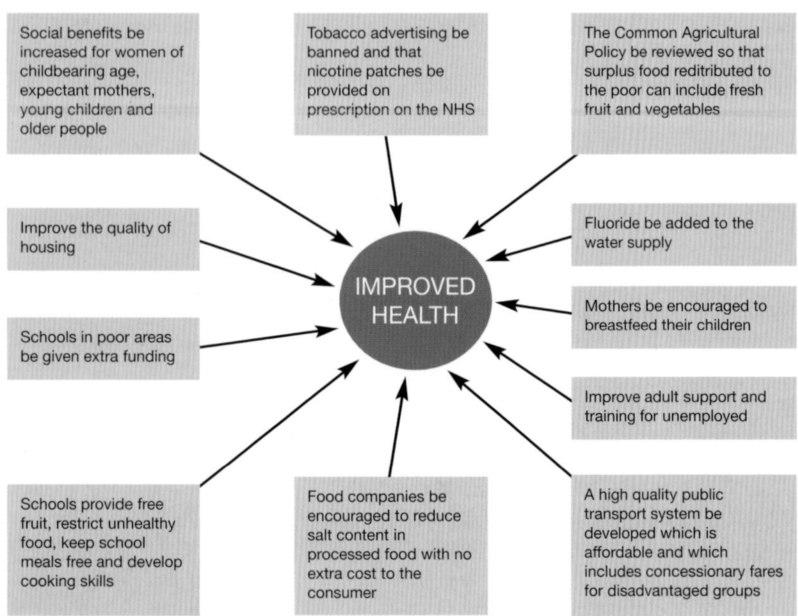

Figure 29.4: Recommendations made by the government's chief medical officer that might lead to an improvement in health for the UK's poorest citizens. The degree of coordination required between different government departments would be considerable in delivering these recommendations.

The Government's chief medical officer has made a number of recommendations that could result in an improvement of health for the poorest citizens in the United Kingdom (see Figure 29.4). The MAIGIS website was a first step towards developing the cooperation required between different areas of government to help make positive changes to people's lives. The site was particularly good at identifying areas in the Midlands that have the worst combination of social, health and environmental conditions. Those areas identified as being worst off could become priority areas for funding and testing to see whether the types of recommendations made in Figure 29.4 can actually work.

As well as creating partnerships, the Government also wants to improve how the public accesses its services. By using internet GIS, both national and local government organisations hope to improve public accessibility to services and important information. The Surrey Alert GIS portal (see Figure 29.5 overleaf) provides the general public living in Surrey, England, with access to information concerning any major incidents that may be happening in the local area.

Figure 29.6 opposite shows the national GIS planning portal. Using such a system, local authorities are able to share important policy initiatives and provide the public with access to important planning services out of hours. By funding such a resource the Government is helping to ensure that both local authorities and the general public have access to the most up-to-date information to inform their decision-making. Providing such a service can enable home owners to

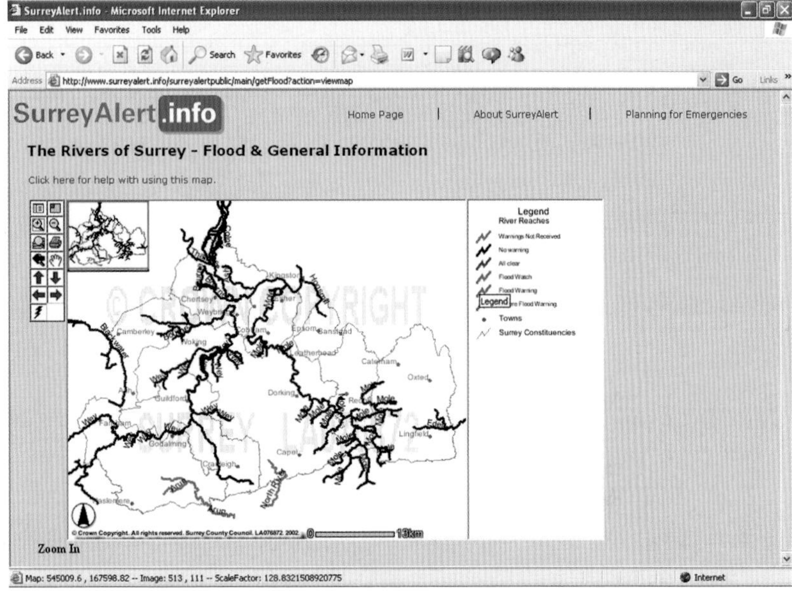

Figure 29.5: A screenshot from Surrey Alert, the emergency GIS portal hosted by Surrey Local Authority, England, showing a spatially interactive flood warning GIS for local residents. Source: *www.surreyalert.info/surreyalertpublic/main*. OS base mapping reproduced with permission.

check such things as whether an application to build an extension is likely to be accepted or rejected. It can help developers identify areas of land that are free for development and it can help local authorities define planning policy. GIS online also provides public access to the information used by national and local government in order to make important policy decisions. This means that decision-making processes become more open and subject to constructive critical analysis.

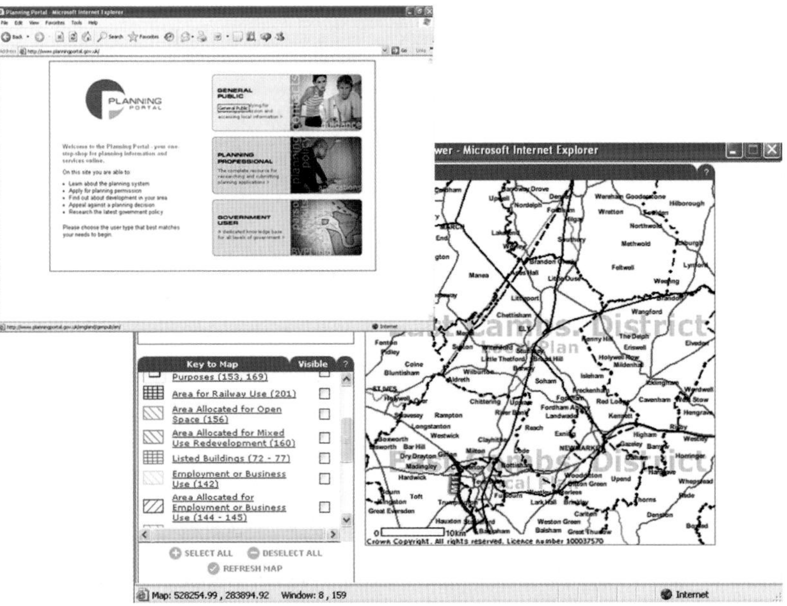

Figure 29.6: The planning GIS portal provides the general public, planning professionals and government organisations access to a spatial planning database covering most of the UK. OS base mapping reproduced with permission.

Providing GIS over the internet is also a way of encouraging public participation in Government decision-making (see Figure 29.1). Research suggests that users of internet GIS start by using the resource for information only, but later graduate to taking transactions online, and finally use GIS to participate in online decision-making through local government initiatives. The ability to engage policy-makers and the general public in this way could lead to innovations in the way public services are provided.

Table 29.1 identifies a number of examples of GIS internet websites that have been established by local authorities across the UK. The Government has provided £78.8 million for establishing the partnerships from which these GIS websites have been developed.

Table 29.1: Examples of local authority services provided by internet GIS. Adapted from Beaumont *et al*. (2005).

Local authority service name	Website address	Types of service and data provided
Leeds Statistics	http://statistics.leeds.gov.uk	• User access to interactive statistical maps of Leeds area. • Data on crime, health and census statistics. • User flexibility to select area of interest.
Buckinghamshire Accessible Services Partnership (BASP)	www.bucksonline.gov.uk	• Online access to community facilities, planning and building control information. • Facility to plot circles around areas of interest and request e-mails of details of current planning applications. • Facility to register for notification of future planning applications in selected area. • Facility to locate conservation areas, preservation areas and public rights of way. • Facility to report problems requiring council attention.
Wiltshire and Swindon Pathfinder GIS	www.maps-direct.co.uk	• Online facility to locate recycling sites, schools and colleges, residential centres, nursing and residential homes, leisure centres and libraries, youth centres, electoral districts, wards and districts boundaries. • Facility to initiate service requests. • Access to frequently asked questions, e.g. identifying local councillors, identifying service levels and availability.
Surrey Alert	www.surreyalert.info	• Online information on major incidents and emergencies, e.g. flooding, fuel availability, progress of foot and mouth disease. • Interactive mapping applications include flood extent and level monitoring.
Worcestershire County Council Joined Up Information System (JUIS)	http://worcestershire.whub.org.uk/home/wcc-pep-ri-index-census-whereilive-juis	• Visualisation of relationships between pooled data. • Includes 2001 Census data.
East of England Data Observatory	www.eastofenglandobservatory.org.uk/mapping.asp	• This site provides an information gateway to the East of England region. • It is for people and organisations interested in discovering more about the region and its social, economic and environmental development.

Local authority service name	Website address	Types of service and data provided
Multi Agency Internet Geographic Information Service (MAIGIS)	maigis.wmpho.org.uk	• Multi-agency internet GIS website operated between 2005-2008 providing health and health-related information within the West Midlands.
Derbyshire Partnership	derbyshiremaps.derbyshire.gov.uk	• A mapping website covering the county and all districts. Providing access to information including councillors, car parking, leisure facilities, schools and police.
London Borough of Brent	www.brent.gov.uk (to view mapping applications, click on 'Maps' on the main menu and follow instructions)	• Numerous map and distance-based applications including: – property lookup (commercial lettings and sales) – moving home to Brent – getting around Brent.
Westminster City Council	www3.westminster.gov.uk/maps	• Provides access to a range of map-based information for a prominent area of London. Serves an important business and tourist community requiring easy online access to services.
Chichester District Council	www.maps-direct.co.uk/mapsdirect	• Provides simple access via a map-based interface to details about councillors, tourist attractions and recycling centres.
Cornwall County Council	http://mapping.cornwall.gov.uk	• Interactive map providing access to community information including libraries, approved marriage venues and register offices.
Worcestershire County Council	www.worcestershire.whub.org.uk/home/wcc-gis.htm	• Interactive map-based applications including tourism, school locations, find your councillor, streetlight fault reporting, election results and public rights of way.
Cheshire County Council	http://maps.cheshire.gov.uk/cheshirecc.interactivemapping.web.internet/Default.aspx	• Interactive map-based application allowing users to navigate by postcode or place name to locate information on parks, libraries, schools, residential homes, youth centres and recycling centres.
West Sussex County Council	http://www.westsussex.gov.uk/ccm/navigation/leisure-and-tourism/public-rights-of-way	• Public rights of way.

Questions

- How is GIS promoting inter-agency communication?
- What benefits might organisations gain from sharing information via GIS?
- How can GIS portals help promote open government?

Topic I: GIS applications

30 The Environment Agency and GIS over the internet

What is the Environment Agency?

The Environment Agency is the leading public body responsible for protecting and improving the environment in England and Wales. Its main responsibilities are to ensure that air, land and water are looked after by everyone in today's society. On a practical level its role includes tackling flooding and pollution incidents, reducing industry's impacts on the environment, cleaning up rivers, coastal waters and contaminated land, conserving natural resources and improving wildlife habitats.

The Environment Agency was established by the UK Government under the 1995 Environment Act, which gives the organisation a number of powers to carry out its responsibilities and duties. In 2005/06 the Environment Agency had an operating budget of £986 million (see Table 30.1), employing approximately 11,000 people. Figure 30.1 gives a breakdown of how it spends its resources.

Table 30.1: Sources of Environment Agency funding. Source: *www.environment.agency.gov.uk*.

Sources of funding	**Income in sterling**	**Percentage of income**
Government and other grants	£640 million	65%
Charges and levies	£309 million	31%
Other income	£37 million	4%
Total	**£986 million**	100%

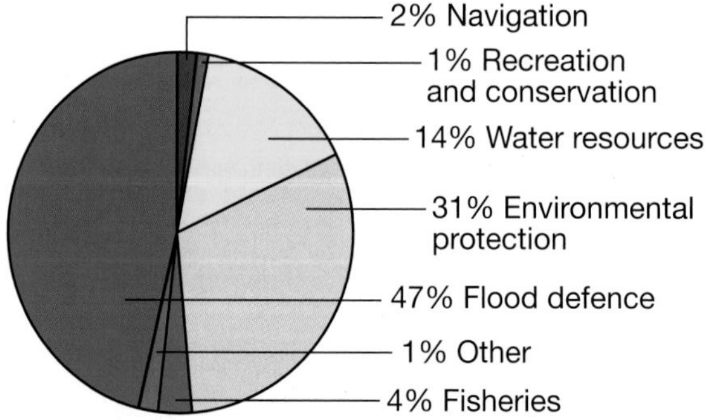

Figure 30.1: A breakdown of how the Environment Agency spends its money. Source: *www.environment-agency.gov.uk*.

The Environment Agency and GIS

Since the year 2000, the Environment Agency has invested more than £1.5 million in GIS technology, and sees the use of geographic information as a crucial tool in delivering its aims. A significant part of this investment has been the provision of publicly accessible GIS over the internet. The Environment Agency has set up a GIS information-rich website called 'What's in your backyard' (see Figure 30.2), which has been operating since 2000.

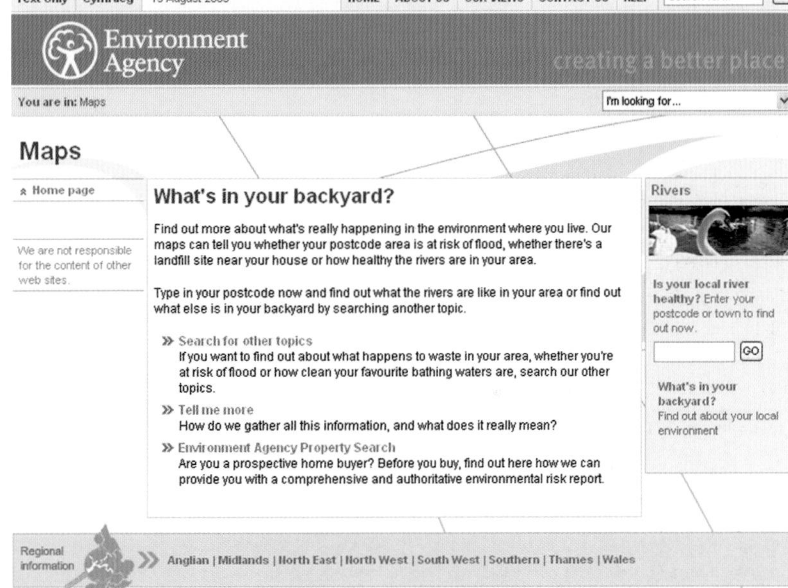

Figure 30.2: The Environment Agency 'What's in your backyard' home page. Source: *www.environment-agency.gov.uk/maps*.

The site provides access to 13 major databases (see Table 30.2), all linked to Ordnance Survey mapping at scales of 1:20,000, 1:100,000, 1:650,000, 1:2,500,000 and 1:6,700,000. The maps can be zoomed and panned at will and the databases can be searched using a postcode or place name. Selecting a query layer can reveal further attribute data such as text, tables and graphs.

1	Bathing Waters Directive
2	OSPAR (discharges to sea)
3	Water source protection zones
4	Floodplain maps
5	Flood warning areas
6	Landfill sites
7	Pollution inventory
8	Pollution hazards and factories
9	River water quality assessment
10	River quality objectives
11	Agency office locations
12	Catchment abstraction management
13	Environment Agency boundaries

Table 30.2: The 13 data sets that are available using the Environment Agency's GIS internet website 'What's in my backyard'.

The main aim of the website is to provide the public with information to help make informed decisions. Its further objectives are:

- to build public trust and confidence in the operations of the Environment Agency
- to enhance the Agency's reputation
- to encourage an understanding of the Agency's environmental actions and policies
- to influence public policy and opinion

- to increase understanding of the Agency's role
- to improve the public's understanding of environmental hazards
- to reduce the public's vulnerability to environmental hazards
- to change attitudes and behaviour
- to achieve an improved environment and quality of life for people living in England and Wales.

According to evidence collected by the Environment Agency, since 2004 the site has been routinely recording more than 400,000 hits per month. Such statistics show that the public are clearly participating in the use of GIS over the internet.

Internet GIS and flood risk management

Some 1.9 million properties in England and Wales, together worth more than £200 billion, are at risk from flooding. Given the number of people involved and the fact that there are 40,000km of watercourses in England and Wales, the task of informing people of the likelihood of

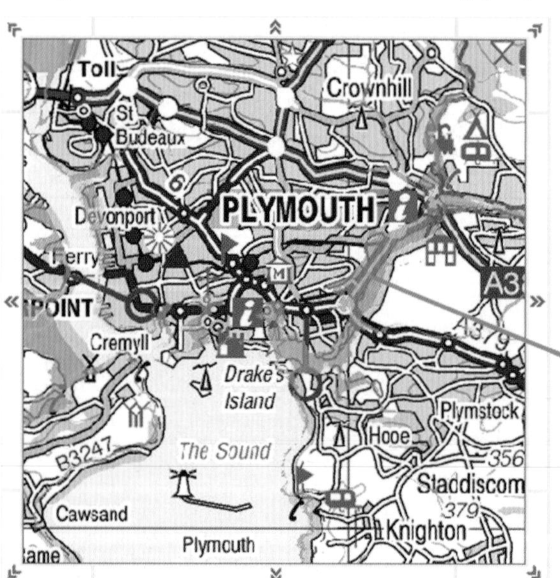

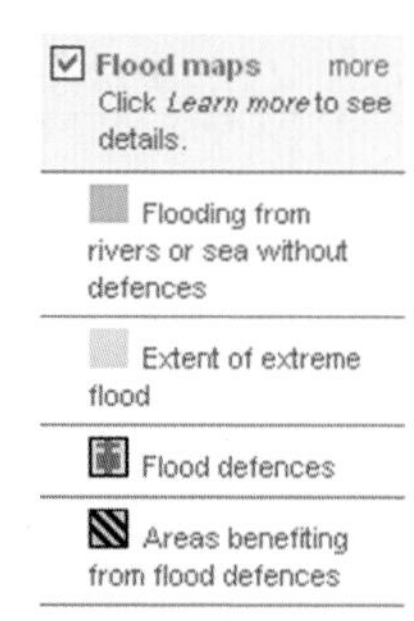

Be prepared

The location you have selected is in an area which fell outside the extent of the extreme flood, at the time of our assessment of the likelihood of flooding. Generally this means that the chance of flooding each year from rivers or the sea is 0.1% (1 in 1000) or less. The Flood Map shows our current best information on the extent of the extreme flood from rivers or the sea that would occur without the presence of flood defences.

For a fuller explanation of flood likelihood, click here.

Be aware:

- Our maps only cover flooding from rivers and the sea. Flooding can occur at any time and in any place from sources such as rising ground water levels, burst water mains, road drains, run-off from hillsides, sewer overflows etc. Click here to find out more.
- To find out how to be prepared for all types of flooding go to our Floodline pages or call Floodline on tel: 0845 988 1188.
- The information on the likelihood of flooding is not intended to be used by people applying for planning permission for new developments. To find out how the Flood Map can help when planning a new development, click here.

Figure 30.3: A flood map for the area of Plymouth shows the areas likely to be affected by an extreme flood. If the query layer is turned on, further information is provided about the likelihood of flooding in this area. Source: *www.environment-agency.gov.uk/maps/*. OS base mapping reproduced with permission.

their home flooding is a difficult one. However, the Agency's GIS website is a major help.

Figure 30.3 (see previous page) shows a floodplain map that can be used to identify whether a home is in a likely flood area. In designated flood warning areas (see Figure 30.4) the maps are updated every 15 minutes on any flood threat. Taking into account up-to-date information on rainfall, groundwater and river conditions, one of four escalating warning codes is assigned to an area (see Figure 30.5).

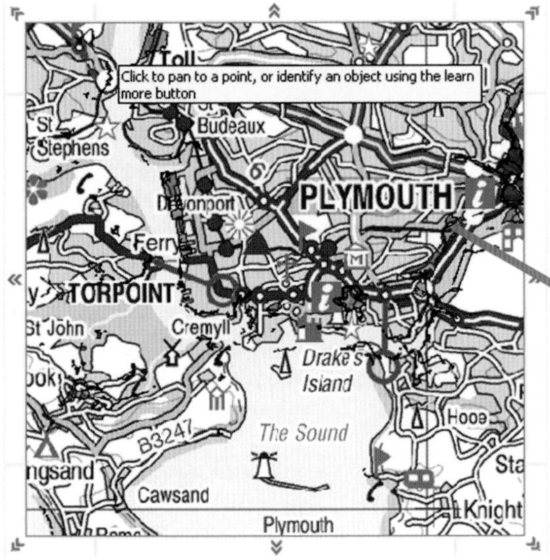

Flood warning areas more

☑ Flood warning areas more
Click *Learn more* to see details.

Areas covered by flood warnings.

Click here to find out what else is in your backyard.

South Cornwall Coast from Lands End to Plymouth

Page last updated: 11:00 on 30-Oct-2004
Flood status checked every 15 minutes.

Current status:	No Warning in Force
Status last changed at:	11:00 on 30-Oct-2004
Location:	Including Millbrook, Kingsand, Cawsand, Seat[...] Looe, Fowey, Mevagissey, Truro, Falmouth, Penryn, Porthleven, Marazion, Penzance and Newlyn.

Figure 30.4: Flood warning areas for Plymouth are updated every 15 minutes to indicate the level of flood risk in a flood event. With the query layer turned on, clicking on the map identifies if a flood warning is in place. Source: *www.environment-agency.gov.uk/maps/*. OS base mapping reproduced with permission.

Flooding possible. Be aware! Be prepared! Watch Out!

Flooding expected affecting homes, businesses and main roads. Act now!

Severe flooding expected. Imminent danger to life and property. Act now!

An all clear will be issued when flood watches or warnings are no longer in force. Flood water levels receding. Check all is safe to return. Seek advice.

Figure 30.5: The four warning codes associated with the Environment Agency's flood warning map. Source: *www.environment-agency.gov.uk/commondata/acrobat/167219*.

The maps are vitally important to any household living in a flood-prone zone. Any individual could use the maps in Figures 30.3 and 30.4 as a way to link to other information provided by the Environment Agency. For example, the booklet shown in Figure 30.6 explains a range of methods that could be used to reduce the damage done to a home during a flood event.

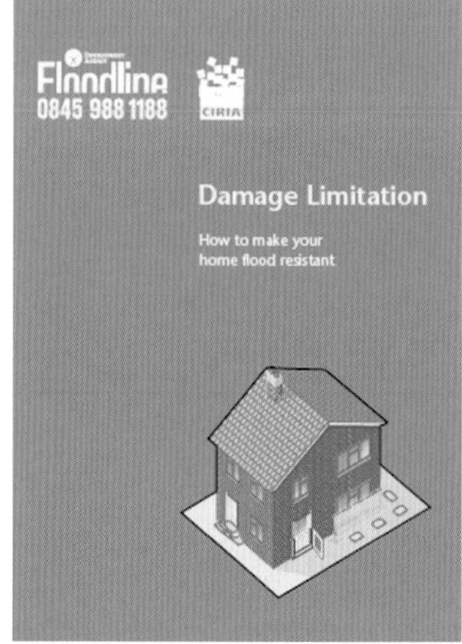

Figure 30.6: The Environment Agency's website provides details of its booklet entitled *Damage limitation: How to make your home flood resistant*. Source: *www.environment-agency.gov.uk/commondata/acrobat/167219.*

The Environment Agency produces a range of documents that could help every household in England and Wales to come up with an individual flood plan. This plan should describe what the household should do before, during and after a flood event (see Figure 30.7). In particular, it should identify what actions can be taken before a flood occurs to reduce the potential damage from flooding. Taken together, the GIS capability of the Agency's website, and its suggestion on how to develop a flood plan, offer a very effective way to reduce the vulnerability of households in England and Wales to the risks of flooding.

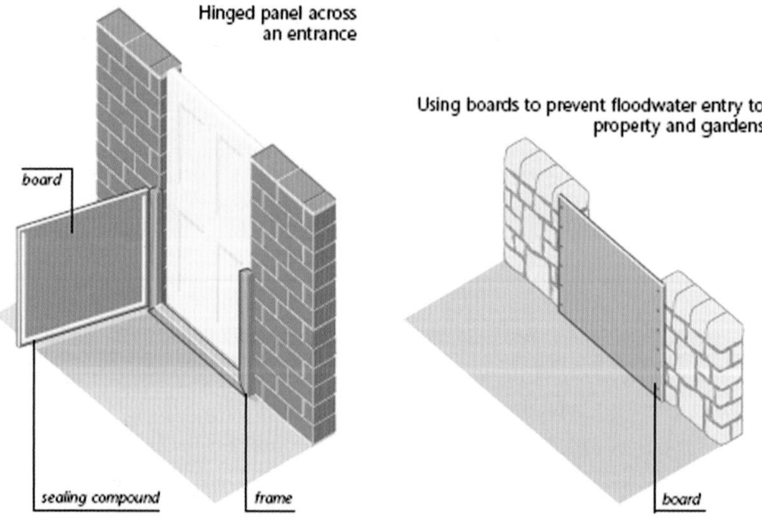

Figure 30.7: An example of the type of action that can be taken as part of a flood action plan. Here boards are used to stop flood water entering a property up to a height of one metre. Source: *www.environment-agency.gov.uk/commondata/acrobat/167219.*

Questions

- What is the function of the Environment Agency?
- What types of information is the Environment Agency providing via its GIS portal?
- How is the Environment Agency, via its GIS portal, helping to reduce flood vulnerability in the UK?

Norwich Union, GIS and flood insurance

Norwich Union is the UK's largest insurer, with a market share of around 20%, insuring more than 700,000 businesses, one in five motor vehicles and one in five households in the UK (see Figure 31.1).

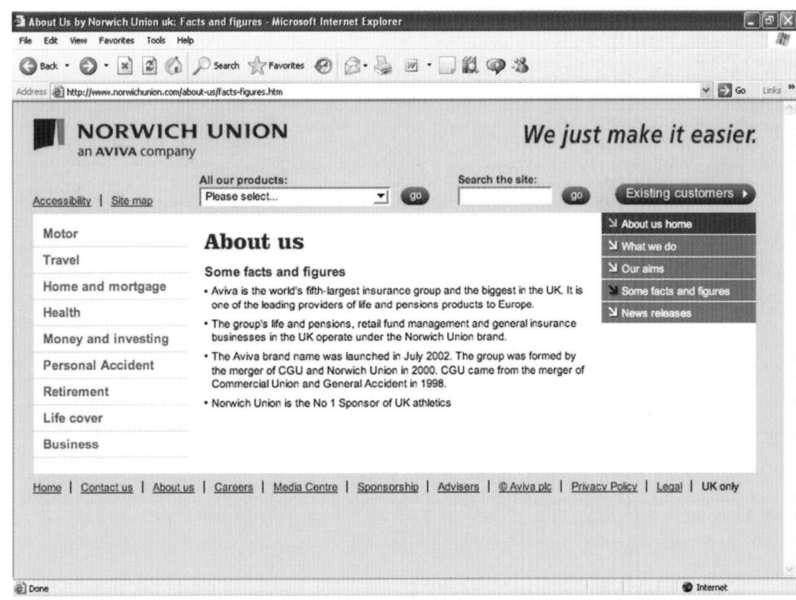

Figure 31.1: The Norwich Union website provides a range of information on the nature of the company's activities. Source: *www.norwichunion.com/about-us/facts-figures.htm.*

Damage caused by flooding already costs insurers around £800 million per year. Norwich Union typically pays out £70 million annually on claims relating to flooding. The floods that swept through England in the autumn of 2000 resulted in insurance claims, including those of associated storm damage, totalling over £1.3 billion – yet this was not an isolated event. Flooding during Easter 1998 resulted in five deaths and caused £150 million of insured property damage. All of the available evidence points to an increased frequency of flooding over the coming years. The Environment Agency, which is responsible for flood warning in England and Wales, recently stated that flooding is now twice as frequent as 100 years ago, and predicted that there will be a ten-fold increase in flood risk over the next century. Also, the number of people at high risk of river and coastal flooding could increase from 1.6 million in 2005 to between 2.3 and 3.6 million by the 2080s.

The need for GIS and improved mapping

Figure 31.2: A 200-year flood outline for Tower Hill and Southwark, London, England. The green hatching represents the flooded area.
Source: *www.environment-agency.gov.uk/maps.* OS base mapping reproduced with permission.

Given the increasing financial impact of flooding, Norwich Union recognised that having a more detailed view of flood risk across the UK could benefit not only the company through reduced business risk, but also its customers through a more accurate system of flood insurance premiums. Norwich Union wanted to take steps which would equip it to give accurate predictions, identifying properties at risk from flooding and how badly they would be affected. Providing more accurate and realistic insurance quotes not only lessens the risk on the insurance company itself but provides customers with fairer quotes.

Until recently, Norwich Union based its quotes for flood insurance on data from the Environment Agency. However, this was not ideal for Norwich Union or its customers. Figure 31.2 shows the type of flood that you might expect to occur in an area of London once every 200 years. It indicates which properties are sited on the floodplain, but doesn't indicate the elevation of the properties above the water level. For example, a street may be located in a flood plain, but if it is sited on a hill, properties at the top will be at less risk than those at the bottom. Norwich Union therefore needed to add another dimension to the data used to predict flood risk – namely the height of the land – so that premiums could be set more accurately.

The development of an improved flood model for the UK using GIS

In order to provide customers with a more accurate quote, Norwich Union needed to develop a GIS that included:

- elevation readings of the terrain across the UK which show the gradients of the landscape and the heights at which properties are located
- a hydrological model that could predict how deep and extensive flooding is likely to be
- address point data for every property in the UK.

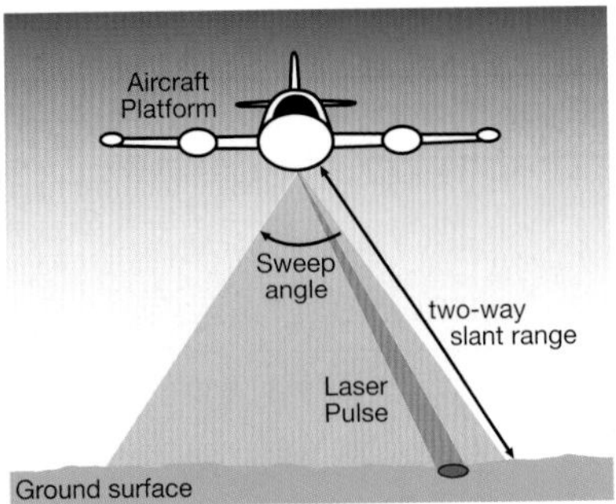

Figure 31.3 (above): Light detection and ranging (LIDAR) is an airborne mapping technique which uses a laser to measure the distance between the aircraft and the ground. This technique results in the production of a height (terrain) map suitable for assessing flood risk. The aircraft flies at a height of about 800m above ground level and a scanning mirror allows a ground width of about 600m to be surveyed during a flight. Individual measurements are made on the ground at 2m intervals, allowing a highly resolved model of the terrain to be generated. Source: *www.environment-agency.gov.uk /science/.*

Figure 31.4 (right): The plane was also used to collect a radar image which can be used as a base layer for displaying with other imagery. When a radar signal is emitted from the plane, water absorbs the radar, which is why it appears black in the image. However, the buildings strongly reflect the radar so that they appear white. Source: Norwich Union.

The collection of such data was no small task and required massive investment by the organisation. Norwich Union worked with Intermap, who collected data using LIDAR and an airborne radar system (see Figures 31.3 and 31.4) to produce a digital elevation model that shows the height of the ground above sea level (Figure 31.5 overleaf). This was combined with a software model provided by JBA Consulting to produce the final map showing where floods are likely to occur, how they can spread and how far they can extend (see Figure 31.6 overleaf). This information was then analysed using a GIS supplied by ESRI (UK).

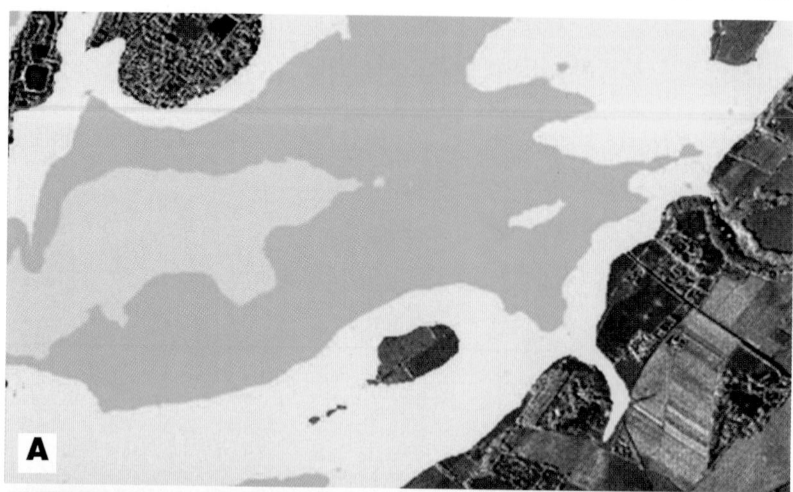

Figure 31.5: A) a 10m contour map showing the level of accuracy that was available from the Ordnance Survey before Norwich Union undertook its mapping programme. **B**) A 1m contour map showing the level of detail that is now available using the LIDAR data. Source: Norwich Union.

The collection of the height data marks the first time elevation mapping of an entire nation has been funded and carried out by a commercial organisation without government involvement. As a consequence, Norwich Union has access to elevation data for the UK that is more accurate than anything held by any government department, including the Environment Agency and Ordnance Survey. However, mechanisms are now being established to share this data with both the Government and other private companies.

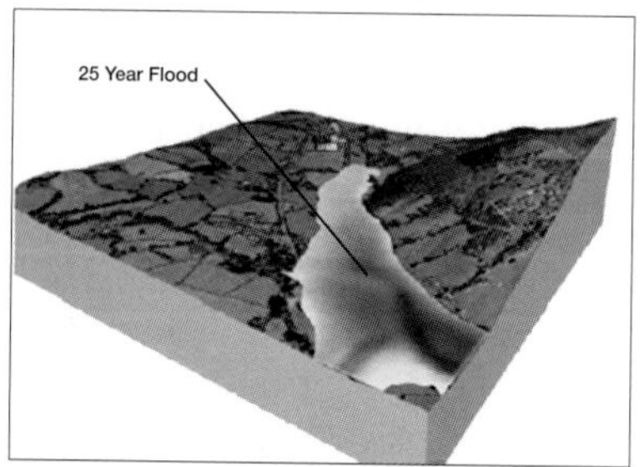

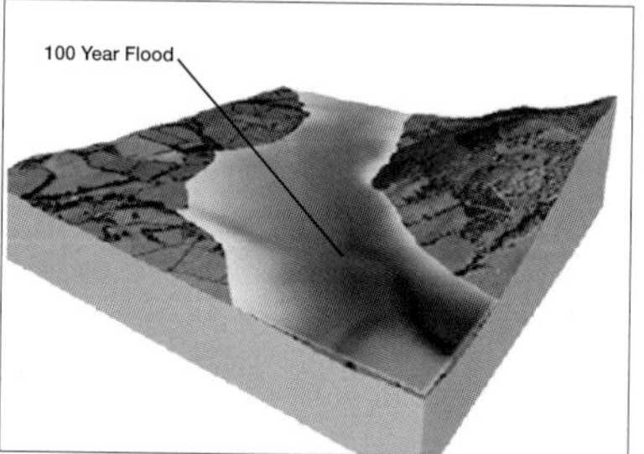

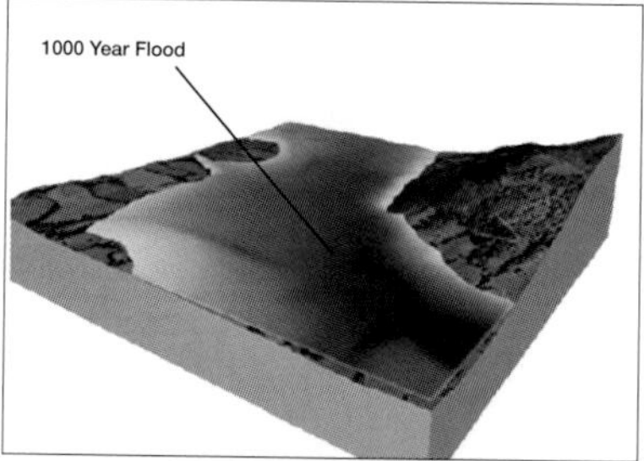

Figure 31.6: Simplified examples of the types of output produced by the JBA Consulting hydrological model. The model is used to predict the extent and depth of flooding for seven return periods of 10, 25, 50, 75, 100, 250 and 1000 years. Put another way, it is possible to estimate the largest flood that is likely to occur over different timescales. Source: Laurence Loughnane PowerPoint, Norwich Union.

The GIS now being used by Norwich Union can predict three key factors for each property in the UK:

- the overall likelihood of flooding
- the extent of flooding
- the likely cost of the damage.

It can then use this analysis to make decisions on whether to insure a property or not and at what level to set the premiums.

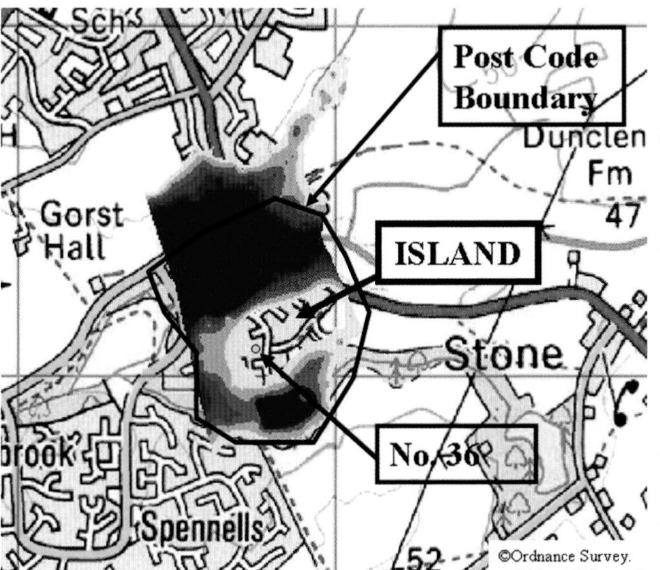

Figure 31.7: The blue area on the map represents areas at risk from flooding. When postcodes have been used in the past to assess flood risk, every house within the boundary has been assigned equal risk. This approach does not provide an accurate assessment of risk, as can be seen above. In this example, No 36 is located on an elevated 'island' within the postcode area, making it a relatively low risk for insurance. The use of address point data, with every house being assessed individually, means that many more houses across the UK have become insurable. Source: Norwich Union. OS base mapping reproduced with permission.

The use of address point data within the GIS has also considerably improved the accuracy of flood risk assessment. For example, in the past flood maps worked according to postcodes – a system that can be unfair to home owners who have no history of flooding but are unfortunate enough to live in a postcode that does have some high flood risk areas (Figure 31.7). The result is higher premiums for all householders in that postcode. However, with the use of GIS and address point data, maps can be produced that accurately pinpoint specific houses rather than whole areas.

Benefits of using GIS

More than 600,000 properties in flood risk areas could now qualify for insurance thanks to the new flood maps being produced by Norwich Union. The ability to pinpoint whether an individual house is on a hill or raised ground, and how floodwaters will flow, is invaluable in the fight against flood damage. The new information will help to convey to customers just how severe the flooding risk to their property will be and how often a flood can be expected. This means that the five million people living or working in flood risk areas, as defined by the Environment Agency, will be charged more accurate premiums and will have a better understanding of the risk to their property. This should mean that at least some home owners currently denied cover because they are perceived to be a high risk could now qualify for insurance.

Questions

- How is Norwich Union using GIS to manage flood risk?
- How was height data collected by Norwich Union?
- How does the use of address point data improve flood prediction for individual households?

32 West Midlands Police and GIS

West Midlands Police Service is responsible for England's second-largest city, Birmingham, which has a population of over 1 million people, over 400,000 households and the largest local authority in Europe. It is also a very young city, with almost 26% of the population under 18, and a city of great diversity, with approximately a quarter of the population from black and minority ethnic backgrounds.

Figure 32.1: The policing areas covered by the West Midlands Police Force and its location within England.
Source: *www.west-midlands.police.uk.* OS base mapping reproduced with permission.

West Midlands Police has been attempting to use GIS to reduce crime and the fear of crime in the Aston area of Birmingham. Aston is an area which presents some significant policing challenges. As regards urban deprivation, it is 27th on an index of some 8,000 districts in the UK (see Figure 32.2). There is a 50% unemployment rate, some 45 languages are heard in the district, and a quarter of children cannot speak a word of English on their first day at school.

Despite these challenges, crime in Aston and Birmingham as a whole has been in decline (see Figure 32.3). However, at the same time there is a steady and seemingly irrational increase in the public's fear of crime. The role of the police is evolving as a result. As well as simply catching criminals, the police want to make people feel secure and safe in their daily lives.

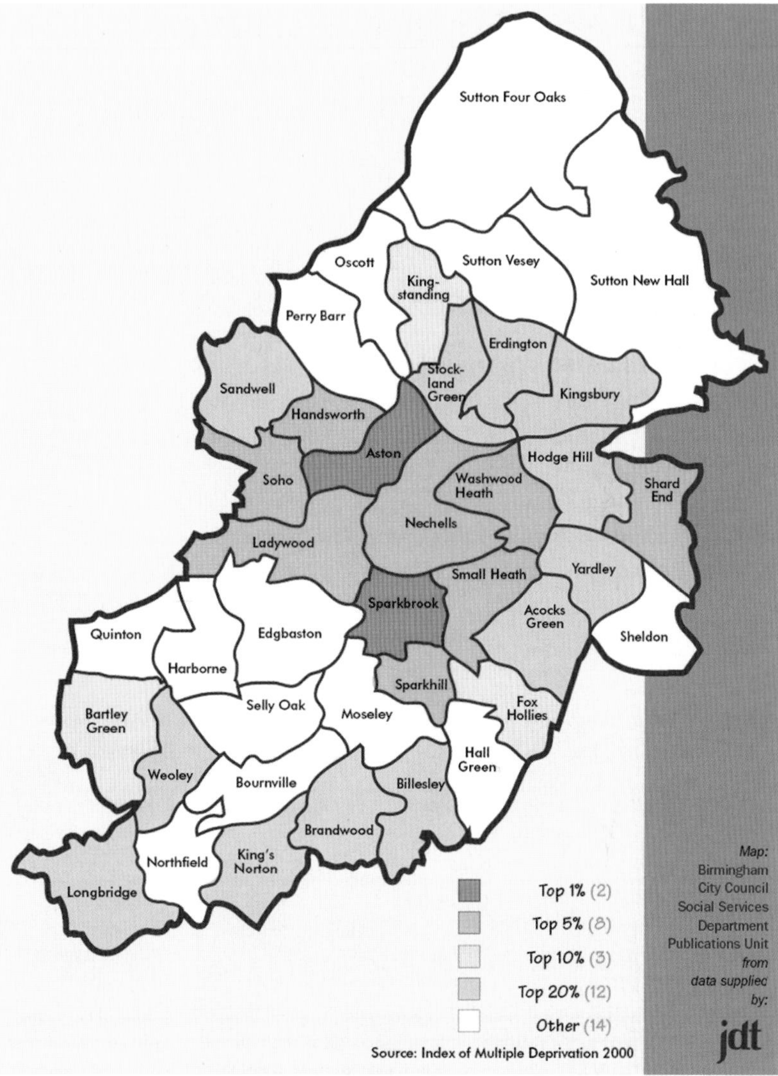

Figure 32.2: The location of Aston within the Birmingham area. Aston is in the top 1% of the most-deprived areas within the UK according to the Multiple Deprivation Index. The index uses several measures to indicate how deprived an area is. These include: income deprivation; employment deprivation; health deprivation and disability; education, skills and training deprivation; barriers to housing and services; living environment deprivation; crime. Source: Birmingham Community Safety Partnership (2002).

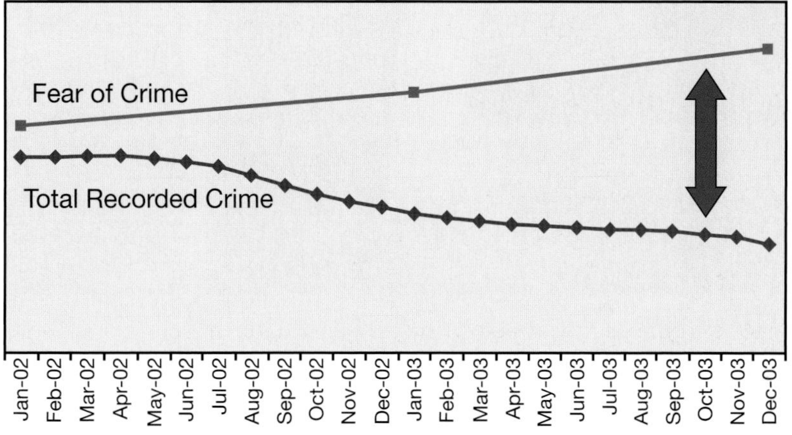

Figure 32.3: Total recorded crime in Birmingham has been reduced. However, at the same time the public's fear of crime has been increasing. Source: West Midlands Police.

Explaining people's growing fear of crime

The West Midlands Police Force and other researchers believe that people's growing fear of crime relates to the concept of 'signal events' or 'signal disorders'. These are minor nuisances and signs of antisocial behaviour which project negative messages to passers-by about the kind of environment they live in. The sight of minor crimes leads people to believe that they are more likely to become victims of crime.

To help reduce Aston residents' fear of crime West Midlands Police initiated a local reassurance project. The establishment of the programme was a joint partnership between, amongst others, the Police, Birmingham City Council and Encams, the body behind Keep Britain Tidy. The project was funded by the Home Office together with 15 similar projects across the country. The first stages of the project involved identifying what types of signal crime Aston's residents were most concerned about, mapping the occurrences of these and other crimes, and then allocating resources to tackle the issues using GIS analysis.

Figure 32.4: Examples of 'signal crime' that may lead to the undermining of an individual's personal feeling of safety. A **signal crime** or **signal disorder** is a criminal incident, or a physical or social disorder, that is interpreted by members of the public as a warning signal about their level of security. In effect, exposure to the signal crime causes people to alter their beliefs or actions in some way, as a reflection of the increased risk that they perceive. Photos: Chelle, Alan Stanton, Fin Fahey at Morguefile

Aston's residents attended local meetings to establish what constitutes signal crime in their view. Residents expressed their crime-fighting priorities by voting with hand-held keypads. This ensured that what

was to be mapped using the GIS was relevant to local people. Electronic voting helped to ensure accurate representation: instead of producing a conclusion decided by a few dominant characters among the audience, it allowed everyone an equal say. The voting revealed, surprisingly to the police, that fly-tipping and litter were the number-one concern of local people (see Figure 32.5).

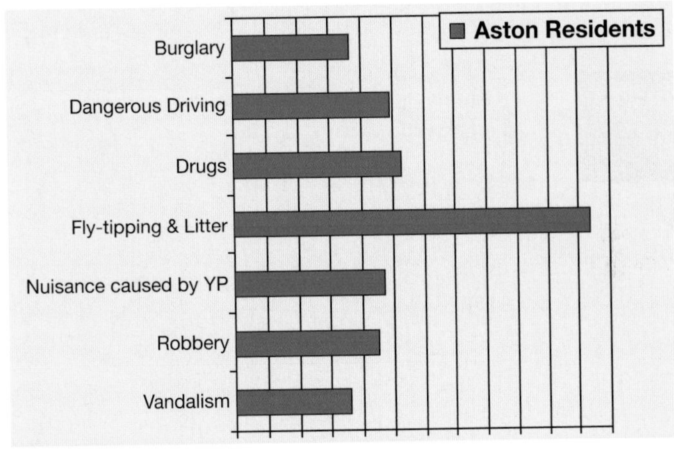

Figure 32.5: Voting from Aston's residents identified that fly-tipping was its number-one policing priority. Source: West Midlands Police.

Mapping using GIS

Mapping was carried out by police officers and community wardens using hand-held GIS (see Figure 32.6). The location of the fly-tipping and other incidents of interest was recorded by touching the screen of

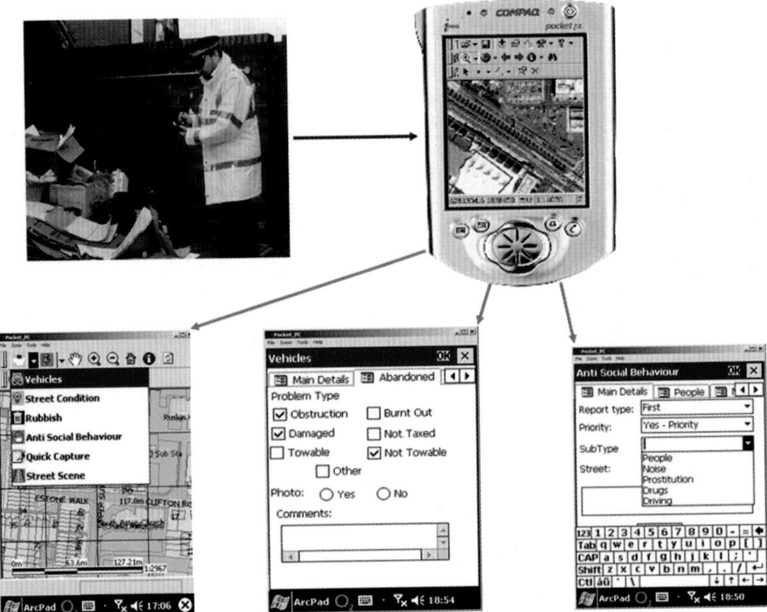

Figure 32.6: A police officer uses a hand-held mobile GIS to record the location of a fly-tipping incident in Aston, Birmingham. The mobile GIS can also record other types of incidents such as abandoned cars, antisocial behaviour and vandalism. Source: West Midlands Police.

the hand-held device. Location was recorded accurately through the use of Ordnance Survey mapping held in the device. Attribute data was recorded through a series of drop-down menus and checklists. Pictures of the area were also recorded.

Over a period of time maps were built up indicating areas where incidents were most likely to occur (see Figure 32.7). These areas were then targeted by the police in an attempt to reduce any illegal activity.

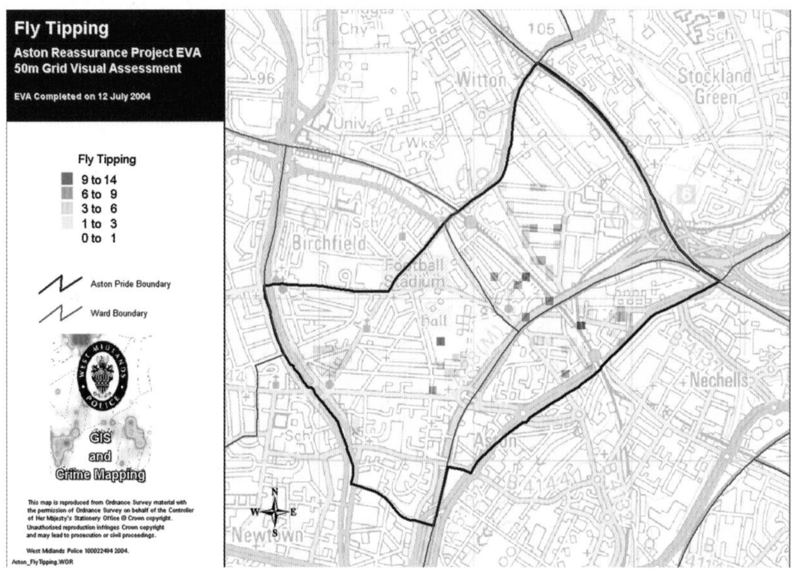

Figure 32.7: An example of the maps that were produced to indicate areas of fly-tipping in Aston. Source: West Midlands Police. OS base mapping reproduced with permission.

The collected information was also made available over the internet (see Figure 32.8). In addition, whenever an incident was recorded, local council officials automatically received an e-mail describing the nature and location of the incident. The local council could then immediately action the clean up of the area, reducing the time the incident remained visible to the community.

Figure 32.8: The system structure for recording, mapping and sharing the GIS-produced information. The data gathered by the hand-held devices was collated on a hosted internet site from which it could be correlated with other data, including police incidents, recorded crime and census information. The internet part of the system was hosted by the specialist GIS company ESRI (UK). Source: West Midlands Police.

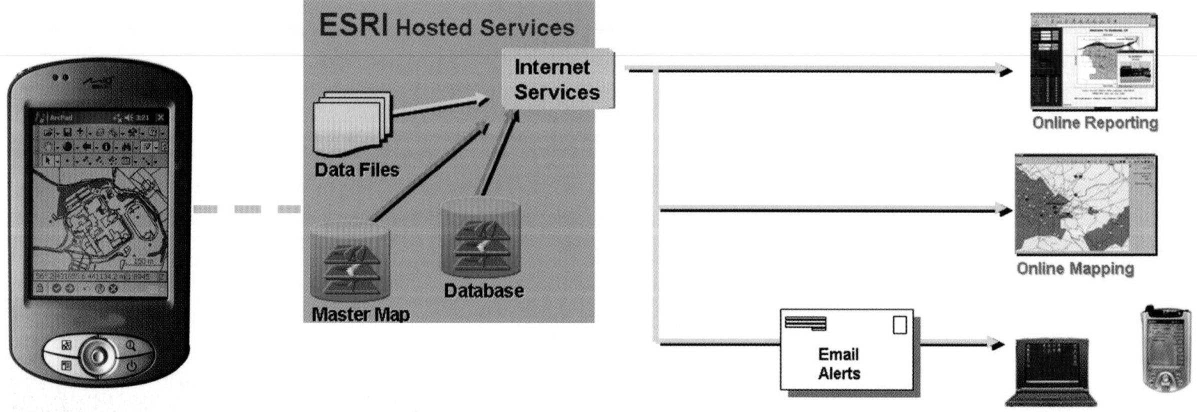

The benefits of using GIS

The action taken by West Midlands Police and Birmingham City Council to remove signal crime from the Aston area had a number of important impacts. For example, a row of shops that had been plagued by fly-tipping was cleaned up and the number of police patrols in the area increased. Shop owners reported an 80% increase in turnover during the reassurance project. Growing evidence from the area leads one to hope that, while serious violations such as armed crime are an occasional feature of the district, tackling minor offences with the use of GIS will not only reassure the public but also modify local culture so that further crimes of this and possibly other kinds are less likely to be committed.

Questions

- Why is Birmingham's fear of crime levels unusual given the total recorded crime figures for the area?
- How was crime mapping carried out in Aston?
- What are the likely impacts of crime mapping in Aston?

33

National and local conflict: wind power and GIS

Site selection for wind power generation is a growing source of tension between the UK Government, environmentalists and local populations. The paragraphs below examine some of the issues involved and how GIS is being used as a tool for negotiation and persuasion in the selection of wind power sites.

CO_2 reduction and wind power

There is now consensus that carbon dioxide emissions are causing climate change. The UK Government have responded to the dangers of climate change by promoting the development of renewable energy sources, including wind power, to reduce emissions of carbon dioxide and other greenhouse gases from the generation of electricity (see Figure 33.1). Government policy is aimed towards obtaining 10% of the UK's electricity from renewable sources by 2010, with an aspiration to source 20% by 2020.

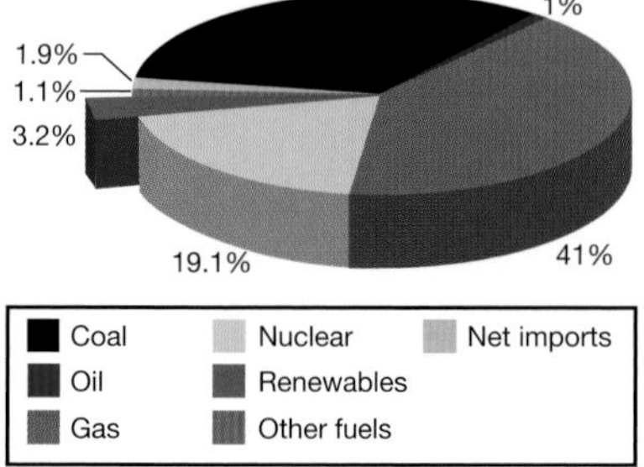

Figure 33.1: Electricity generation by fuel source in 2004. The Government wants the percentage of electricity produced from renewable sources to increase from 3.2% in 2004 to 10% by 2010. Source: Sustainable Development Commission (2005).

After a public consultation between 1999 and 2000, the Government decided that a Renewables Obligation (RO) was their preferred solution for achieving reductions in CO_2 emissions through renewable electricity generation. The Renewables Obligation requires electricity generators to produce 10% of their electricity resources from renewable sources by 2010. The Renewables Obligation became law in April 2002, and covers England and Wales.

As the UK has the best wind resources in Europe (see Figure 33.2) and the method is perceived to be economical (see Table 33.1 opposite), many electricity generators are choosing to meet their Renewables Obligation through the use of wind power.

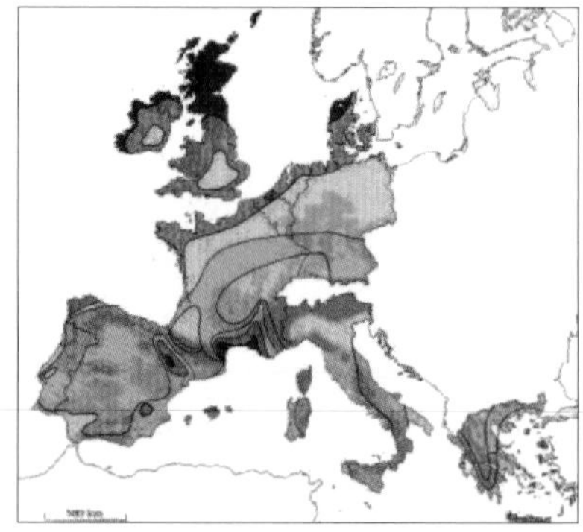

Figure 33.2: The dark-blue (>9.0ms^{-1}) and red (8.0–9.0ms^{-1}) areas on the map show the best areas in Europe for wind power generation because of the high wind speeds in these areas. As can be seen the UK has the best potential for wind power generation in Europe. Source: Sustainable Development Commission (2005).

Wind power and conflict over land use

With power companies obligated by the Government to switch to generating electricity from renewable resources, the search is on for suitable sites. However, there is often intense opposition from local residents and environmental organisations to proposed wind power

Table 33.1: Today the generation costs of onshore wind power are around 3.2p/kWh, and offshore around 5.5p/kWh, compared to a wholesale price for electricity of around 3.0p/kWh. However, generation costs for wind power are projected to decrease over time, making this one of the most cost-efficient ways of producing electricity by 2020. Source: Sustainable Development Commission (2005).

Technology	Cost in 2020	Confidence in estimate	Cost trends to 2050
Conventional fuels			
Coal (IGCC[XVI])	3.0-3.5p/kWh	Moderate	Decrease
Gas (CCGT)	2.0-2.3p/kWh	High	Limited decrease
Fossil generation with CO_2 capture & sequestration	3.0-4.5p/kWh	Moderate	Uncertain
Large HP (gas)	under 2p/kWh	High	Limited decrease
Micro CHP (gas)	2.5-3.5p/kWh	Moderate	Sustained decrease
Nuclear	3.0-4.0p/kWh	Moderate	Decrease
Renewables			
Onshore wind	1.5-2.5p/kWh	High	Limited decrease
Offshore wind	2.0-3.0p/kWh	Moderate	Decrease
Energy crops	2.5-4.0p/kWh	Moderate	Decrease
Wave	3-6p/kh	Low	Uncertain
Solar photovoltaics	10-16p/kWh	High	Sustained decrease

generation projects. Opponents to development are most often concerned about the potential impacts of:

- visual changes to the landscape
- noise from turbines
- interference with television and radio signals from blade rotation
- interference with radar for civilian and military navigation
- environmental or ecological effects on local habitats, wildlife and flora
- impact on house prices and other local economic factors
- disturbance during construction.

The result is that people's attitudes towards wind power developments may sometimes change, from being favourable in principle to being opposed when people are faced with the prospect of having a wind farm in their locality. While people recognise the need to reduce CO_2 emissions they often do not want the outcomes of these policy decisions in their backyard.

The role of GIS

In order to help in these matters, Government, local authorities, researchers and power companies are using GIS to identify sites for wind power generation that minimise the potential for conflict. The Government has also instructed local councils to be active in trying to identify sites suitable for renewable energy as a means of translating national targets into suitable development on the ground.

To take one example, researchers from the University of Glamorgan have developed a GIS query to identify the best sites in Wales for the

Are not within 3km of an airport;
Are not within 1km of a National Park;
Are not within 1km of a National Trust property;
Are not within 1km of a military danger zone;
Are not within 1km of a Scenic Area;
Are not within 1km of a Forest Park;
Are not within 2km of a built-up area;
Are not within 5km of a city;
Are not within 2.5km of an urban area;
Are not within 1.5km of a town;
Are not within 1km of a small town or village;
Are not within 750 metres of a small village, hamlet or isolated settlement;
Are not within 250 metres of a lake, marsh or reservoir;
Are not within 300 metres of a motorway, A-road or B-road;
Are not within 250 metres of a railway;
Are not within 200 metres of a river or canal;
Are not within 250 metres of a radio or TV mast;
Are above 100 metres in elevation
Are not within 1km of a 'picturesque' or scenic feature, including:
Battlefields, Castles, Country Parks, Historic Sites, Houses or Gardens, Nature Reserves or Scenic Viewpoints.

Figure 33.3 A GIS query used by researchers from the University of Glamorgan, Wales, to identify potential sites for wind turbines while avoiding features of significant potential conflict in Wales. Source: Sparkes and Kidner (1996).

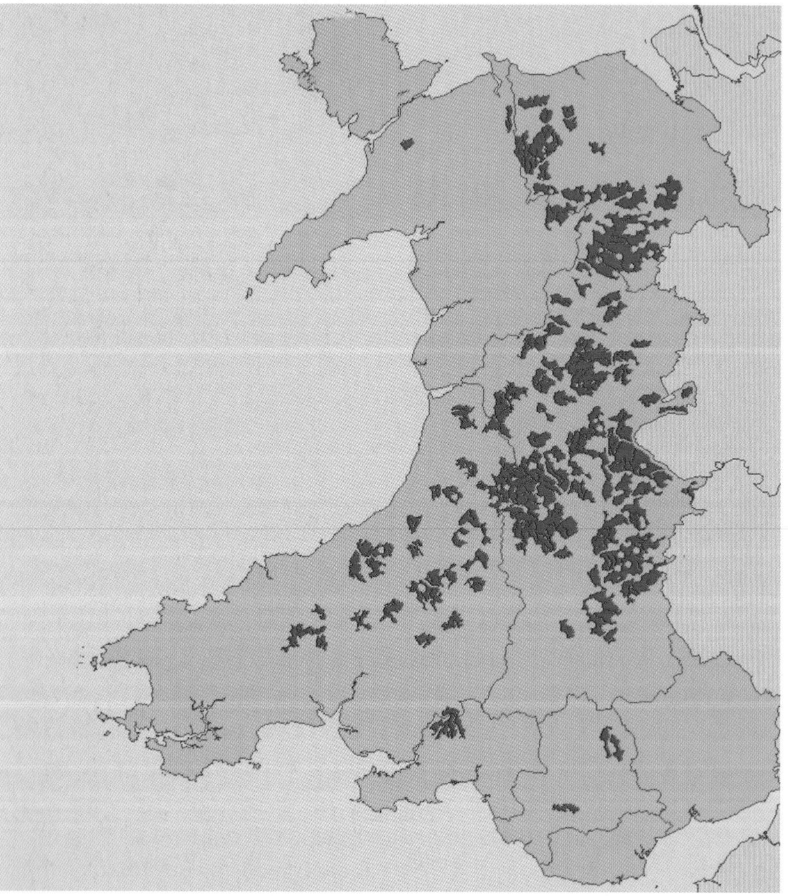

Figure 33.4: The best potential sites (areas greater than 5 kilometres) in Wales for the location of wind turbines as defined by the criteria in Figure 33.3. Source: Sparkes and Kidner (1996).

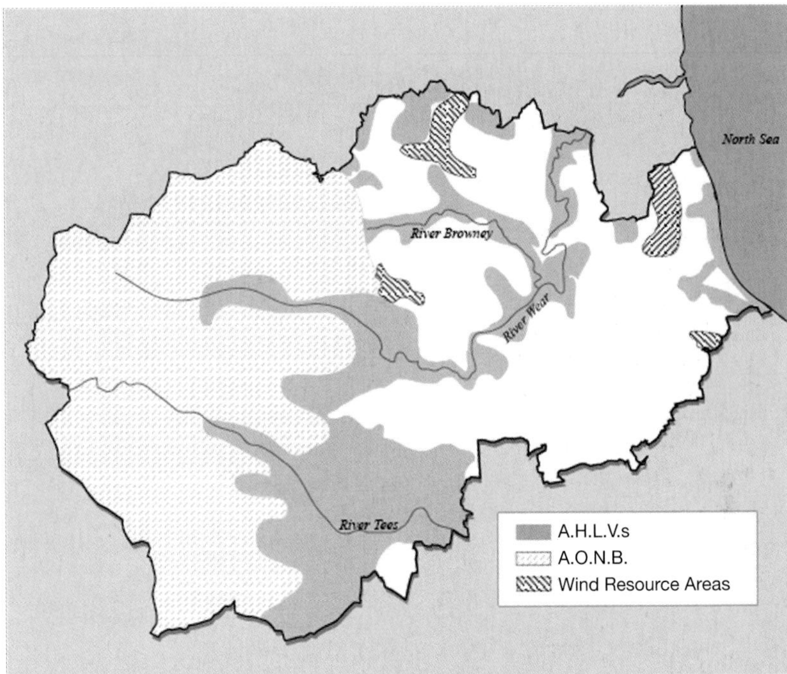

Figure 33.5: Durham County Council have used GIS query techniques to identify potential sites in the county where planning permission for wind power generation is most likely to be given. The sites shown avoid areas of outstanding natural beauty (AONB) and areas of high landscape value (AHLV). Source: Durham County Council (1999).

location of wind turbines while avoiding areas where there is likely to be significant conflict with local populations (see Figure 33.3). The results of this query are shown in Figure 33.4.

GIS thus offers the potential for combining complex search criteria representing the interests of local people, environmental groups and power companies. The views of local people are increasingly being included as part of the process of defining the criteria for identifying potential new sites for wind turbines. The techniques developed by Glamorgan University are being replicated across the country. In particular, local authorities and county councils are starting to use these techniques as part of their sustainable development strategies (see Figure 33.5).

Using GIS to visualise the impact

GIS technology has been used not only to identify potential sites for wind turbines, but also to help people visualise how the turbines will appear in the landscape. In this way GIS is being used to bridge the gap between people's perceptions and the reality of how the wind turbines will actually appear in the landscape (see Figures 33.6 and 33.7 overleaf).

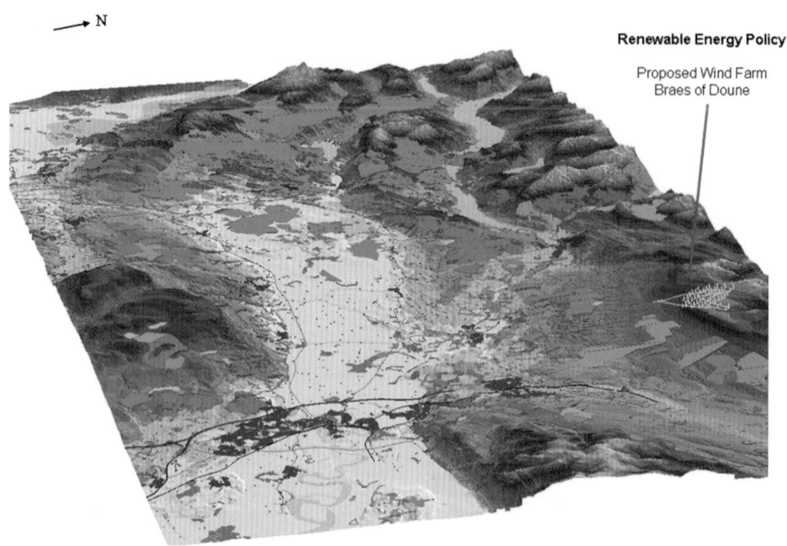

Figure 33.6: Visualising the site and situation of a proposed wind farm near Stirling in Scotland using GIS techniques. Source: Stirling Council (2005).

Figure 33.7: Visualising the site of a proposed wind farm locations using GIS. Source: Sparkes and Kidner (1996).

A very important technique in this area is called viewshed analysis (see Figure 33.8 opposite). Viewshed analysis allows individuals to determine how much of an object can be seen from different points in the landscape. This would, for example, enable individual households to determine how many turbines, or how much of a turbine, would be visible from their home.

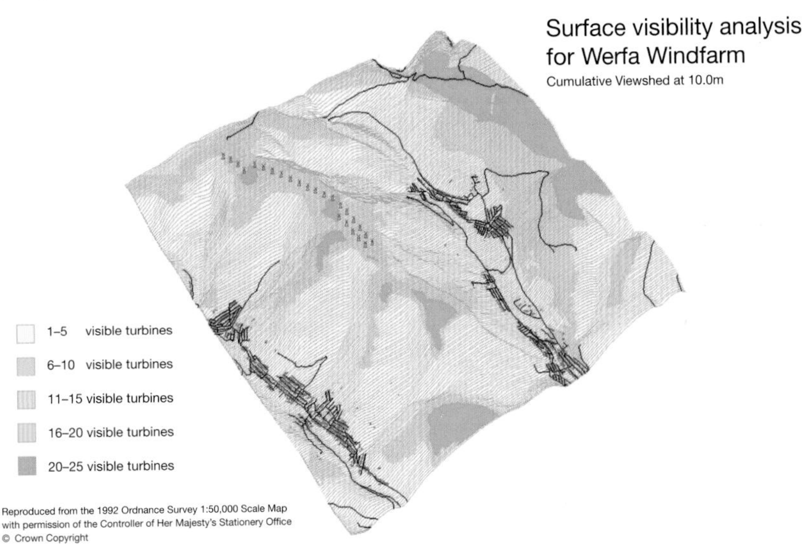

Figure 33.8: A viewshed analysis of a proposed wind farm in Wales. Each colour on the map shows how many turbines can be seen from the corresponding location. This is a very powerful technique for enabling people to see how much a proposed wind farm will intrude visually on the location where they live. Source: Sparkes and Kidner (1996).

The importance of GIS to national energy policy

The use of GIS by local councils and local authorities to define potential sites for wind farm development is helping to speed up the planning process so that power companies can meet government renewable energy targets. At the same time, planners are using GIS to limit the potential impact of development by applying a rigorous set of site selection criteria. This in turn helps to minimise the potential for conflict between different interest groups.

It is of course impossible to remove the potential for conflict completely. Where conflicts arise, however, GIS visualisation techniques are being used to inform the debate so that the different parties involved have the best possible evidence to put before the decision-makers as to which site should be chosen.

Questions

- What is the Renewables Obligation?
- Why are some communities against wind power?
- How is GIS being used to manage land-use conflict in relation to the location of wind farms?

GIS helping to reconstruct Ice Age Britain

34

Introduction

It has been known for over 150 years that large parts of Britain were inundated by an ice sheet during the last glaciation. Many investigations by geologists in the UK have yielded a vast range of publications reporting field evidence suggesting the extent and dynamics of the last (Devensian) ice sheet. The information base is so large – most likely exceeding 2,000 publications – that all the pieces of the jigsaw have never been assembled (Clark *et al.*, 2004). To address this problem, a team of researchers in the UK have attempted to pull together all the glacial data into one single source using GIS.

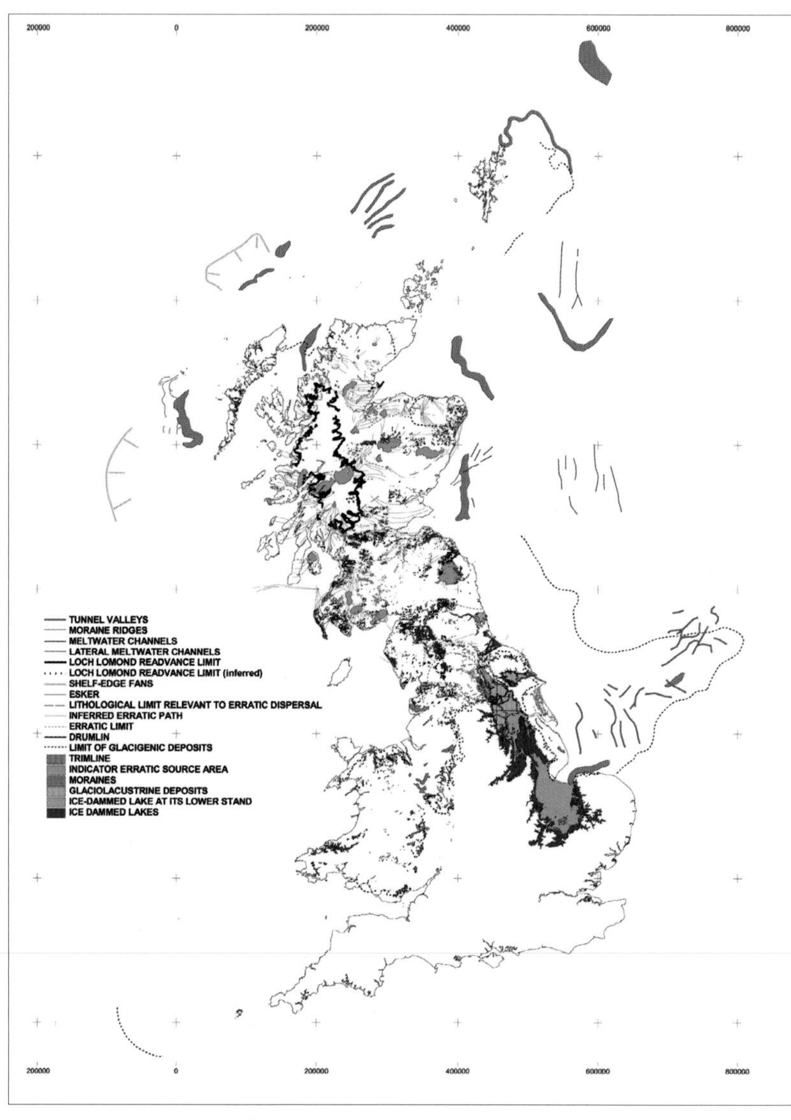

Figure 34.1: Overview of all 20 thematic layers displayed within the GIS, including terrestrial and offshore features. The database comprises over 20,000 individual features split into the thematic layers of moraines, eskers, drumlins, meltwater channels, tunnel valleys, shelf-edge fans, trimlines, limits of key glacigenic deposits ('drift limits'), glaciolacustrine deposits, ice-dammed lakes, erratic dispersal and the West Highland Loch Lomond Readvance limit. Source: Clark *et al.* (2004).

Mapping Ice Age Britain

Professor Chris Clark from the University of Sheffield and his team (Clark *et al.*, 2004) carried out a review of all the academic literature and British Geological Survey mapping in order to produce a 'glacial map' of the UK. In addition they built a GIS database of features related to

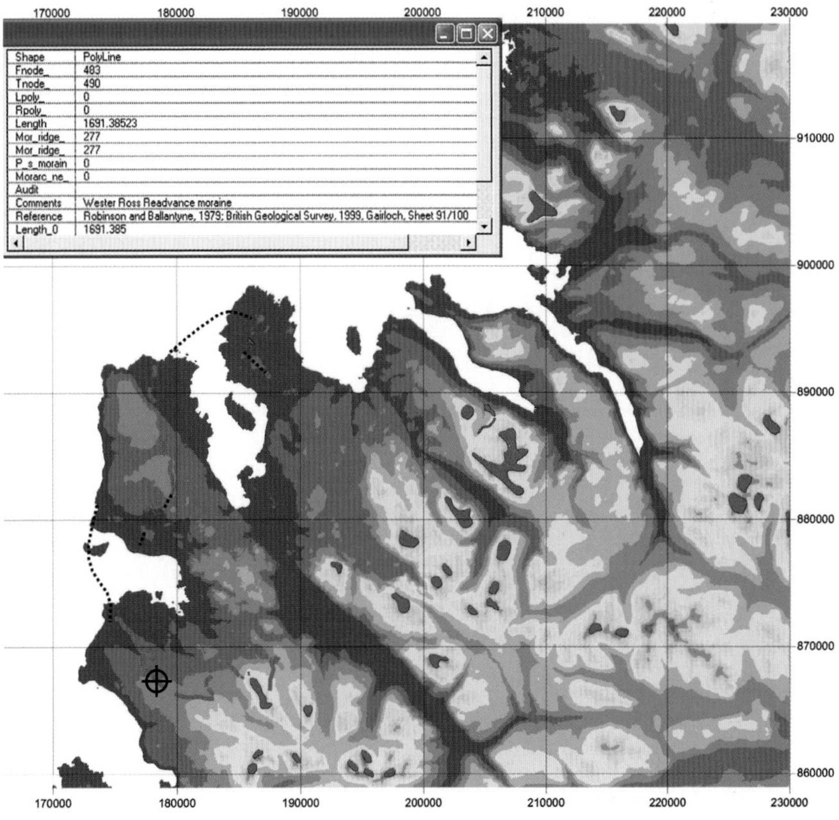

Figure 34.2: On-screen view of some of the GIS layers for part of Wester Ross, Scotland – trimlines (nunataks) in red, moraine ridges in brown, and limits of glacigenic deposits dotted in black – overlaid on a DEM of the topography. This illustrates how it is possible to interrogate any individual feature and receive information on the published source from which it derives together with a brief explanatory comment. Source: Clark *et al.* (2004).

the last (Devensian) British ice sheet (see Figure 34.1). The data is freely available by web download from the following site: *www.shef.ac.uk/geography/staff/clark_chris/britice.html*.

The database represents a significant achievement and shows how the technology can be used to pull together and share information. The GIS contains over 20,000 features split into thematic layers. Individual features are attributed in such a way that they can be traced back to their published sources by carrying out a GIS query (Figures 34.2 above and 34.3 overleaf). This facility is important as the sources used to construct the GIS database date back over 150 years. It is essential that we should be able identify these sources in order to assess the reliability of the mapping.

The researchers hope that the database will stimulate greater use of existing published data, assist in palaeoglaciological reconstructions and facilitate the use of field evidence in numerical ice-sheet modelling. It may also help direct field workers in the future by identifying sites for potential investigation.

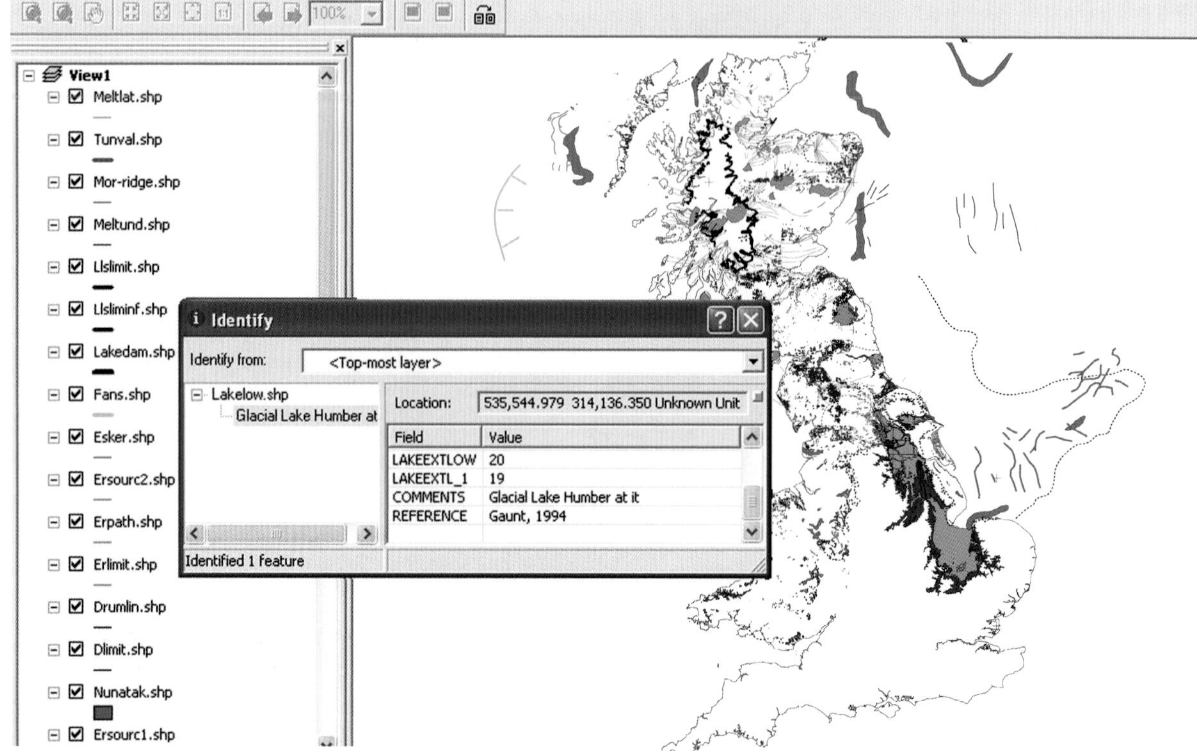

Figure 34.3: An image of the downloaded GIS glacial database in ArcMap 9.2. Source: *www.shef.ac.uk/geography/staff/clark_chris/britice/html*

Questions

- Download the GIS database from the following website: *www.shef.ac.uk/geography/staff/clark_chris/britice.html*
- From the database, produce a map of your area showing its main glacial features.
- From the resources that come with the glacial GIS identify the main limitations associated with the construction of the map.

35 Mapping social values with GIS

Introduction

In many urban areas the demand for new construction sites leads to the infilling of existing green locations with other urban land uses. This is in response to the need to protect green belt land outside the city and to slow down the process of urban sprawl. The utilisation of existing urban spaces is seen by many urban planners as a way of ensuring sustainable development.

However, in making these planning decisions, are the views and feelings of urban dwellers being fully taken into account? For example, green areas contribute greatly to people's quality of life in cities, allowing recreational opportunities and improving the home and work environment, as well as impacting on physical and mental health. It is therefore important to ask:

- How much green area (and of what kinds) should be provided for residents in urban areas?
- Do suburban green areas provide high-quality benefits for residents?
- Where do residents find attractive and meaningful green areas and what are the characteristics of these areas?

In asking and mapping the answers to such questions, urban planners may well be in a better position to make decisions that ensure the protection of our most-valued urban green spaces.

A new approach to urban planning in Finland

Researchers in Finland (Tyrvainen *et al.*, 2007) are developing new tools and approaches for using GIS to map social attitudes towards urban green areas so that the views of local residents can be integrated into the planning process.

The researchers based their work (Figure 35.1 overleaf) in Helsinki, the capital of Finland, which lies on the south coast of the country. The city is home to approximately 560,000 inhabitants, covers some 18,535ha of land and owns 5,510ha of green areas, most of which is accessible to the public. A majority of the green space – 3,570 ha – consists of woodland.

A postal questionnaire was sent to 1,000 residents aged 15–75. The questionnaire dealt with mapping the social values of green areas. A map of the green areas being investigated was included in the questionnaire. Respondents were asked to identify areas on the map with the following positive values: beautiful landscape, valuable nature site, the feeling of forest, space and freedom, attractive park, peace and quiet, opportunities for activity, and history and culture.

Furthermore, they were asked to identify areas with the negative values of unpleasantness, scariness and noise.

Figure 35.1: The case study area in eastern Helsinki. Source: Tyrvainen *et al.* (2007).

Mapping the results of the postal questionnaire

The social values of green areas identified by each respondent were compiled into a database per unit area, which produced the number of times an area had been identified as having a specific social quality. The database with social value scores was imported into a GIS, making it possible to present the results on a series of maps (see

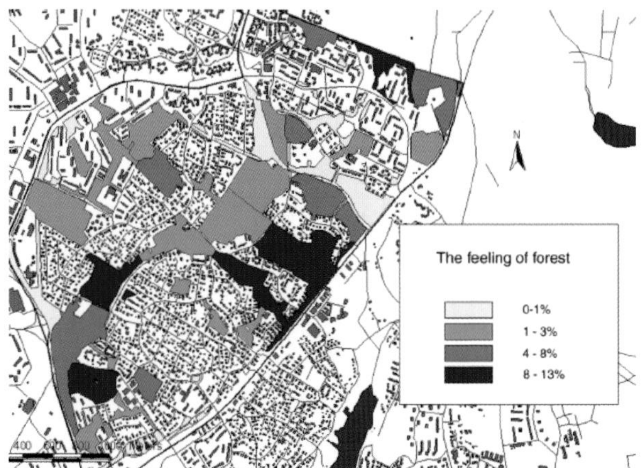

Figure 35.2: Areas in which the respondents experience the sense of being in a forest (percentage of total scores). Source: Tyrvainen *et al.* (2007).

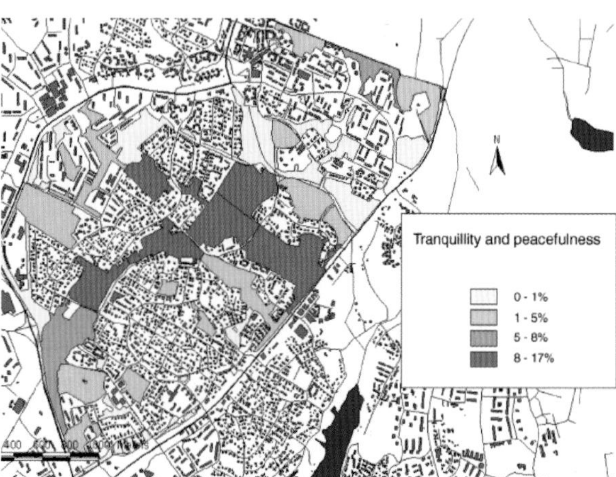

Figure 35.3: Peaceful areas within the study area (percentage of total scores). Source: Tyrvainen *et al.* (2007).

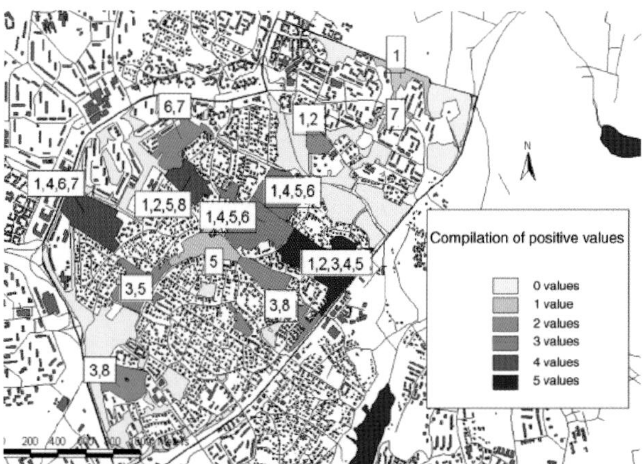

Figure 35.4: A synthesis map of the areas with the highest scores in various social value categories. Key to numbers: (1) beautiful landscape, (2) valuable nature site, (3) the feeling of forest, (4) space and freedom, (5) peace and quiet, (6) attractive parkland, (7) opportunity for activities, (8) history and culture. Source: Tyrvainen *et al.* (2007).

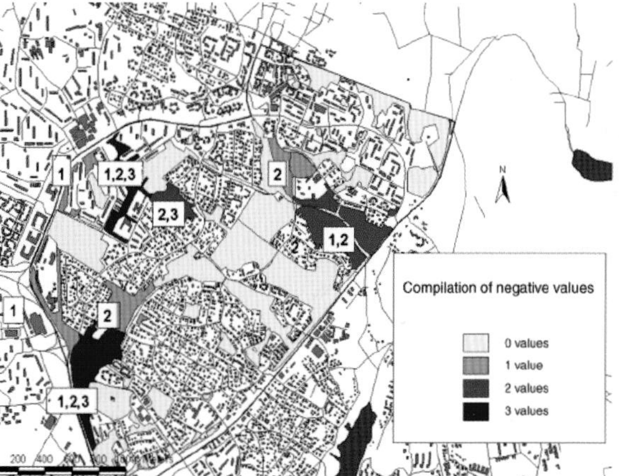

Figure 35.5: A synthesis map of the most negatively experienced areas. Key to numbers: (1) noisy areas, (2) unpleasant areas, (3) scary areas. Source: Tyrvainen *et al.* (2007).

Figures 35.2 to 35.5), combine it with other geographical information and perform further analysis.

Having successfully completed the mapping, the researchers came to the following conclusions:

- If recorded systematically, the social opinions of residents can be made equally visible as part of the planning process, thus enabling more balanced decisions to be reached.
- The method of GIS analysis facilitates the communication of green

area values, and empowers otherwise silent groups by enabling them to express their opinions.
- The maps show areas with qualities that should also be sustained in the future as well as development areas where values are currently missing.
- For land-use planning, the results highlight the green areas that should be protected from development for other land uses.

The research work conducted in Finland highlights the potential social benefits of GIS use, which has the power to map abstract concepts that might be otherwise difficult to visualise and communicate. The technology can also be inclusive and promote collective rather than minority decision-making.

Questions

- What other kinds of social opinions, not covered by the research in Finland, do you think it would be helpful to map in order to aid the planning process in the UK?
- Do you think it is important to include the views of residents in local planning issues? Fully justify your point of view.

Hazard prediction with GIS

Introduction

The ability of GIS to combine and analyse different layers of information makes it a powerful tool in the modelling of hazards and their mitigation. Virtually all hazard mapping utilises GIS to identify areas of risk. Likewise, GIS enables planners to visualise the spatial variability of hazards and recognise areas that are likely to be most vulnerable to future disasters.

Volcanic hazards: modelling lahars

Of the 220 active volcanoes around the world, only about 12% are monitored adequately. Many countries do not have the funds to conduct research or establish geological survey teams to construct hazard maps. One potential solution to this problem is to base hazard mapping programs on remote sensing and GIS technologies. Using remotely sensed data to construct hazard maps is much cheaper than carrying out labour-intensive field-based investigations. As a result, many hazard mapping programs in LEDCs are now based around remote sensing and GIS technologies.

Mexico: Popocatépetl Volcano

Popocatépetl Volcano (see Figure 36.1 overleaf) is located in the Trans-Mexican Volcanic Belt, 40–60km from large metropolitan areas such as Mexico City, Puebla and Cuernavaca. The region has many millions of inhabitants. The scientists working in this area (Huggel *et al.*, 2007) suggest that lahars are among the most serious and far-reaching volcanic hazards. As a consequence, an assessment of the related hazards in this area is crucial for undertaking appropriate mitigating actions and for reducing the associated risks. The lahar hazards in this area deserve special consideration on account of the glacier ice on top of the volcano and the attendant possibility of lahars triggered by eruption-induced ice-melt processes.

In an attempt to develop mitigation strategies, scientists (Huggel *et al.*, 2007) have tried to model the level of hazard associated with lahar flows surrounding Popocatépetl Volcano using remote sensing and

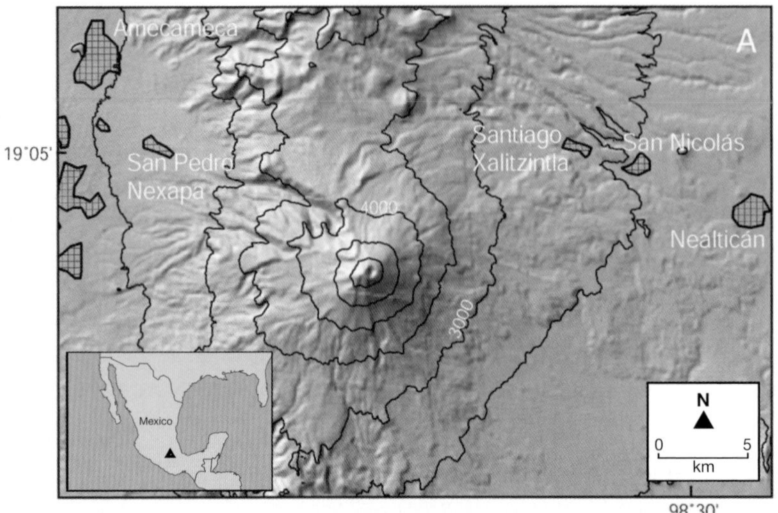

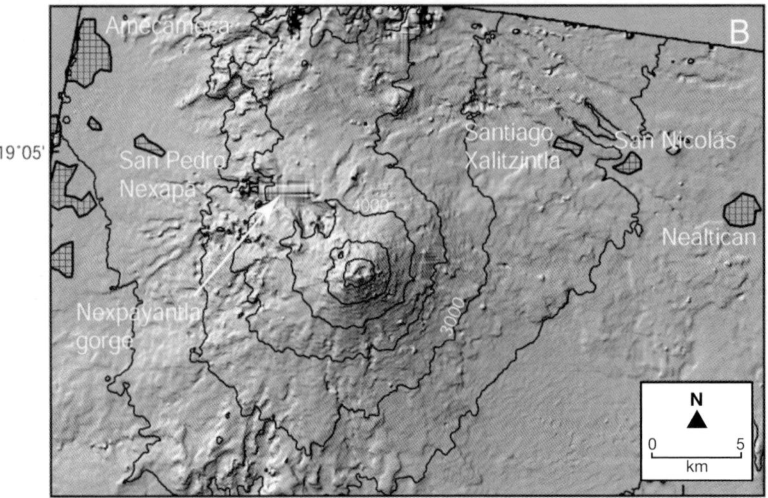

Figure 36.1: The location of Popocatépetl Volcano in central Mexico (inset). Shaded SRTM (A) and ASTER (B) DEMs (see opposite) of the Popocatépetl Volcano area are shown. Contour lines are at 500m intervals. The most important villages and towns relevant for lahar modelling studies are indicated. Note the erroneously shown area in the ASTER DEM at the Nexpayantla Gorge. Source: Huggel *et al.* (2007).

GIS technologies. It is hoped that this information will provide local authorities with the means to carry out effective mitigation planning. Additionally, if the techniques applied to Popocatépetl Volcano are successful, they may also provide a methodology for carrying out hazard mapping in other locations where ground surveying is not possible.

Constructing a hazard model for lahar flow

Lahars flow over a landscape under the influence of gravity. The direction and rate of flow will be determined by changes in topography and gradient. An essential first step in predicting the nature of lahar flow is to construct a digital elevation model (DEM). The lack of available digital elevation data has until recently been a major limiting factor in the construction of cost effective hazard mapping. However, remote sensing technology is now breaking down this barrier. The team of scientists (Huggel *et al.*, 2007) working in Mexico has attempted to use two different sources of digital elevation data:

- Advanced Spaceborne Thermal Emission and Reflection Radiometer (ASTER). The ASTER sensor onboard the NASA Terra satellite provides imagery with visible and near-infrared bands. When stereo pairs of these images are taken, they can be used to generate digital elevation data.
- Shuttle Radar Topography Mission (SRTM). SRTM was a single-pass, synthetic aperture radar interferometry campaign conducted in February 2000. For the first time a global high-quality DEM was achieved covering the earth's area between 60°N and 54°S.

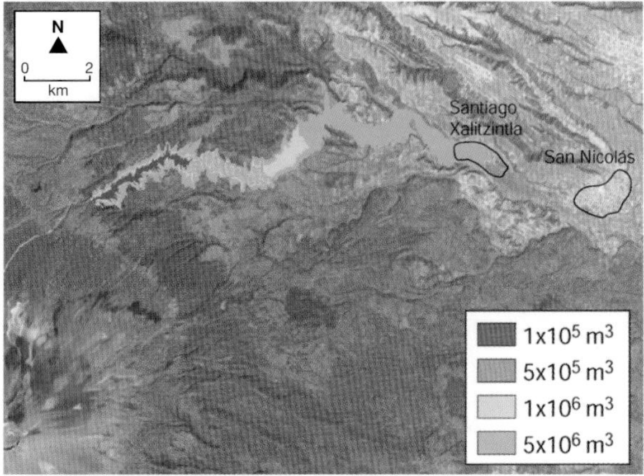

Figure 36.2: Modelled lahars in the Huiloac Gorge using the ASTER DEM with four different lahar volumes. The base image is an ASTER near-infrared image in which vegetation is shown in red (taken on 21 March 2001). Popocatépetl Volcano with its crater is visible in the lower left-hand corner. Source: Huggel *et al.* (2007).

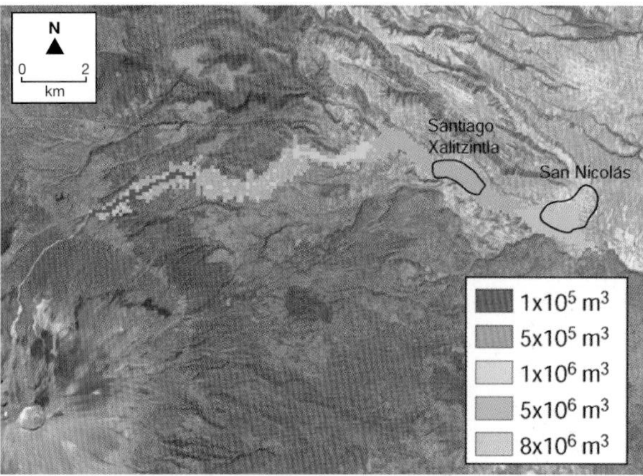

Figure 36.3: Modelled lahars in the Huiloac Gorge using the SRTM DEM with five different lahar volumes. The base image is the same as in Figure 36.2. Note that the predicted travel distances of lahars of equal volume are different from those shown in Figure 36.2. Source: Huggel *et al.* (2007).

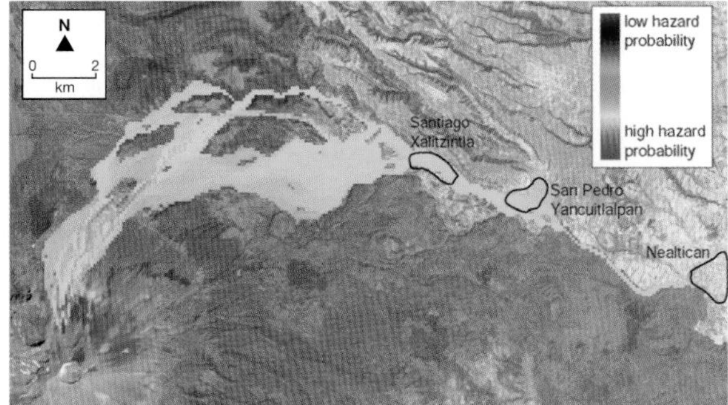

Figure 36.4: A model simulating a probable maximum lahar event in the Huiloac Gorge using the SRTM DEM. Colour coding indicates different degrees of probability for a cell to be affected by the lahar. Source: Huggel *et al.* (2007).

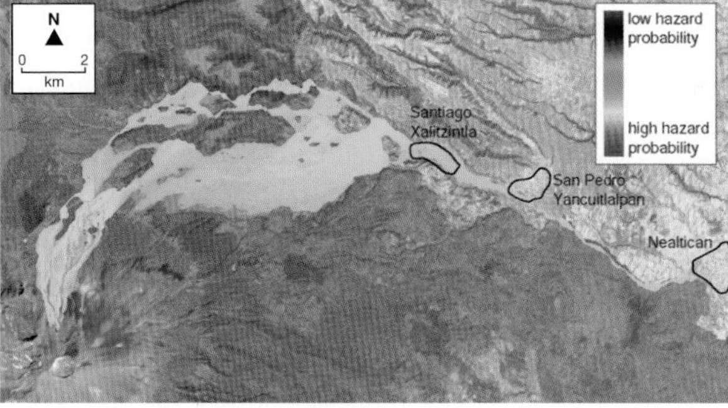

Figure 36.5: A model simulating a probable maximum lahar event in the Huiloac Gorge using the ASTER DEM. Colour coding indicates different degrees of probability for a cell to be affected by the lahar. Source: Huggel *et al.* (2007).

There will always be error in the generation of any DEM. An analysis of the SRTM and ASTER DEMs of Popocatépetl suggested that the SRTM DEM shows a lesser degree of error than the ASTER DEM. The maximum errors of the ASTER DEM were several hundreds of meters greater than those of the SRTM DEM (Huggel *et al.*, 2007).

Once the DEMs have been constructed (see Figure 36.1 on page 162), the next stage of the modelling process involves the integration of the DEMs into a GIS. Geological records of recent lahar events are input into the GIS to determine the size of the lahar flows to be modelled. Flow routing equations are then used to predict the spatial pattern of lahar events. Using this combined approach that merged remote sensing with GIS, the scientists produced a series of lahar hazard maps (see Figures 36.2 to 36.5 on previous page).

Despite the fact that scientists have been able to produce a range of accurate hazard maps, it is important to note that hazard mapping using remotely sensed data requires constant evaluation of data quality. For example, if you compare the different GIS outputs of the hazard modelling process (Figures 36.2 to 36.5), you can see that the choice of DEM will have a significant impact on the results obtained. A very important question, then, is which set of maps are the most reliable? On an initial inspection, you might think that the coarser resolution of the SRTM data might result in less reliable predictions. Yet the ASTER DEM, despite being of higher resolution, has proved less reliable in representing the actual topography (see Figure 36.1). The issue of reliability is not a simple question to answer and the modelling results will also vary depending on the equations used to predict lahar flow direction.

However, even taking these reservations into account, the scientists found that both types of DEMs could be used to produce reliable hazard maps. Given the global coverage of ASTER and SRTM data, we can conclude that lahar modelling studies are possible on virtually any volcano. This is of particular importance in hazard mitigation in LEDCs where volcanoes often lack DEM information (Huggel *et al.*, 2007).

Unit 2:

Practical exercises in GIS using ArcView 9.2

Exercise

Exercise 1: Where are all the people?

Aims

- To map the population density of England using GIS
- To produce a population density map of England suitable for publication

Background

Population density is a measure of how many people live in a given area. The nature and representation of population density figures can vary greatly. For example, an organisation like the United Nations is likely to contrast variations in population density *between* countries, whereas governments are more likely to map variations *within* a country. In this exercise we will map variations in population density across county boundaries in England.

Mapping population density is important as it allows decision-makers to visualise where people live. As a result, resources can be directed to where they are needed the most, or in some cases policies can be implemented to influence or change population distributions.

Another important part of this exercise is to develop skills for the effective sharing of the information we are mapping. We will therefore give careful consideration to the choices that are important in creating good map design for publication.

Launch ArcMap

1 Create a **new folder** where you can save all your future GIS work. Call it **GIS_Exercises**.

2 From the windows taskbar, click **Start**, **All Programs**, **ArcGIS**, **ArcMap**.

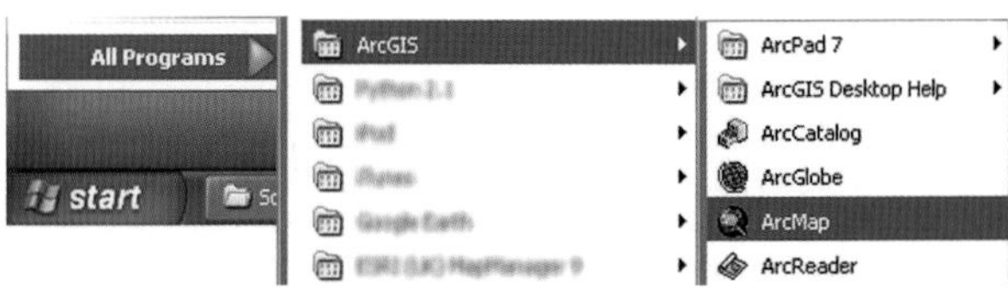

Depending on how ArcGIS and ArcMap have been installed, or which Windows operating system you are using, you may have to use a slightly different navigation menu from which to open ArcMap. Ask your teacher for further instructions.

3 In the resulting ArcMap window, click the **An existing map** radio button and click **OK**.

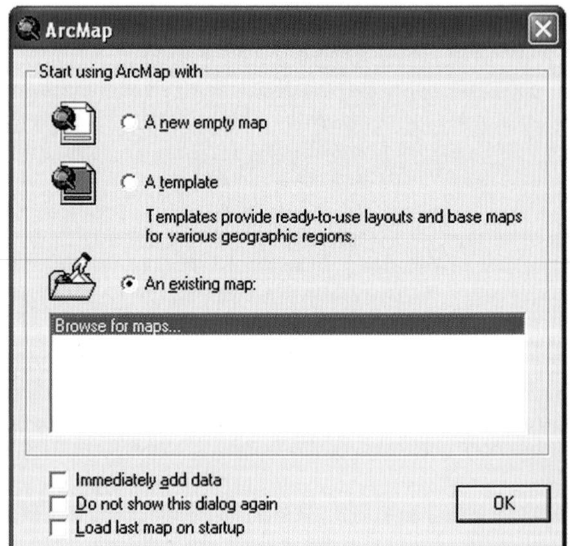

Open an existing map

4. Browse to the drive on which your GIS Exercises have been installed (e.g. GIS_Exercises\Exercise1\Map Documents\Exercise1), click the **Exercise1** icon and click **Open**.

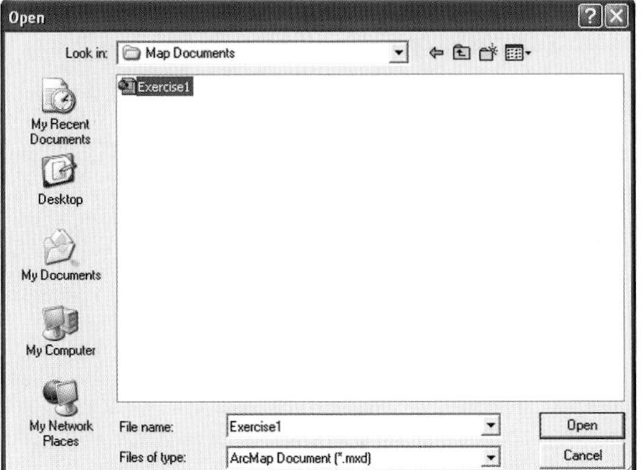

5. The **Exercise1.mxd** project opens in ArcMap showing all the data you have available to complete this exercise.

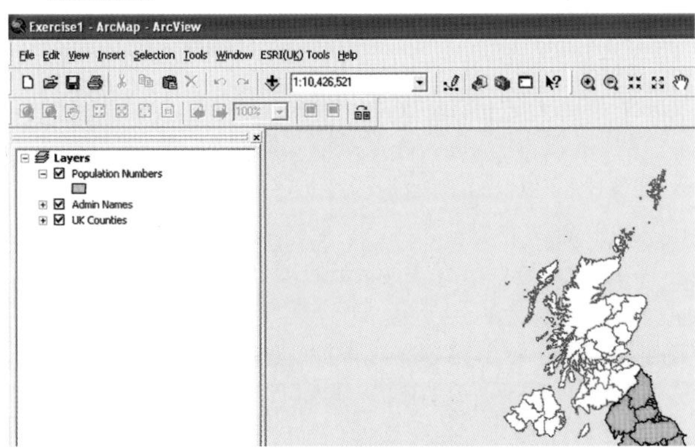

6. **Very Important:** As soon as you have opened the Exercise1.mxd project, save it to your own drive area using **File > Save As...** (e.g. the new project folder that you have just created called **GIS_Exercises**). **Everything that you now do for this project must be saved to the same folder.**

Map layers

Map layers are references to data sources such as historical maps, Ordnance Survey maps, aerial photography or Census 2001 data that can be displayed in ArcView.

Turn a layer ON or OFF

7 Click the small check box to the left of the **Population Numbers** layer in the **Table of Contents** to turn that layer on or off.

The **Table of Contents** is the panel to the left of the view window. If it accidentally closes, click **Window**, **Table of Contents** to reopen it. A check mark appears if the layer is turned on. Nothing appears if it is turned off.

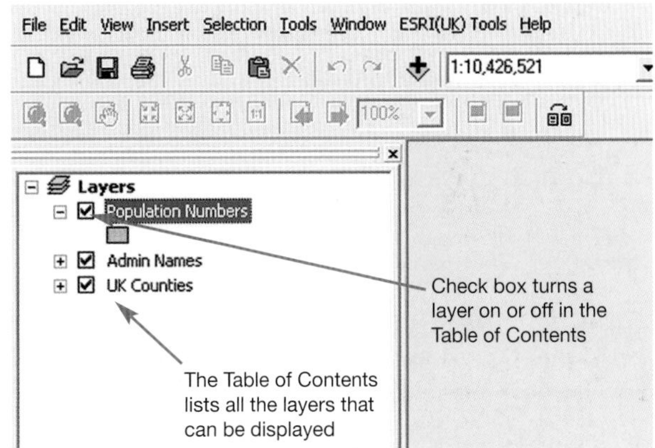

Change the display order of layers

8 In the table of contents click and hold down the left mouse button on the name of the **Population Numbers** layer.

9 Drag the **Population Numbers** layer down to the bottom of the table of contents.

ArcMap draws layers from the top down. Because the **Population Numbers** layer is now drawn last, its lines are now covered by the **UK Counties** layer in the table of contents.

10 Click and hold down the left mouse button on the **Population Numbers** layer.
11 Drag the **Population Numbers** layer back to the top of the table of contents.

Because the **Population Numbers** layer is now drawn first, its areas can be seen again.

Zoom and Pan

Zooming and panning enlarges or reduces the display and shifts the display to show different areas of the map. The **Zoom** and **Pan** buttons are found on the **Tools** toolbar.

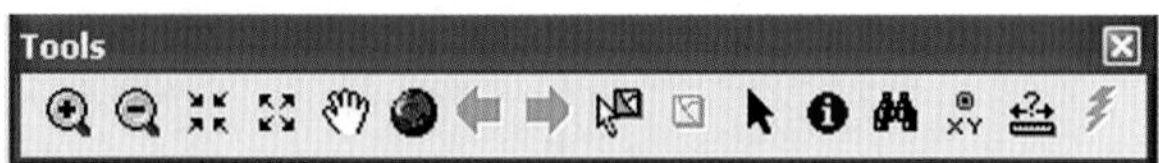

Zoom In

12 Click the **Zoom In** button.
13 Click and hold down the mouse button on a point above and to the left of North-West Scotland.
14 Drag the mouse below and to the right of South-East Scotland and release the mouse button.
15 Click once on the screen to zoom to the rectangle created from the points that you clicked and released.

This is an alternative to dragging a rectangle for zooming in.

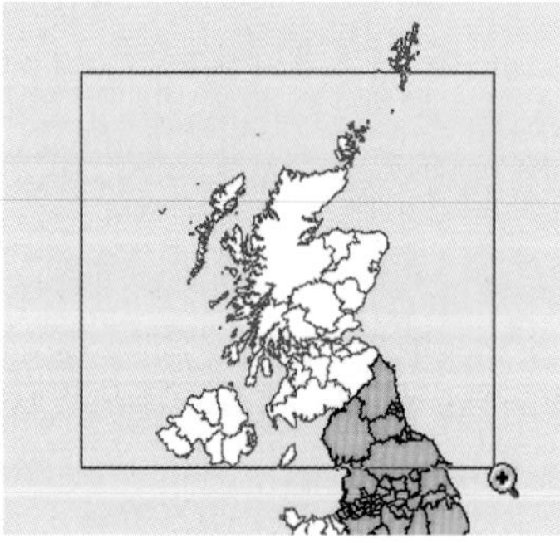

Fixed Zoom In

16 Click the **Fixed Zoom In** button.

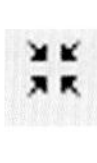

This zooms in a fixed distance on the centre of the current zoomed display.

Fixed Zoom Out

17 Click the **Fixed Zoom Out** button.

This zooms out a fixed distance from the centre of the current zoomed display.

Pan

Panning shifts the current display to the left, right, up or down without changing the current scale.

18 Click the **Pan** button.

19 Move the cursor anywhere onto the map display.
20 Hold down the left mouse button and drag the mouse in any direction.
21 Release the mouse button.

Zoom to Full Extent

22 Click the **Zoom to Full Extent** button.

This zooms to a full display of all layers, regardless of whether they are turned on or off.

Zoom to Previous Extent

23 Click the **Zoom to Previous Extent** button.

This returns the map display to its previous extent. Continue to click this button to step back through views.

Zoom to Next Extent

24 Click the **Zoom to Next Extent** button.

This moves forward through the sequence of zoomed extents you have viewed. You can continue to click this button until you reach the most recently viewed extent.

Identify features

The **Identify Tool** displays the data attributes of a feature by clicking the feature on the map. This tool is the easiest way to learn something about a location in a map.

*An **attribute** describes the characteristics associated with a feature drawn on a map. In this exercise the **attribute data** describes the characteristics of the number of people who live in each county in England.* *See page 37 for a fuller description of attributes.*

Identify the number of people living in any county in England

25 Make sure that the **Population Numbers**, **Admin Names** and **UK Counties** layers are turned on.

26 From the **Tools** toolbar, click the **Identify** button.

27 Click inside any of the **County Boundaries** (polygon areas) for England.

The **County** (polygon) that you choose will flash temporarily and its attributes will appear in the **Identify Results** dialog box.

This function is an important feature of GIS. The power of GIS comes from being able to ask questions about the information that lies behind the map. By using the **Identify Tool** we are asking the GIS programme to display the attribute information it has for that county. Such information can be very quickly searched and displayed from the very large attribute tables that are connected to the map.

Map layers and attribute data

We will now look more closely at the attributes table that is linked to the map of **Population Numbers**.

28 In the table of contents left-click on the layer **Population Numbers**.

29 With the right mouse button click once on the layer **Population Numbers**.

30 From the drop-down menu that appears select **Open Attribute Table**.

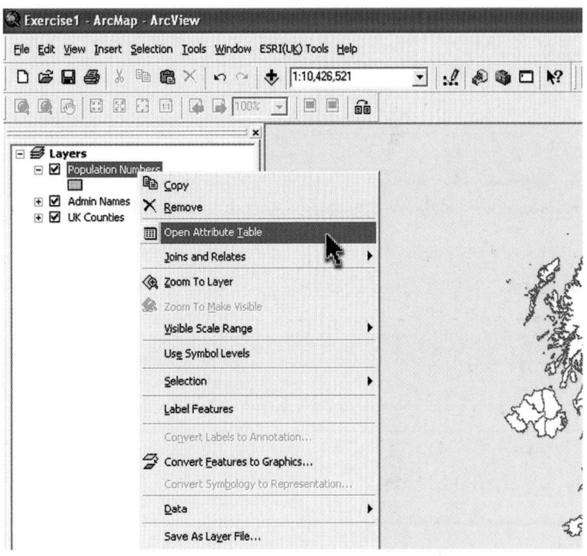

What is an **attribute**?

The attributes table for the **Population Numbers** layer will open up.

31 Use the scroll bars in the attributes table to explore the data.

An important feature of GIS is that the data in any attributes table is constantly linked to the mapping layer that is displayed in the data view.

There is a constant link between a **map layer** and its **attributes.**

Attributes of Population Numbers

FID	Shape *	PROV3NAME	PROV3ABBR	NATION	CNTRYNAME	CNTRYABBR	SQKM	COLORMAP
0	Polygon	Cornwall County	Corn	44	United Kingdom	GB	3547.11367	1
1	Polygon	Devon County	Devon	44	United Kingdom	GB	6546.90087	9
2	Polygon	City of Plymouth	Plmth	44	United Kingdom	GB	84.34328	5
3	Polygon	Torbay	Torbay	44	United Kingdom	GB	62.50331	2
4	Polygon	Somerset County	SOM	44	United Kingdom	GB	3406.28845	4
5	Polygon	Wiltshire County	Wilts	44	United Kingdom	GB	3216.73132	3
6	Polygon	Bath and North East Somerset	Bath	44	United Kingdom	GB	345.39721	8
7	Polygon	Dorset County	Dors	44	United Kingdom	GB	2533.5611	1
8	Polygon	City of Portsmouth	Pomth	44	United Kingdom	GB	54.20576	9
9	Polygon	City of Southampton	Soton	44	United Kingdom	GB	58.97936	2
10	Polygon	Hampshire County	Hants	44	United Kingdom	GB	3653.72705	6
11	Polygon	Isle of Wight	IOW	44	United Kingdom	GB	377.60689	7
12	Polygon	Bournemouth	Bmth	44	United Kingdom	GB	46.42251	6
13	Polygon	Poole	Poole	44	United Kingdom	GB	73.38199	3
14	Polygon	Bromley	Broml	44	United Kingdom	GB	148.34089	2
15	Polygon	Croydon	Croyd	44	United Kingdom	GB	86.675	4
16	Polygon	Surrey County	SRY	44	United Kingdom	GB	1644.38031	7
17	Polygon	Brighton and Hove	Brton	44	United Kingdom	GB	80.15912	1
18	Polygon	Kingston upon Thames	KingT	44	United Kingdom	GB	38.61018	2

Record: 1 Show: All Selected Records (0 out of 149 Selected) Options

32 Click on the table column title **PROV3NAME**.
The column should turn blue.

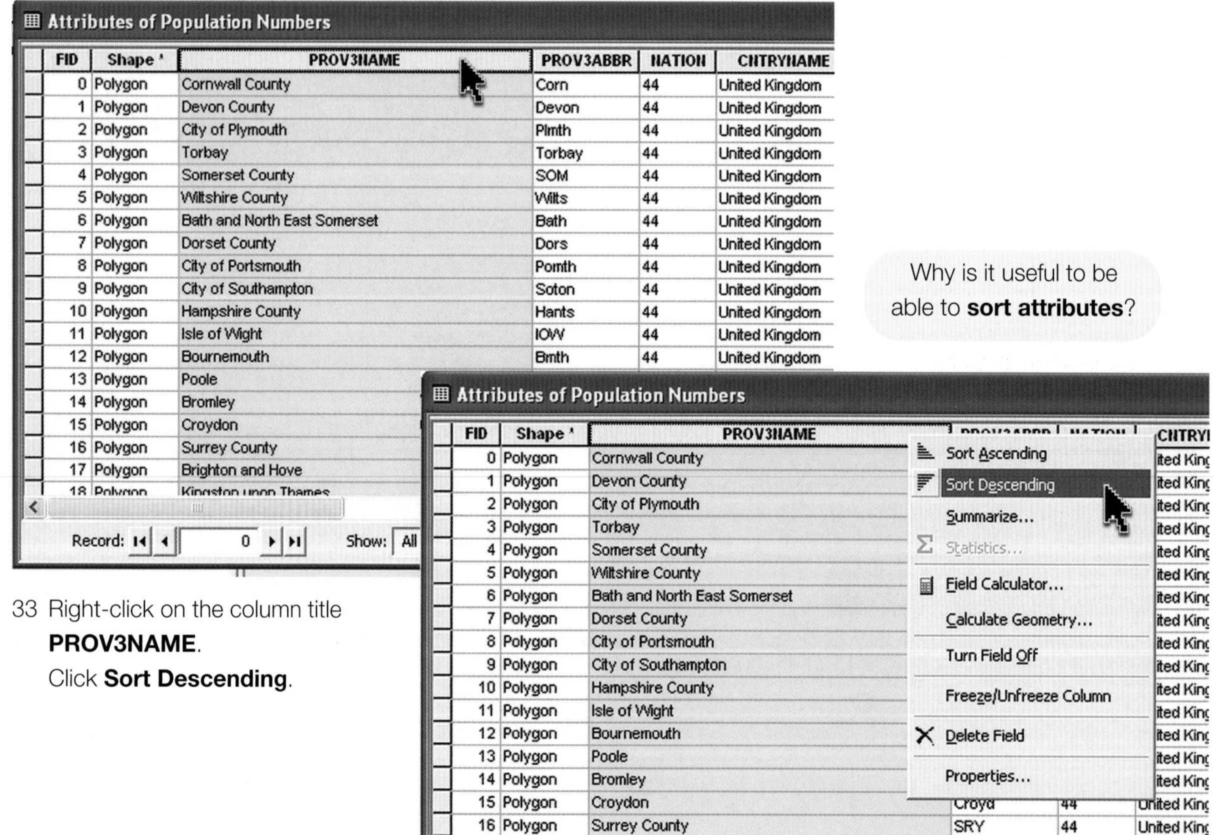

Why is it useful to be able to **sort attributes**?

33 Right-click on the column title **PROV3NAME**.
Click **Sort Descending**.

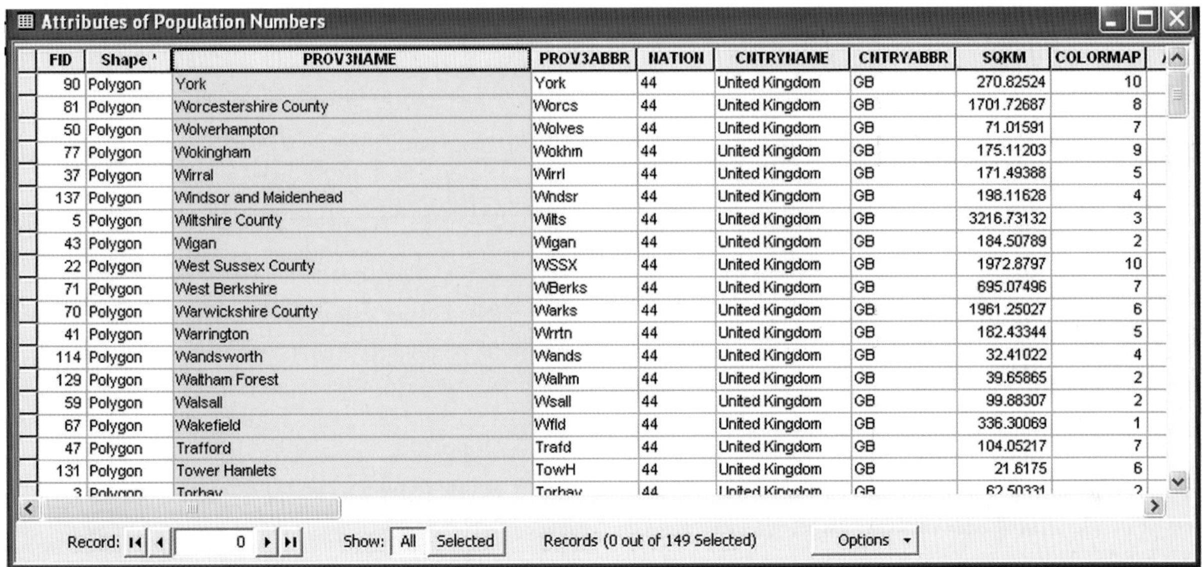

Attributes of Population Numbers

FID	Shape *	PROV3NAME	PROV3ABBR	NATION	CNTRYNAME	CNTRYABBR	SQKM	COLORMAP
90	Polygon	York	York	44	United Kingdom	GB	270.82524	10
81	Polygon	Worcestershire County	Worcs	44	United Kingdom	GB	1701.72687	8
50	Polygon	Wolverhampton	Wolves	44	United Kingdom	GB	71.01591	7
77	Polygon	Wokingham	Wokhm	44	United Kingdom	GB	175.11203	9
37	Polygon	Wirral	Wirrl	44	United Kingdom	GB	171.49388	5
137	Polygon	Windsor and Maidenhead	Wndsr	44	United Kingdom	GB	198.11628	4
5	Polygon	Wiltshire County	Wilts	44	United Kingdom	GB	3216.73132	3
43	Polygon	Wigan	Wigan	44	United Kingdom	GB	184.50789	2
22	Polygon	West Sussex County	WSSX	44	United Kingdom	GB	1972.8797	10
71	Polygon	West Berkshire	WBerks	44	United Kingdom	GB	695.07496	7
70	Polygon	Warwickshire County	Warks	44	United Kingdom	GB	1961.25027	6
41	Polygon	Warrington	Wrrtn	44	United Kingdom	GB	182.43344	5
114	Polygon	Wandsworth	Wands	44	United Kingdom	GB	32.41022	4
129	Polygon	Waltham Forest	Walhm	44	United Kingdom	GB	39.65865	2
59	Polygon	Walsall	Wsall	44	United Kingdom	GB	99.88307	2
67	Polygon	Wakefield	Wfld	44	United Kingdom	GB	336.30069	1
47	Polygon	Trafford	Trafd	44	United Kingdom	GB	104.05217	7
131	Polygon	Tower Hamlets	TowH	44	United Kingdom	GB	21.6175	6
3	Polygon	Torbay	Torbay	44	United Kingdom	GB	62.50331	2

Record: 0 Show: All Selected Records (0 out of 149 Selected) Options

The attributes table should now be sorted so that **York** is at the top of the table.

34 If you scroll down the table, you will see that the data is now sorted in reverse alphabetical order.

35 Hold down the **Ctrl** key and with the left mouse button select the first 16 attribute rows (York to Wakefield).

36 Close the attributes table. The map that is now displayed will show the counties that you have highlighted in the attributes table.

Click here to select a row of data from the attribute table

Attributes of Population Numbers

FID	Shape *	PROV3NAME	PROV3ABBR	NATION	CNTRYNAME	CNTRYABBR	SQKM	COLORMAP
90	Polygon	York	York	44	United Kingdom	GB	270.82524	10
81	Polygon	Worcestershire County	Worcs	44	United Kingdom	GB	1701.72687	8
50	Polygon	Wolverhampton	Wolves	44	United Kingdom	GB	71.01591	7
77	Polygon	Wokingham	Wokhm	44	United Kingdom	GB	175.11203	9
37	Polygon	Wirral	Wirrl	44	United Kingdom	GB	171.49388	5
137	Polygon	Windsor and Maidenhead	Wndsr	44	United Kingdom	GB	198.11628	4
5	Polygon	Wiltshire County	Wilts	44	United Kingdom	GB	3216.73132	3
43	Polygon	Wigan	Wigan	44	United Kingdom	GB	184.50789	2
22	Polygon	West Sussex County	WSSX	44	United Kingdom	GB	1972.8797	10
71	Polygon	West Berkshire	WBerks	44	United Kingdom	GB	695.07496	7
70	Polygon	Warwickshire County	Warks	44	United Kingdom	GB	1961.25027	6
41	Polygon	Warrington	Wrrtn	44	United Kingdom	GB	182.43344	5
114	Polygon	Wandsworth	Wands	44	United Kingdom	GB	32.41022	4
129	Polygon	Waltham Forest	Walhm	44	United Kingdom	GB	39.65865	2
59	Polygon	Walsall	Wsall	44	United Kingdom	GB	99.88307	2
67	Polygon	Wakefield	Wfld	44	United Kingdom	GB	336.30069	1
47	Polygon	Trafford	Trafd	44	United Kingdom	GB	104.05217	7
131	Polygon	Tower Hamlets	TowH	44	United Kingdom	GB	21.6175	6
3	Polygon	Torbay	Torbay	44	United Kingdom	GB	62.50331	2

Record: 0 Show: All Selected Records (16 out of 149 Selected) Options

Shows the number of attribute rows selected from the total dataset

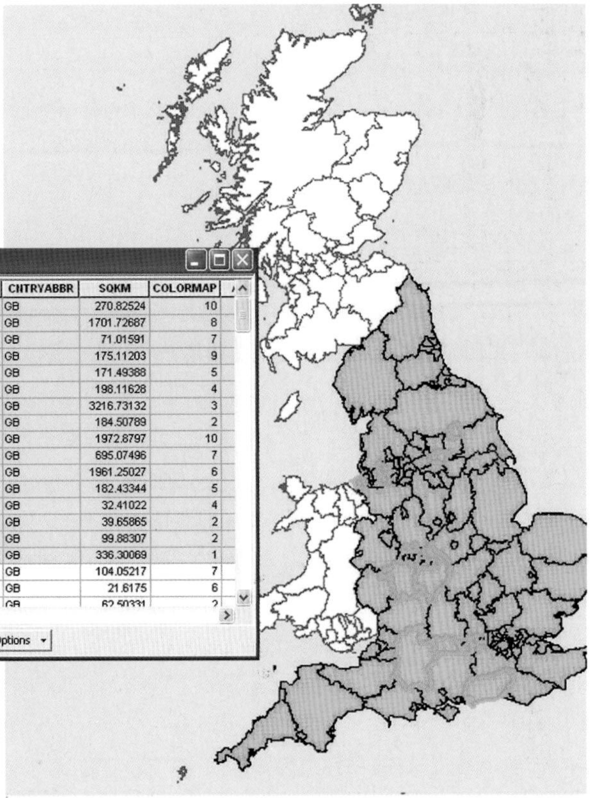

The steps that you have followed show how the data in the attributes table is constantly linked to the maps you are viewing. To deselect the data in the attributes table, click on **Selection** and **Clear Selected Features**.

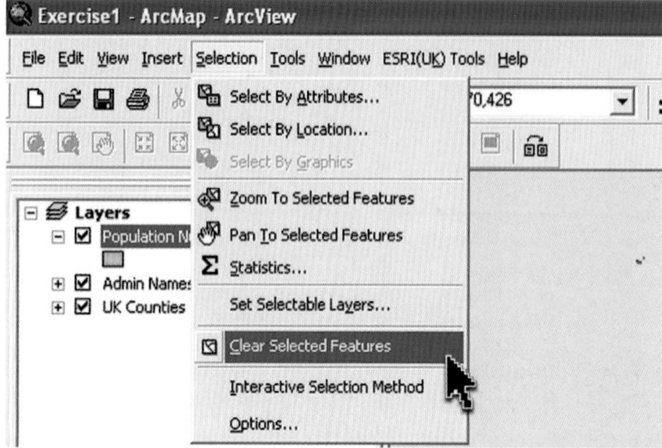

Mapping and symbolising attribute data

The next stage of this exercise is to try to map variations in population density across counties in the UK.

37 Double-click on the layer name **Population Numbers** in the table of contents. (Make sure you double-click on the layer name and not on the symbol beneath it.)

The **Layer Properties** menu will open. Click on the **Symbology** tab ('symbology' is just another word for map key).

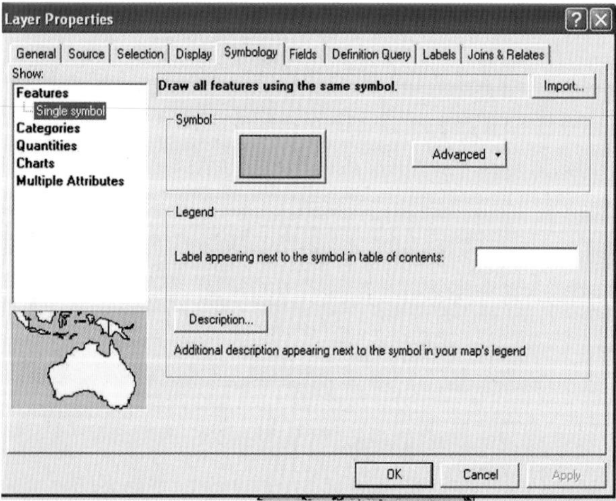

38 From the **Show** menu select **Quantities**, then **Graduated colors**.

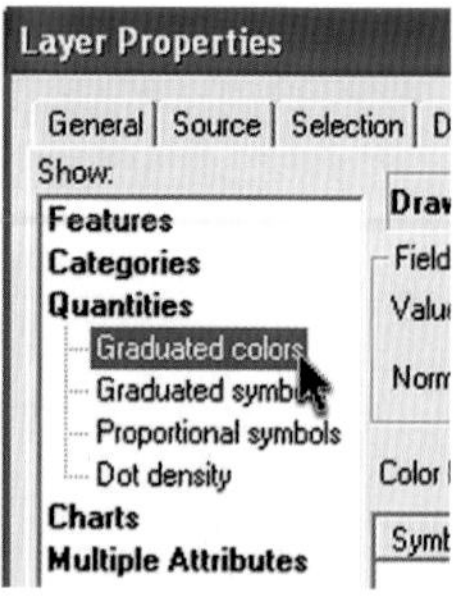

By what other name do you think a **graduated colours** map might be known?

All the options in the **Value** field are the titles of the columns in the attributes table that we have previously examined.

39 From the **Fields** menu click the drop-down button next to the **Value** field and select **No. of People**.

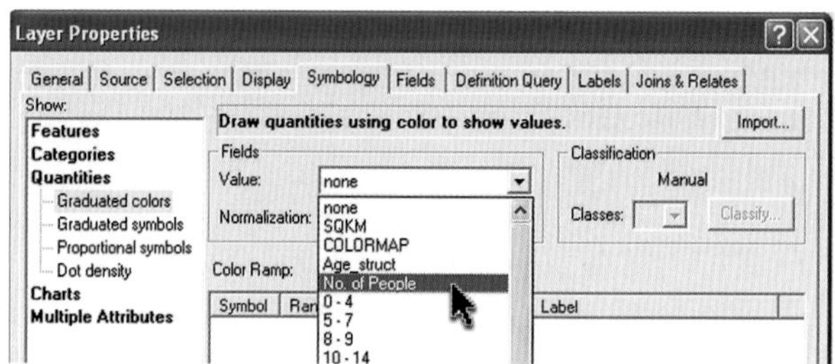

40 Use the **Color Ramp** drop-down menu and select **Orange Bright** as your display colour. Note that the number of **Classes** is set to five in the **Classification** box.

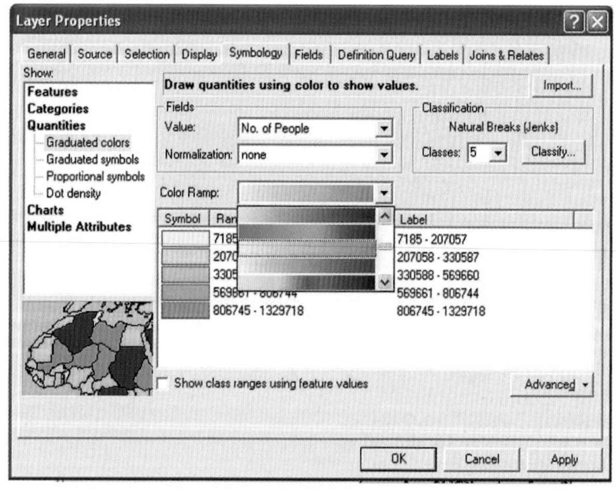

41 Click **OK**.

How do you think the choice of colour could affect the quality of map design?

You have now created a map showing the number of people living in different counties across England.

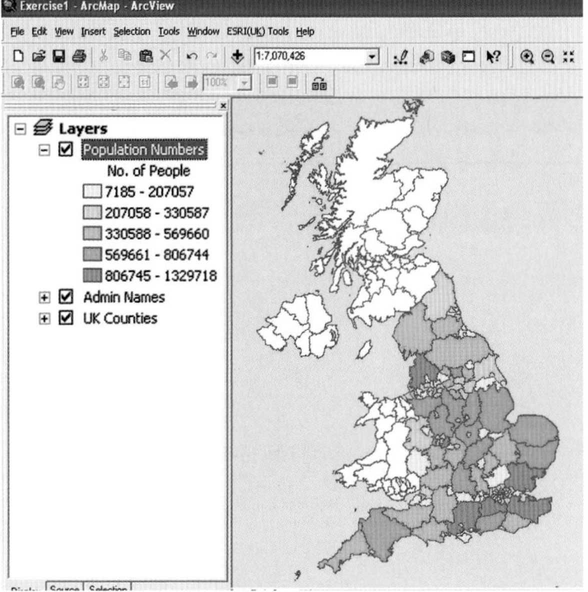

However, this map is of limited value as it only provides a simple count of the number of people living in each county. To make the map more useful for comparing where people live in England, we need to create a population density map.

42 Double-click the **Population Numbers** layer name in the table of contents with the left mouse button to get back to **Layer Properties**.

43 From the **Fields** menu click the drop-down menu next to **Normalization** and select **SQKM**.

The **SQKM** field gives the number of kilometres squared associated with each county in England. By selecting this value in the **Normalization** field we are dividing the number of people living in each county by the size of the county to give a population density figure.

Experiment with the number of classes to see how it affects the patterns shown on your map.

44 Select the orange to red colour shown below from the **Color Ramp**. In the **Classification** menu select **10** as the number of **Classes**.

45 Click **OK**.

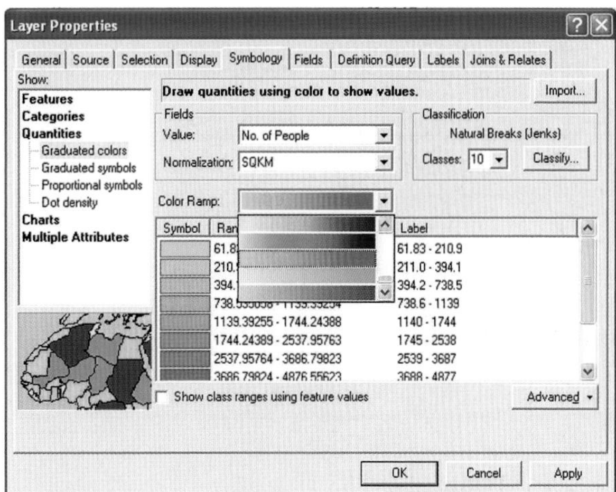

You have now created a population density map of England. The units given with the legend are the number of people living in a given square kilometre.

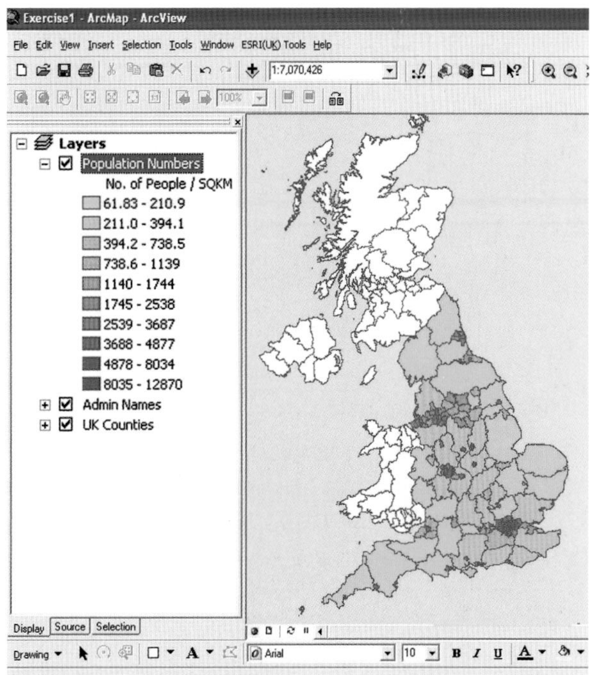

Producing a map for printing

In the next part of this exercise you will learn how to produce a map for printing. This allows you to share information with other interest groups.

46 Click the **View** menu and click **Layout View**.

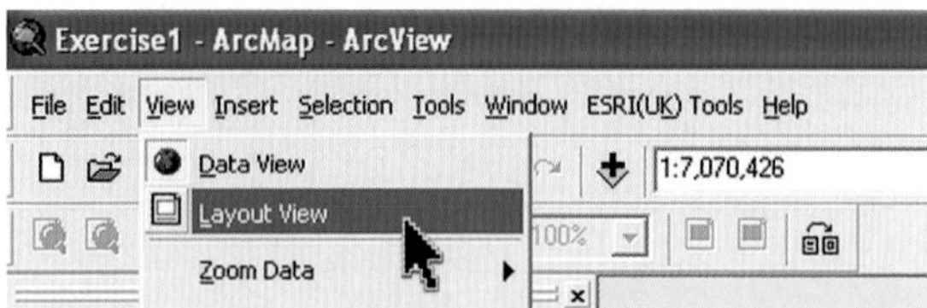

Your map is now sketched on a virtual page. There is also a new navigation toolbar for **Layout** view as shown below.

47 Use the different page symbols to move around your map.

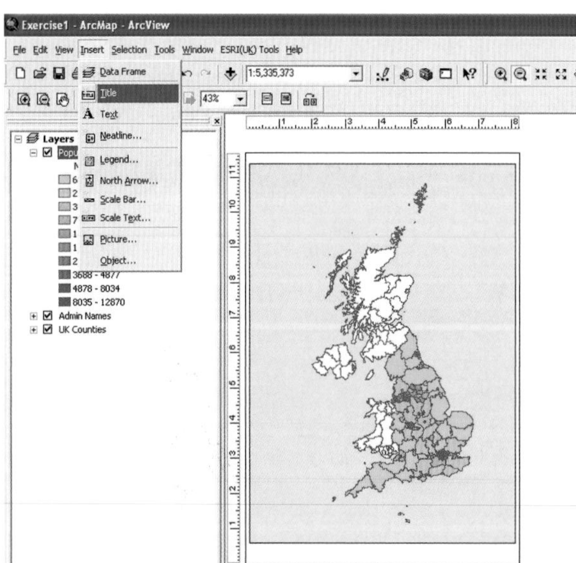

48 In **Layout** view click the **Insert** menu and click **Title**.

A text box is added to the page. The default title is the name of your ArcMap document.

49 In the text box, type in a well thought-out title that reflects clearly the content of your map (e.g. **Population Density**) and press **Enter**.

50 If you make a mistake and need to change the text after pressing **Enter**, double-click on the title to open its **Text Properties**. You can change the properties of the text, including text colour and font, by clicking on the **Change Symbol** button in the **Properties** box.

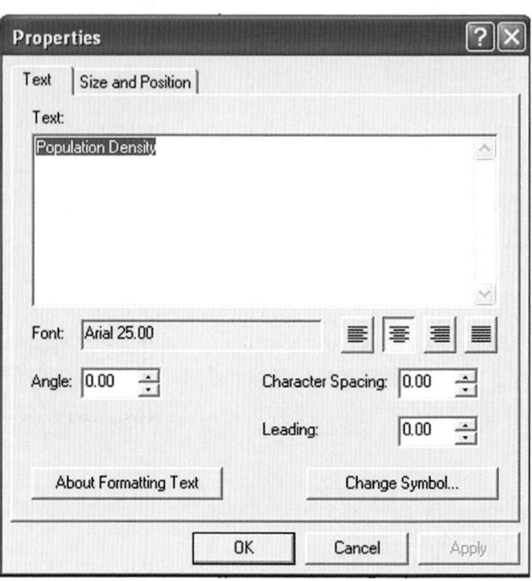

51 You can move the position of the title by clicking and dragging.

52 You can also change the properties of your title by using the **Drawing** toolbar.

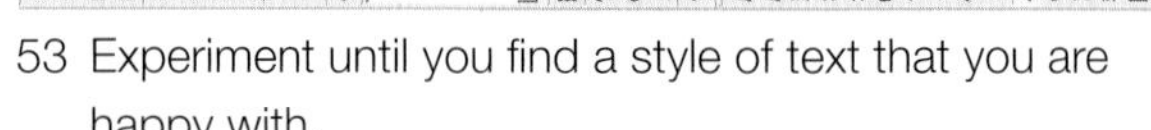

53 Experiment until you find a style of text that you are happy with.

54 You can add a subtitle like the one shown below by clicking the **Insert** menu and then **Title**.

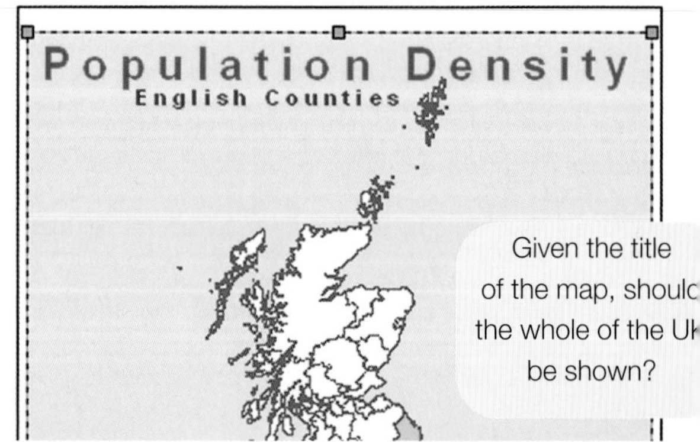

55 Use the **Insert Title** function to add your name (**Map Designed by [your name]**) and the source of the data you are mapping (**Data Source: Navteq, Census 2001**).

Next you need to add a legend/key to your map.

56 Click the **Insert** menu and click **Legend** to open the **Legend Wizard**.

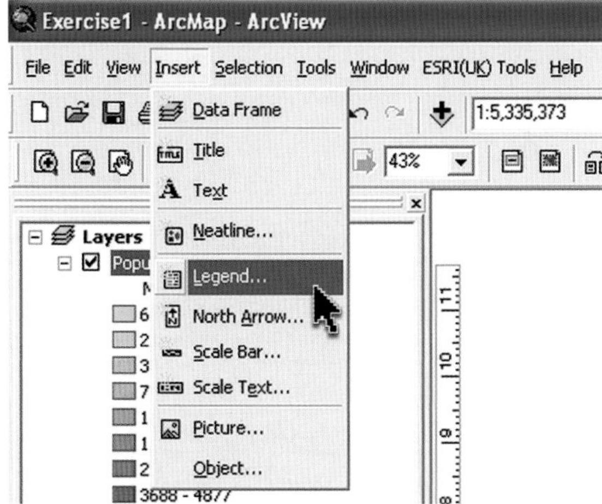

The **Legend Wizard** will open.

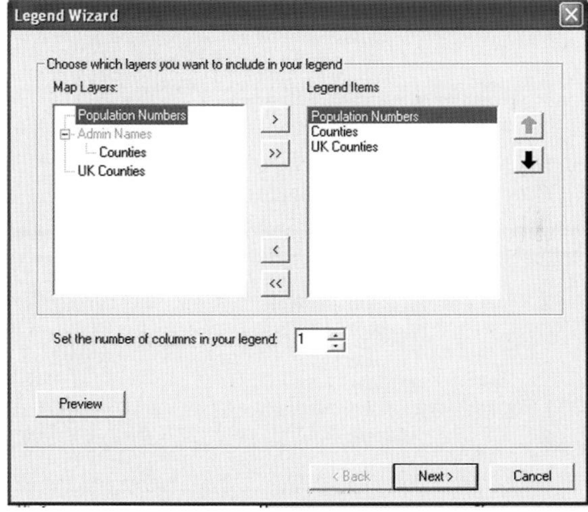

57 By default, the legend includes all layers from the map and the number of legend columns is set to one.

58 To remove a layer from the items legend, click and highlight it on the right-hand side, under **Legend Items**, then click the arrow button pointing to the left.

Make sure that **Population Numbers** is the only layer remaining in the **Legend Items** column. Click **Next**.

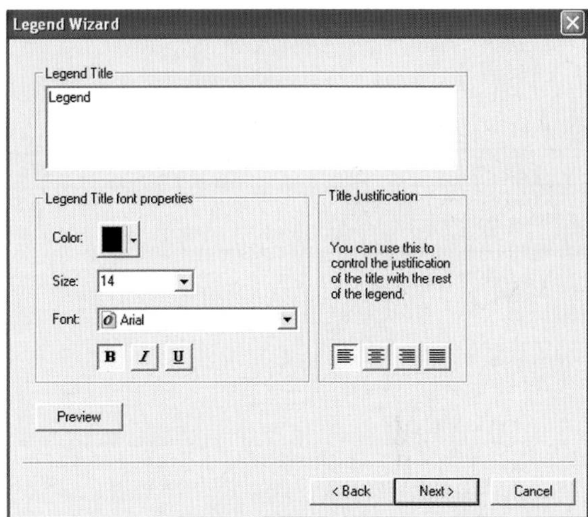

59 In the **Legend Title** box, type in an appropriate title for your legend – for example, **Population Density**. Click **Next**.

60 In the legend **Frame** window leave the **Border** box blank and select **Lt Blue** from the **Background** menu.

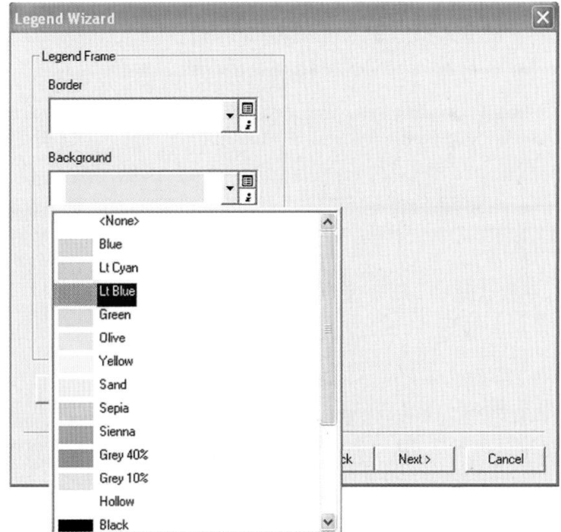

61 The next two panels set symbols and spacing for the legend, but you need not change these, so click the **Next** button twice and click **Finish**.

62 Make sure you move your legend to an appropriate position on the page.

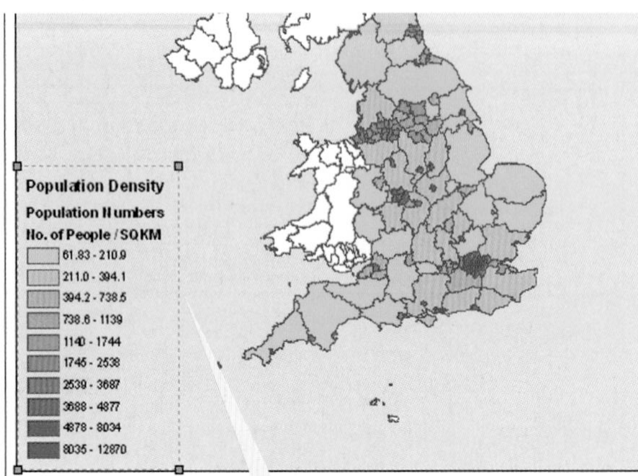

What criteria do you think should be used to decide an appropriate location for the map key?

63 You can move the position of your title and legend by using the **Select Elements** button on the **Tools** toolbar.

64 Edit the legend by double-clicking on the inserted legend using the **Select Elements** button.

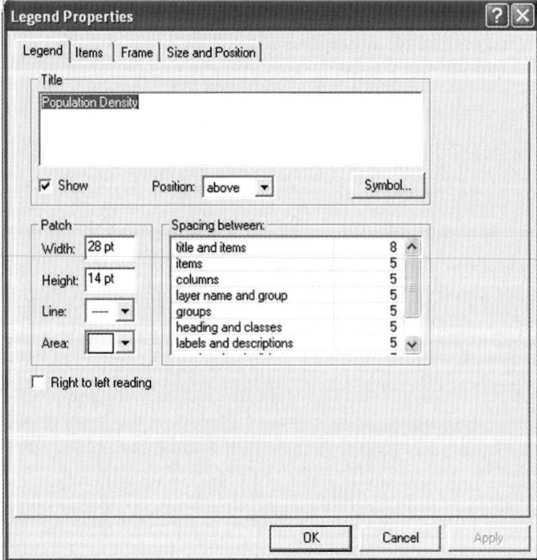

65 Select the **Items** tab and highlight the **Population Numbers** layer in the **Legend Items** column.

66 Click **Style**.

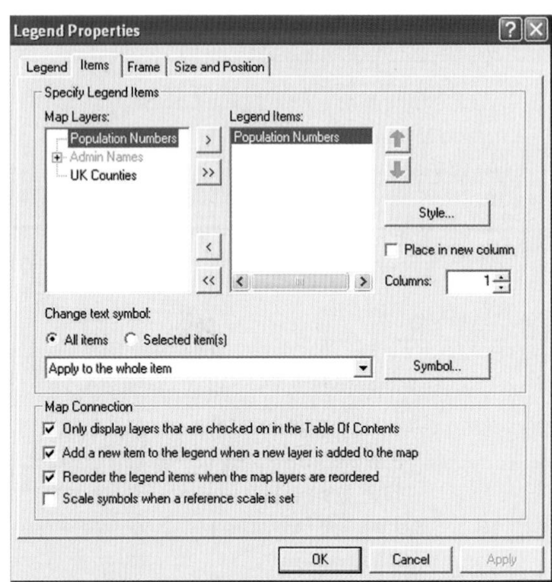

67 Select the legend style as shown below.

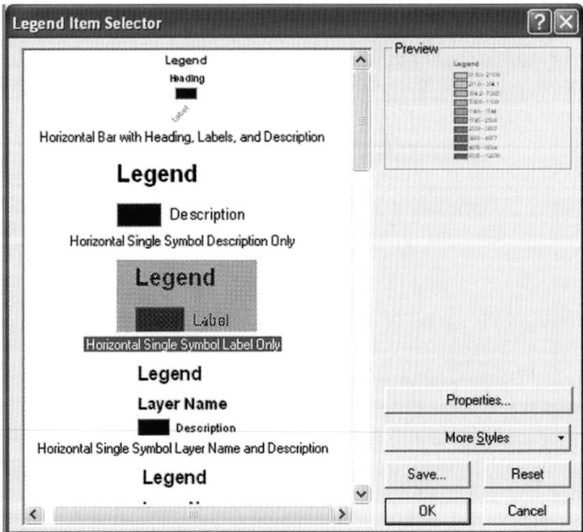

68 Click the **Legend** tab and type in the **Title**: **Population Density**, **km squared**. Click **OK**.

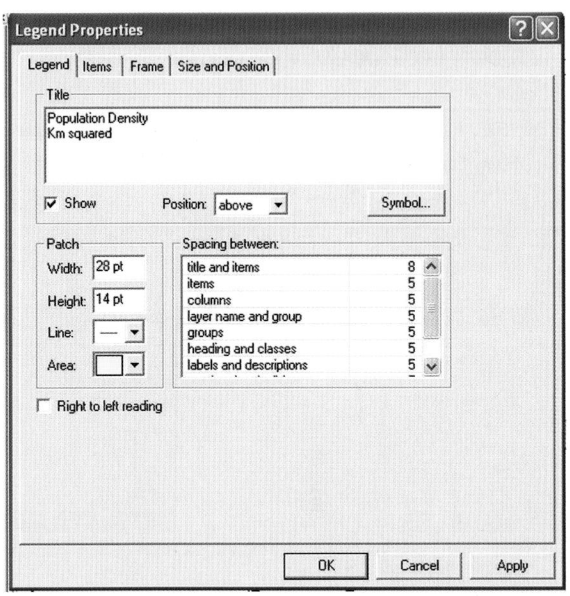

69 When you have finished editing your legend, use the **Insert** menu to enter a north arrow and scale bar on your map.

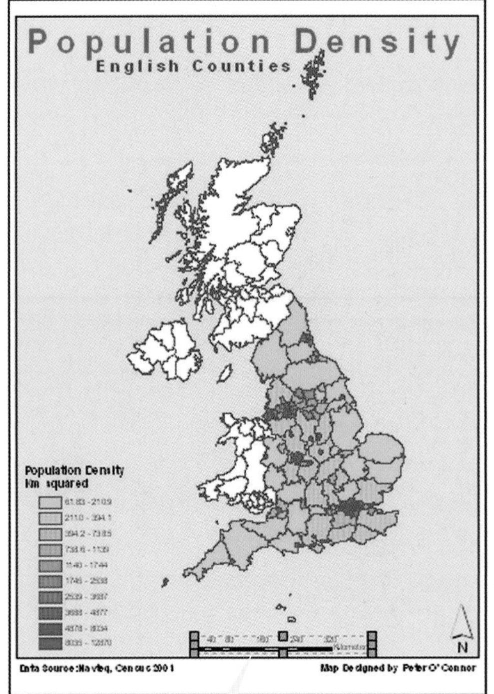

Are a scale bar and north arrow necessary on this map?

Describe the variation in population density within England.

70 If the area of your map appears to be too small on the page use the **Zoom** tool to position the map more like the image shown above.

Once you are happy with the layout of your map and its presentation, you need to export your map as a JPEG file so that it can be easily incorporated into a word-processing package later on.

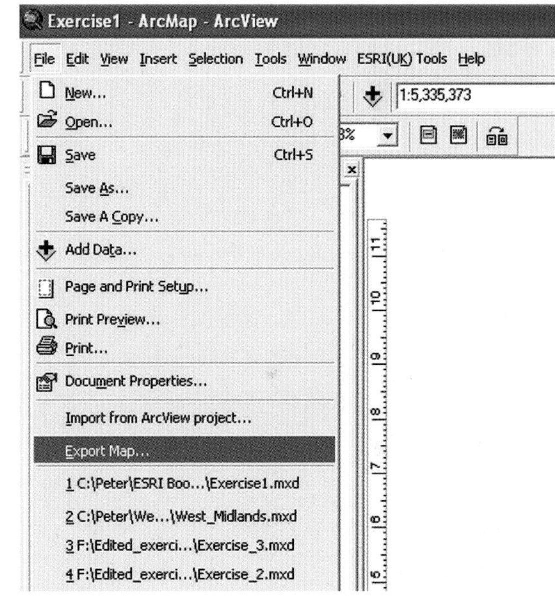

71 From the **File** menu click **Export Map**.

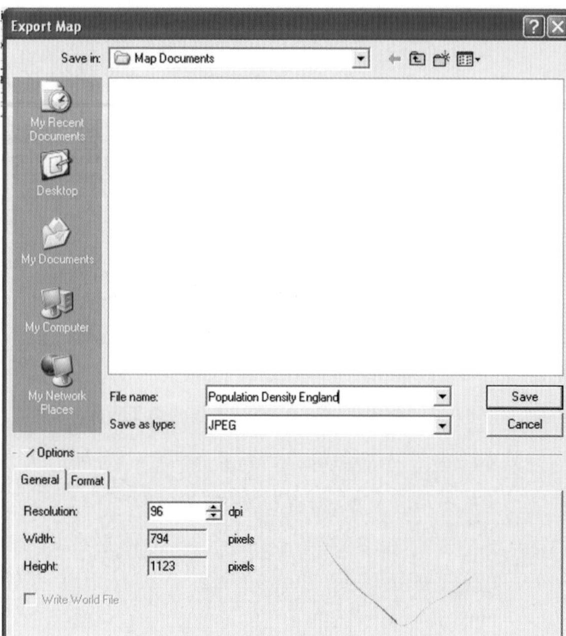

72 When the directory window appears, navigate to your GIS project folder.

73 Give the map an appropriate file name such as **Population Density England**.

74 From the **Save as type** drop-down menu select **JPEG** and click **Save**.

75 Open up the **Paint** software package from the **Start** menu and check that the JPEG that you have just saved opens correctly. At a later stage you can copy this image from Paint into Word to describe the patterns shown on the map.

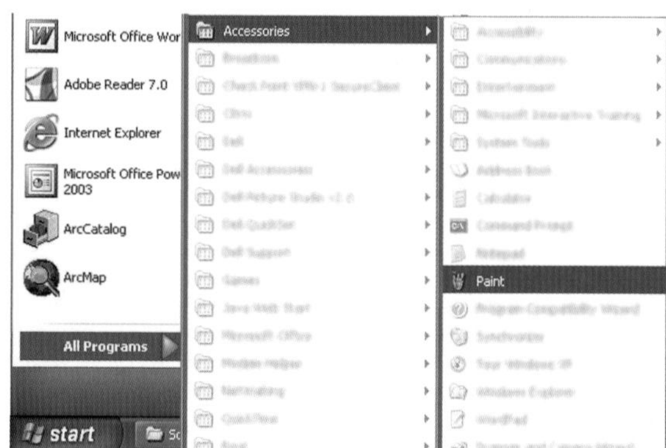

76 Now complete the additional activities associated with exercise 1 on the CD.

How do patterns of crime vary across England and Wales?

Aims

- To map variations in patterns of crime across England and Wales
- To identify which police forces in England and Wales have the highest and lowest incidences of crime
- To consider the nature of police authorities with high and low levels of crime

Introduction

Increasingly, issues surrounding crime and the fear of crime have begun to influence people's perception of place and even how we behave in the areas we live. Crime is a major political issue and, consequently, governments and police forces have invested many resources collecting statistics about the nature of crime and where it occurs. Such statistics are used to assess the performance of different police forces, to determine the allocation of resources and to establish policing priorities.

This exercise looks at how GIS can be used to present crime statistics for police forces in England and Wales.

Launch ArcMap

1 Make sure you have created a folder where you can save all your GIS work. Call it **GIS_Exercises**.

2 From the windows taskbar, click **Start**, **All Programs**, **ArcGIS**, **ArcMap**.

Depending on how ArcGIS and ArcMap have been installed or which Windows operating system you are using, you may have to use a slightly different navigation menu from which to open ArcMap. Ask your teacher for further instructions.

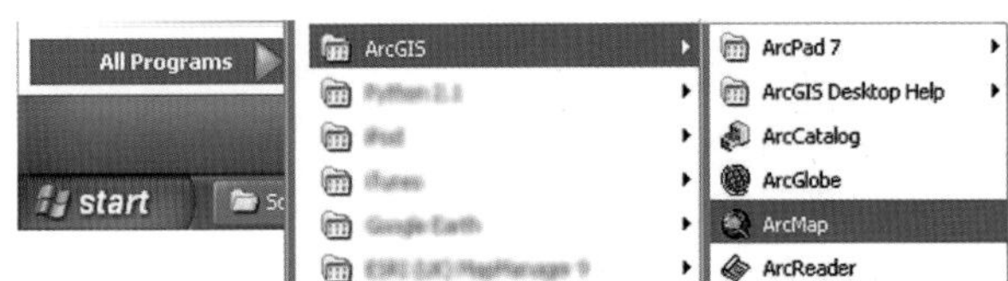

3 In the resulting **ArcMap** window, click the **An existing map** radio button and click **OK**.

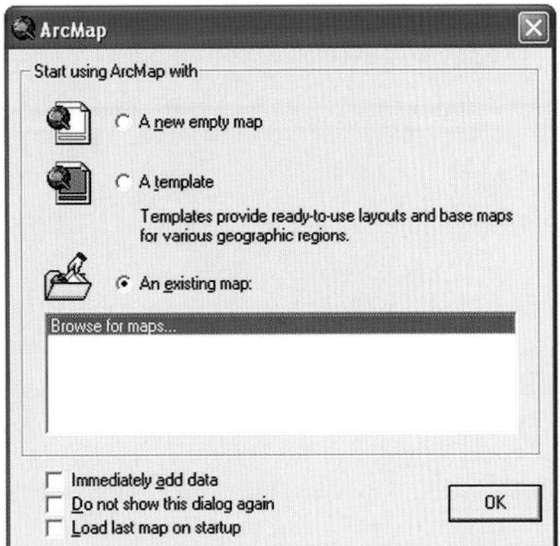

Open an existing map

4 Browse to the drive on which your GIS Exercises have been installed (e.g. GIS_Exercises\Exercise2&3\Map Documents\Exercise2), click the **Exercise_2** icon and click **Open**.

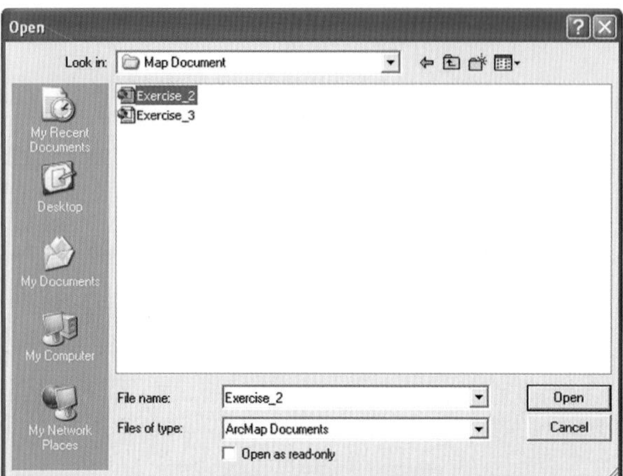

5 The **Exercise_2.mxd** project opens in **ArcMap** showing all the data you have available to complete this exercise.

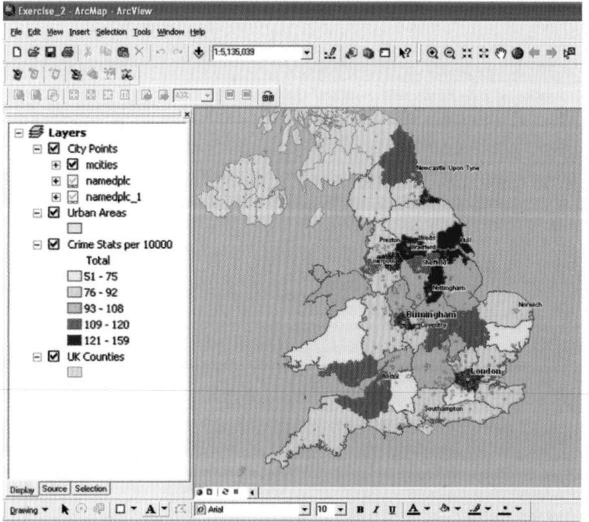

6 Very important: As soon as you have opened your Exercise_2 project, save this information to your own drive area (e.g. the new project folder that you have just created called GIS_Exercises). **Everything that you now do for this project must be saved to the same folder.**

Background to the police data

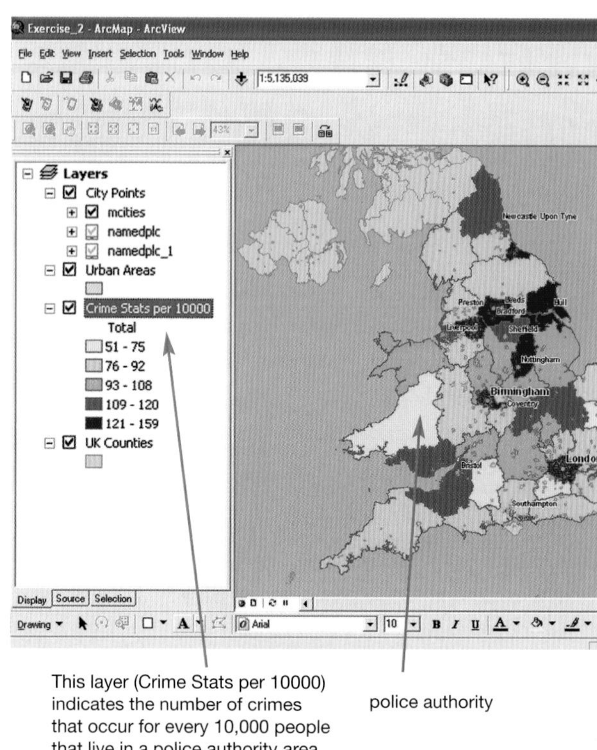

This layer (Crime Stats per 10000) indicates the number of crimes that occur for every 10,000 people that live in a police authority area.

police authority

The layer **Crime Stats per 10000** indicates the number of crimes that occur in each police authority for every 10,000 people that live in that area. For example, if the map states that 53 crimes occur for every 10,000 people living in a police authority and the police authority has a population of 50,000, that means 265 criminal incidents have occurred in total in that area. The figures are given in this format in order to take account of variations in population levels between different police authorities. For example, if we simply counted the number of criminal incidents, those areas with the largest populations would nearly always have the largest number of crime incidents. The data is provided by the Home Office, the part of the UK Government which has responsibility for policing.

Mapping areas with the lowest crime levels

7 With the right mouse button click on the layer **Crime Stats per 10000**.

8 From the drop-down menu select **Open Attribute Table**.

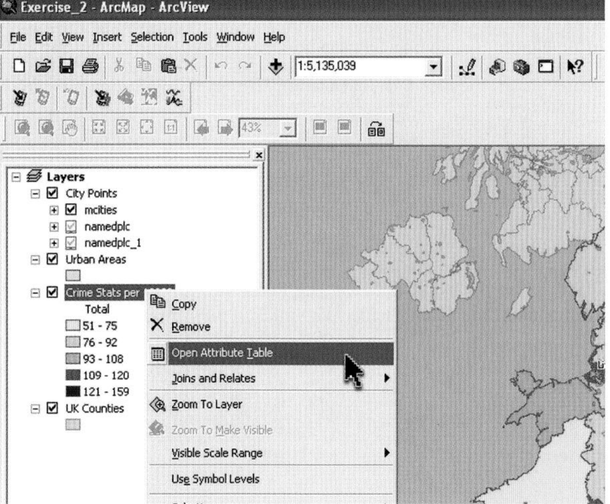

9 With the left mouse button click on the column heading called **Total**. The column should be now highlighted blue. This column of data records the total number of crimes committed for every 10,000 people living in each of the 42 police authorities in England and Wales.

Attributes of Crime Stats per 10000

OBJECTID *	Shape *	POLICE_FORCE	POLICE_AUTHORITY	POLICE_FORCE_1	Total
1	Polygon	Devon and Cornwall	Devon & Cornwall	Devon and Cornwall	83.0000
2	Polygon	Avon and Somerset	Avon & Somerset	Avon and Somerset	117.0000
3	Polygon	Dorset	Dorset	Dorset	90.00000
4	Polygon	Hampshire	Hampshire	Hampshire	86.00000
5	Polygon	Sussex	Sussex	Sussex	88.00000
6	Polygon	Kent	Kent	Kent	83.00000
7	Polygon	Surrey	Surrey	Surrey	65.00000
8	Polygon	Wiltshire	Wiltshire	Wiltshire	72.00000
9	Polygon	Essex	Essex	Essex	84.00000
10	Polygon	Suffolk	Suffolk	Suffolk	75.00000
11	Polygon	Norfolk	Norfolk	Norfolk	89.00000
12	Polygon	Hertfordshire	Hertfordshire	Hertfordshire	83.00000
13	Polygon	Bedfordshire	Bedfordshire	Bedfordshire	108.0000
14	Polygon	Cambridgeshire	Cambridgeshire	Cambridgeshire	120.0000
15	Polygon	Northamptonshire	Northamptonshire	Northamptonshire	117.0000
16	Polygon	Northumbria	Northumbria	Northumbria	120.0000
17	Polygon	Durham	Durham	Durham	87.00000
18	Polygon	Cleveland	Cleveland	Cleveland	136.0000
19	Polygon	Cumbria	Cumbria	Cumbria	77.00000

Record: 0 Show: All Selected Records (0 out of 50 Selected) Options

10 Place the cursor over the column title called **Total** and click with the right mouse button. From the drop-down menu that appears, click **Sort Ascending**. The police authority data is now sorted from those authorities with the lowest crime levels to those with the highest.

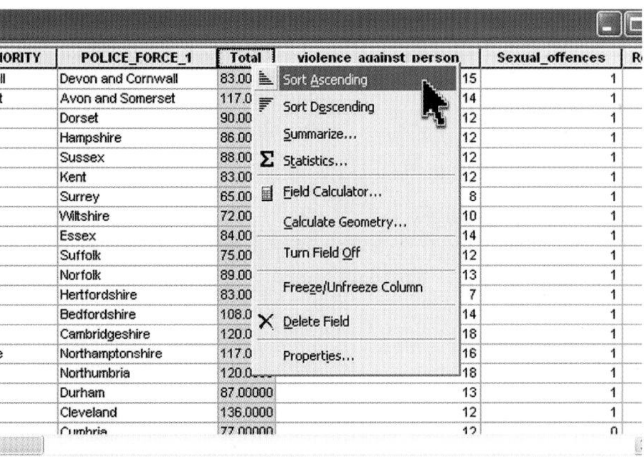

POLICE_FORCE_1	Total	violence against person	Sexual_offences
Devon and Cornwall	83.00	15	1
Avon and Somerset	117.0	14	1
Dorset	90.00	12	1
Hampshire	86.00	12	1
Sussex	88.00	12	1
Kent	83.00	12	1
Surrey	65.00	8	1
Wiltshire	72.00	10	1
Essex	84.00	14	1
Suffolk	75.00	12	1
Norfolk	89.00	13	1
Hertfordshire	83.00	7	1
Bedfordshire	108.0	14	1
Cambridgeshire	120.0	18	1
Northamptonshire	117.0	16	1
Northumbria	120.0	18	1
Durham	87.00000	13	1
Cleveland	136.0000	12	1

11 With the left mouse button and the **Ctrl** key held down, highlight the first five police authorities with the lowest total crime figures.

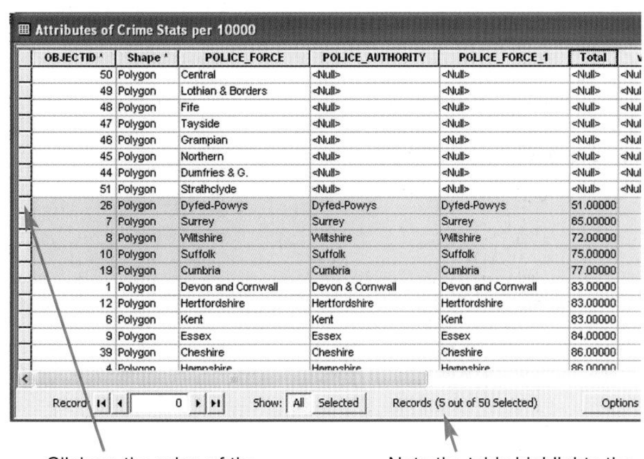

Attributes of Crime Stats per 10000

OBJECTID *	Shape *	POLICE_FORCE	POLICE_AUTHORITY	POLICE_FORCE_1	Total
50	Polygon	Central	<Null>	<Null>	<Null>
49	Polygon	Lothian & Borders	<Null>	<Null>	<Null>
48	Polygon	Fife	<Null>	<Null>	<Null>
47	Polygon	Tayside	<Null>	<Null>	<Null>
46	Polygon	Grampian	<Null>	<Null>	<Null>
45	Polygon	Northern	<Null>	<Null>	<Null>
44	Polygon	Dumfries & G.	<Null>	<Null>	<Null>
51	Polygon	Strathclyde	<Null>	<Null>	<Null>
26	Polygon	Dyfed-Powys	Dyfed-Powys	Dyfed-Powys	51.00000
7	Polygon	Surrey	Surrey	Surrey	65.00000
8	Polygon	Wiltshire	Wiltshire	Wiltshire	72.00000
10	Polygon	Suffolk	Suffolk	Suffolk	75.00000
19	Polygon	Cumbria	Cumbria	Cumbria	77.00000
1	Polygon	Devon and Cornwall	Devon & Cornwall	Devon and Cornwall	83.00000
12	Polygon	Hertfordshire	Hertfordshire	Hertfordshire	83.00000
6	Polygon	Kent	Kent	Kent	83.00000
9	Polygon	Essex	Essex	Essex	84.00000
39	Polygon	Cheshire	Cheshire	Cheshire	86.00000

Record: 0 Show: All Selected Records (5 out of 50 Selected) Options

Click on the edge of the table to highlight a row

Note the table highlights the number of rows selected

Do you think the number of police authorities selected will affect our view of how crime varies across the UK?

12 Close the attributes table for crime stats per 10,000. Those police authorities with the lowest crime figures should now be highlighted on your map.

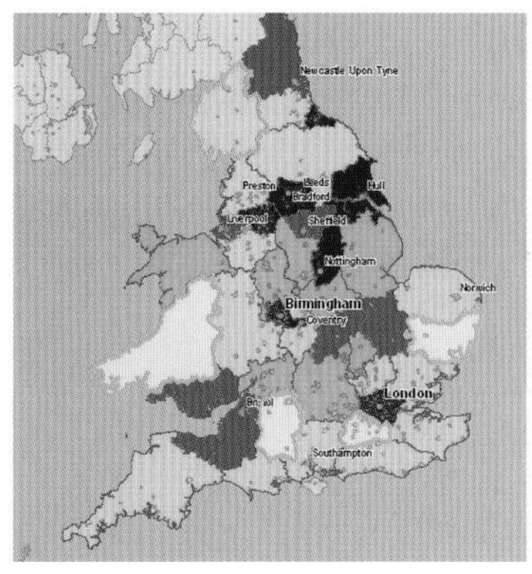

We now want to copy these selected authorities into a separate layer in order to help us see patterns in the data more clearly later.

13 With the right mouse button click on the layer called **Crime Stats per 10000**. From the drop-down menu that appears, click with the left mouse button on **Selection** and then on **Create Layer From Selected Features**.

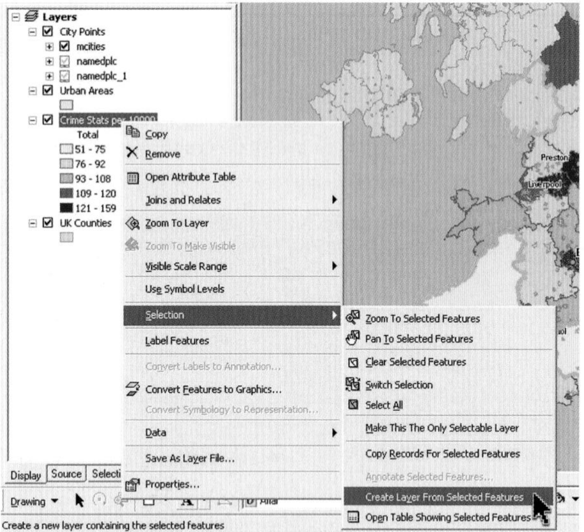

A new layer will appear in the table of contents called **Crime Stats per 10000 selection**. This layer now represents those five police authorities with the lowest total crime levels in England and Wales.

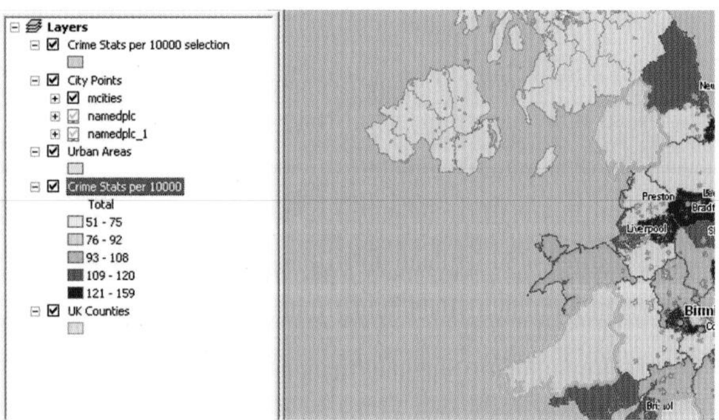

What is the pattern of low crime areas in England and Wales?

Speculate as to why these areas have lower levels of crime.

14 From the main menu click **Selection**, and from the drop-down menu that appears click **Clear Selected Features**.

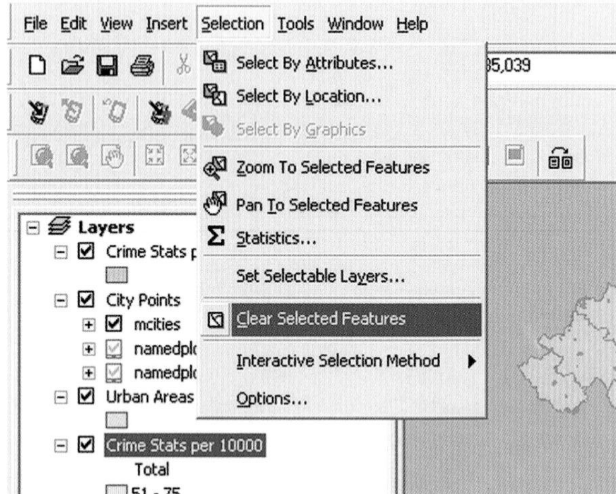

Next we want to tidy up the presentation of our new layer showing the areas of lowest crime.

15 With the left mouse button click on the layer title called **Crime Stats per 10000 selection** and then press the **F2** button on your keyboard. This allows you to edit the layer name. Change the layer title to **Low Crime Police Authorities**.

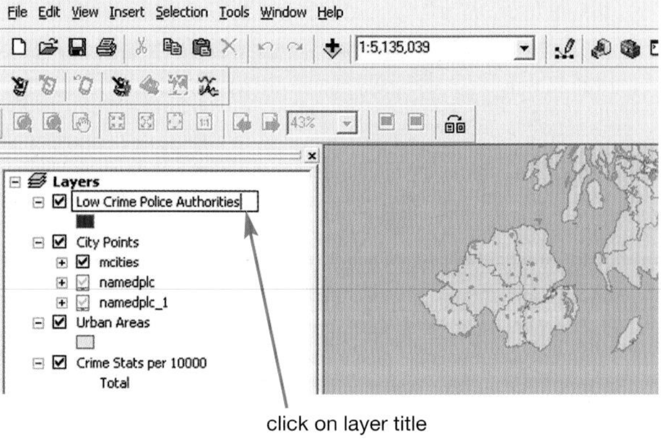

Next we want to change the colour that the layer **Low Crime Police Authorities** is displayed with.

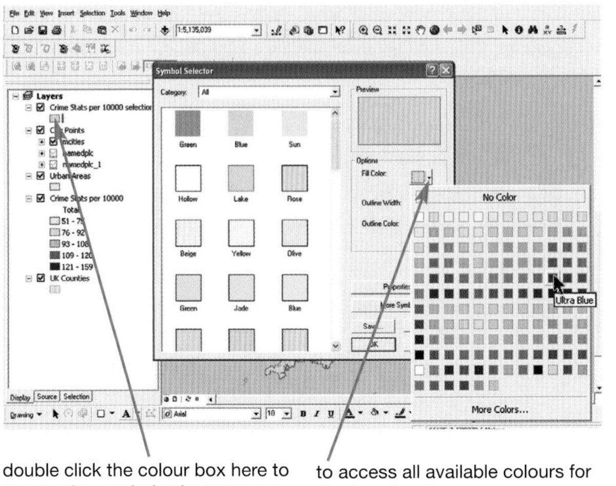

double click the colour box here to access the symbol selector menu

to access all available colours for display click the down arrow here

16 With the left mouse button click the colour box under the layer name **Low Crime Police Authorities**. From the **Fill Color** options drop-down menu move your mouse over the colours and select **Ultra Blue**. Click **OK** on the **Symbol Selector** menu.

> Why change the colour of the layer **Low Crime Police Authorities**?

17 Turn off the layer called **Crime Stats per 10000**. You now have a map that clearly shows the location of those forces with the lowest crime levels.

18 Turn the layer called **Crime Stats per 10000** back on and turn off the layer called **Low Crime Police Authorities**.

> Why choose **Ultra Blue** to display areas of low crime?

Mapping areas with the highest crime levels

19 With the right mouse button click on the layer name **Crime Stats per 10000**.

20 From the drop-down menu select **Open Attribute Table**.

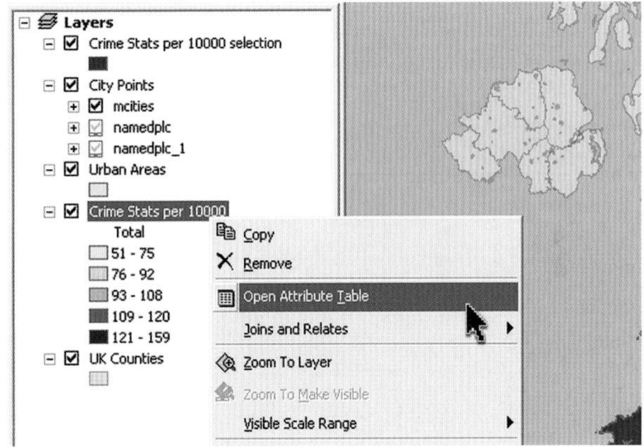

21 With the left mouse button click on the column heading called **Total**.

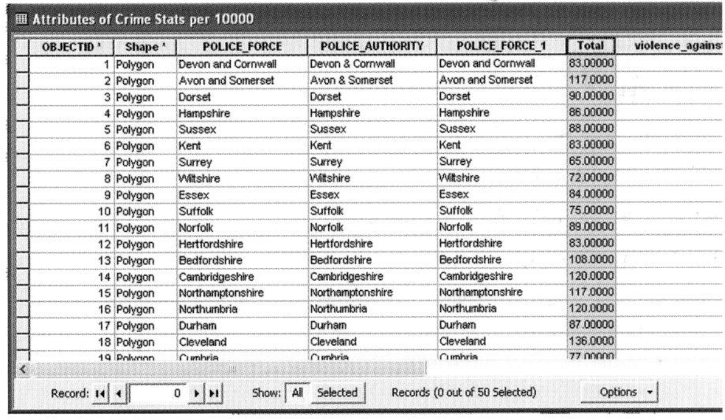

Attributes of Crime Stats per 10000

OBJECTID *	Shape *	POLICE_FORCE	POLICE_AUTHORITY	POLICE_FORCE_1	Total	violence_agains
1	Polygon	Devon and Cornwall	Devon & Cornwall	Devon and Cornwall	83.00000	
2	Polygon	Avon and Somerset	Avon & Somerset	Avon and Somerset	117.0000	
3	Polygon	Dorset	Dorset	Dorset	90.00000	
4	Polygon	Hampshire	Hampshire	Hampshire	86.00000	
5	Polygon	Sussex	Sussex	Sussex	88.00000	
6	Polygon	Kent	Kent	Kent	83.00000	
7	Polygon	Surrey	Surrey	Surrey	65.00000	
8	Polygon	Wiltshire	Wiltshire	Wiltshire	72.00000	
9	Polygon	Essex	Essex	Essex	84.00000	
10	Polygon	Suffolk	Suffolk	Suffolk	75.00000	
11	Polygon	Norfolk	Norfolk	Norfolk	89.00000	
12	Polygon	Hertfordshire	Hertfordshire	Hertfordshire	83.00000	
13	Polygon	Bedfordshire	Bedfordshire	Bedfordshire	108.0000	
14	Polygon	Cambridgeshire	Cambridgeshire	Cambridgeshire	120.0000	
15	Polygon	Northamptonshire	Northamptonshire	Northamptonshire	117.0000	
16	Polygon	Northumbria	Northumbria	Northumbria	120.0000	
17	Polygon	Durham	Durham	Durham	87.00000	
18	Polygon	Cleveland	Cleveland	Cleveland	136.0000	
19	Polygon	Cumbria	Cumbria	Cumbria	77.00000	

Record: 0 Show: All Selected Records (0 out of 50 Selected) Options

22 Place the cursor over the column title called **Total** and click with the right mouse button. From the drop-down menu that appears, click **Sort Descending**. The police authority data is now sorted from those authorities with the highest crime levels to those with the lowest.

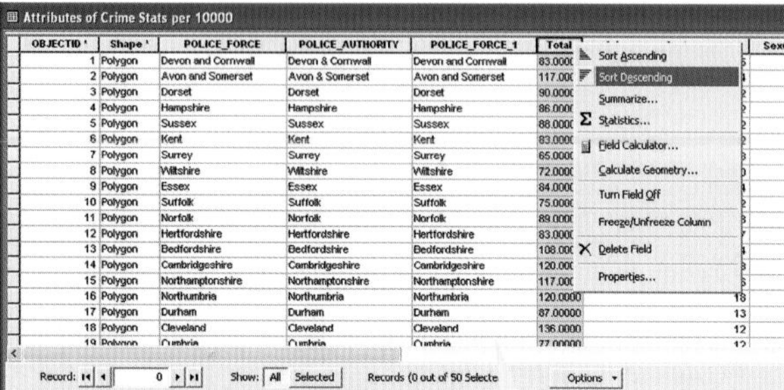

Attributes of Crime Stats per 10000

OBJECTID *	Shape *	POLICE_FORCE	POLICE_AUTHORITY	POLICE_FORCE_1	Total
1	Polygon	Devon and Cornwall	Devon & Cornwall	Devon and Cornwall	83.000
2	Polygon	Avon and Somerset	Avon & Somerset	Avon and Somerset	117.00
3	Polygon	Dorset	Dorset	Dorset	90.000
4	Polygon	Hampshire	Hampshire	Hampshire	86.000
5	Polygon	Sussex	Sussex	Sussex	88.000
6	Polygon	Kent	Kent	Kent	83.000
7	Polygon	Surrey	Surrey	Surrey	65.000
8	Polygon	Wiltshire	Wiltshire	Wiltshire	72.000
9	Polygon	Essex	Essex	Essex	84.000
10	Polygon	Suffolk	Suffolk	Suffolk	75.000
11	Polygon	Norfolk	Norfolk	Norfolk	89.000
12	Polygon	Hertfordshire	Hertfordshire	Hertfordshire	83.000
13	Polygon	Bedfordshire	Bedfordshire	Bedfordshire	108.00
14	Polygon	Cambridgeshire	Cambridgeshire	Cambridgeshire	120.00
15	Polygon	Northamptonshire	Northamptonshire	Northamptonshire	117.00
16	Polygon	Northumbria	Northumbria	Northumbria	120.0000
17	Polygon	Durham	Durham	Durham	87.00000
18	Polygon	Cleveland	Cleveland	Cleveland	136.0000

Why sort the data using this method?

23 With the left mouse button and the **Ctrl** key held down, highlight the first five police authorities.

Attributes of Crime Stats per 10000

OBJECTID *	Shape *	POLICE_FORCE	POLICE_AUTHORITY	POLICE_FORCE_1	Total
32	Polygon	Nottinghamshire	Nottinghamshire	Nottinghamshire	159.0000
22	Polygon	West Yorkshire	West Yorkshire	West Yorkshire	155.0000
37	Polygon	Greater Manchester	Greater Manchester	Greater Manchester	153.0000
21	Polygon	Humberside	Humberside	Humberside	153.0000
40	Polygon	Metropolitan Police	Metropolitan Police	Metropolitan Police	150.0000
34	Polygon	West Midlands	West Midlands	West Midlands	137.0000
18	Polygon	Cleveland	Cleveland	Cleveland	136.0000
27	Polygon	South Wales	South Wales	South Wales	120.0000
16	Polygon	Northumbria	Northumbria	Northumbria	120.0000
14	Polygon	Cambridgeshire	Cambridgeshire	Cambridgeshire	120.0000
23	Polygon	South Yorkshire	South Yorkshire	South Yorkshire	120.0000
38	Polygon	Merseyside	Merseyside	Merseyside	120.0000
2	Polygon	Avon and Somerset	Avon & Somerset	Avon and Somerset	117.0000
15	Polygon	Northamptonshire	Northamptonshire	Northamptonshire	117.0000
28	Polygon	Gwent	Gwent	Gwent	111.0000
36	Polygon	Derbyshire	Derbyshire	Derbyshire	108.0000
13	Polygon	Bedfordshire	Bedfordshire	Bedfordshire	108.0000
30	Polygon	Leicestershire	Leicestershire	Leicestershire	104.0000

Record: 0 Show: All Selected Records (5 out of 50 Selected) Options

24 Close the **Attributes of Crime Stats per 10000** table. Make sure the layer Attributes of Crime Stats per 10000 is turned on.You should now see on your map those police authorities with the highest crime figures highlighted.

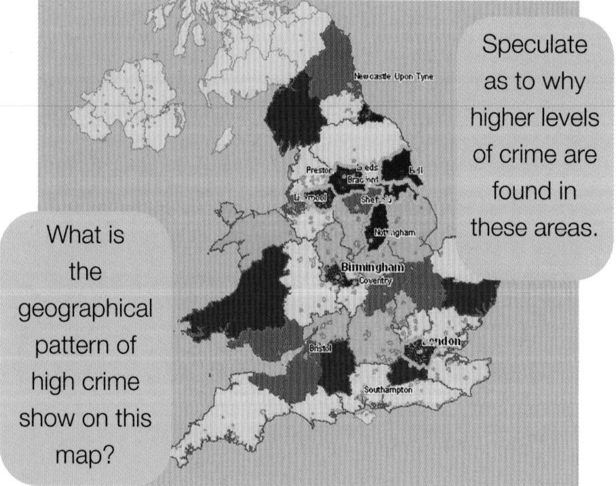

We now want to convert this selection into a layer so that we can examine its patterns more clearly later.

25 With the right mouse button click on the layer called **Crime Stats per 10000**. From the drop-down menu that appears, click with the left mouse button on **Selection** and then on **Create Layer From Selected Features**.

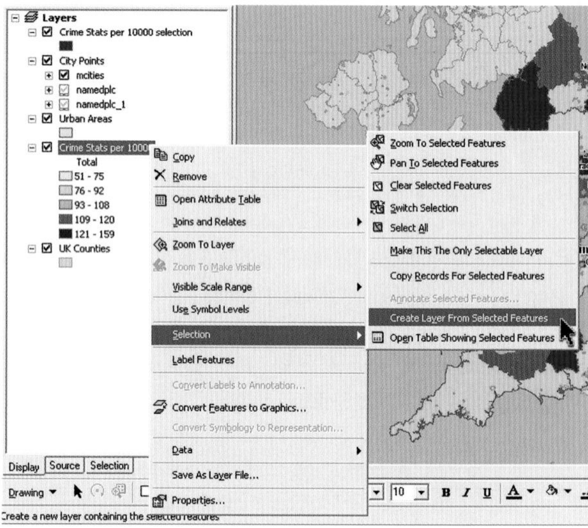

A new layer will appear in the table of contents called **Crime Stats per 10000**. This layer now represents those five police authorities with the highest total crime levels in England and Wales.

26 From the main menu click **Selection**, and from the drop-down menu that appears click **Clear Selected Features**. Alternatively, use the **Clear Selected Features** button on the Tools toolbar.

Next we want to tidy up the presentation of our new layer showing the areas of highest crime.

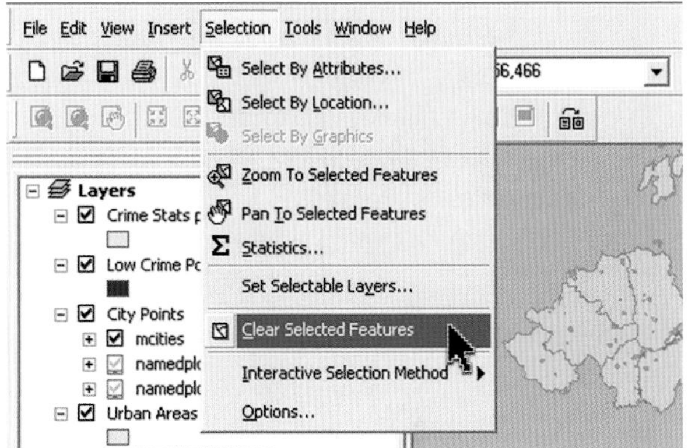

27 With the left mouse button double-click on the layer title called **Crime Stats per 10000**. Change the layer title to **High Crime Police Authorities.**

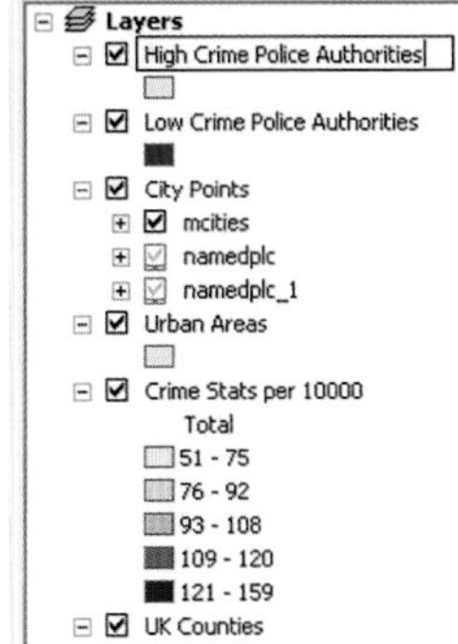

Now we want to change the colour that the **High Crime Police Authorities** layer is displayed with.

28 With the left mouse button click the coloured box under the layer name **High Crime Police Authorities**. Open the **Fill Color** drop-down menu, move your mouse over the colours and select **Mars Red**. Click **OK** on the **Symbol Selector** menu.

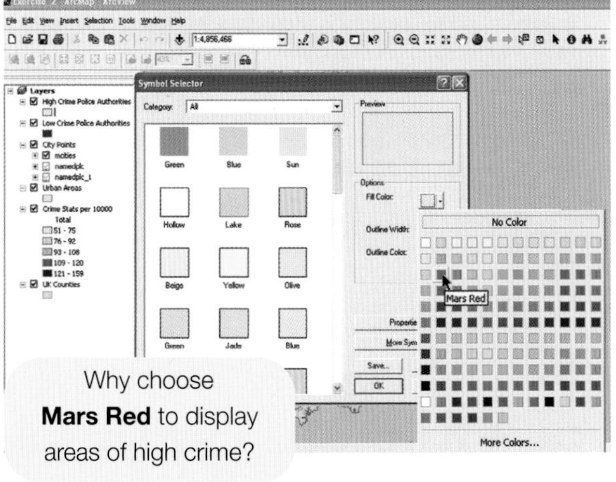

Why choose **Mars Red** to display areas of high crime?

29 Turn off the layers called **Crime Stats per 10000** and **Low Crime Police Authorities**. You now have a map that clearly shows the location of those forces with the highest crime levels.

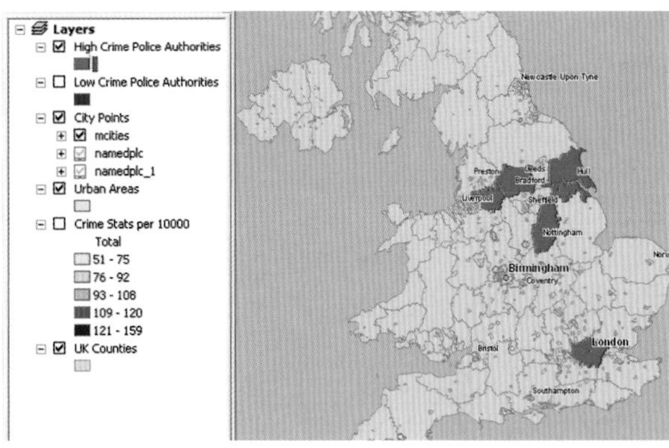

30 Turn back on the layer called **Low Crime Police Authorities**.

You have how produced a clearly defined map showing the locations of the police authorities with the highest and lowest levels of crime. Based on your map evidence, you should now be starting to think about what differences exist between areas defined as having high and low crime levels.

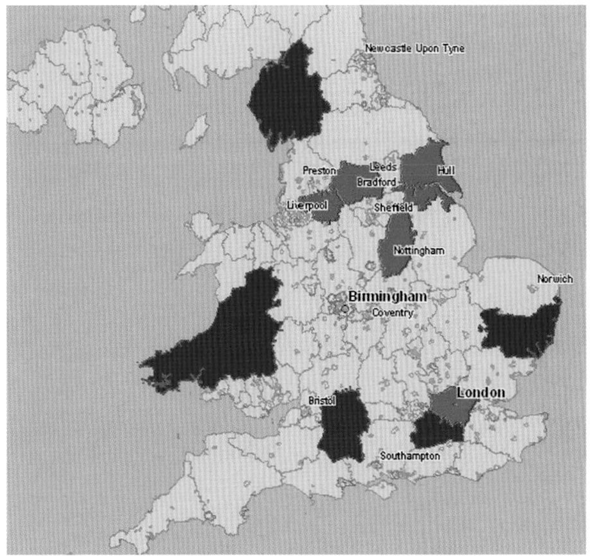

Contrast the locations of high and low crime police authoritites.

Adding graphs to a map

We can enhance our understanding of criminal activity in the areas we have mapped by adding further information. To achieve this we will add two graphs to our map that more clearly define the types of criminal activity that are occurring in the areas we have mapped.

31 From the main menu click on **View**, and from the drop-down menu that appears, click on **Layout View**.

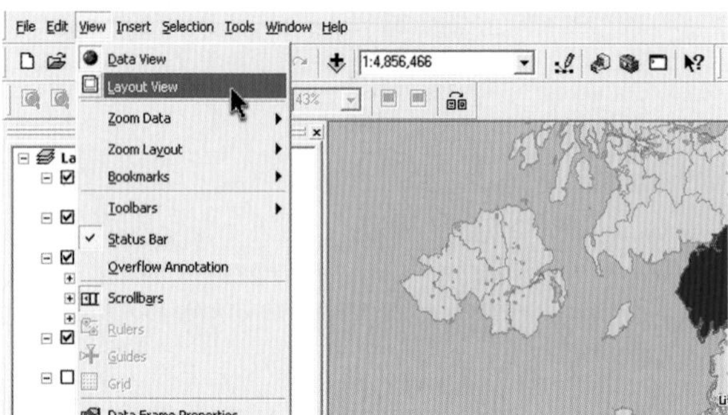

32 In **Layout View** right-click on the layer called **High Crime Police Authorities**. From the drop-down menu that appears, click on **Open Attribute Table**.

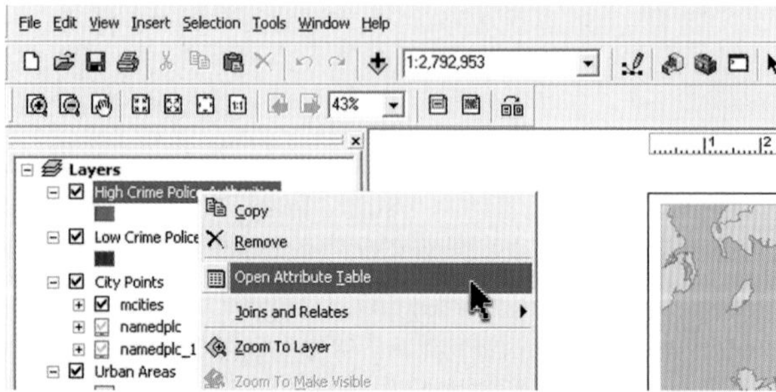

33 With the attribute table open, click on the **Options** tab, and from the pop-up menu that appears, select **Create Graph**.

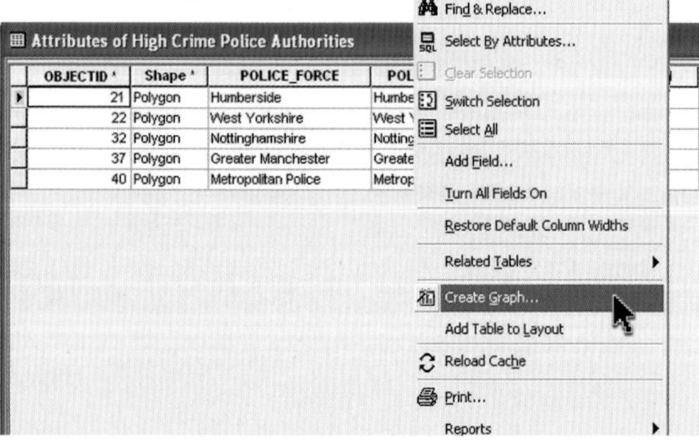

34 Using the **Create Graph Wizard** select the following options as shown in the screenshot below:

- for **Graph type:** select **Vertical Bar**
- for **Layer/Table:** select **High Crime Police Authorities**
- for the **Value field:** select **Total**
- for the **X label field:** select **POLICE_AUTHORITY**
- for **Color:** select **Palette**
- click the check box for the **Show border** option.

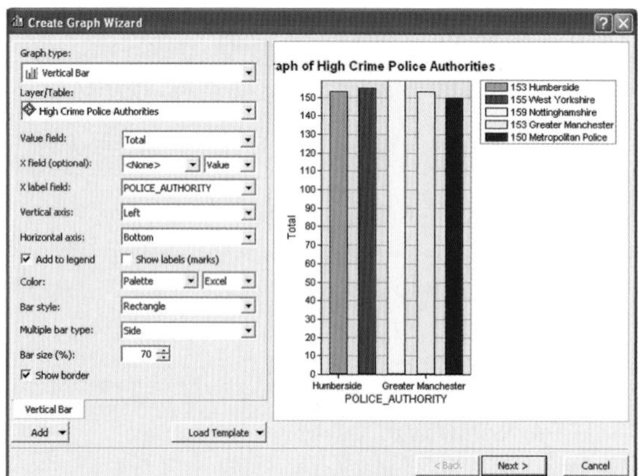

35 Click the **Next** button on the **Create Graph Wizard** menu.

36 In the **General graph properties** box edit the graph title to state **High Crime Police Authorities**. In the **Graph legend** menu select **Top** from the drop-down **Position** menu. From the **Axis properties** menu click on the left tab and type **Total Crimes per 10000** in the **Title** box.

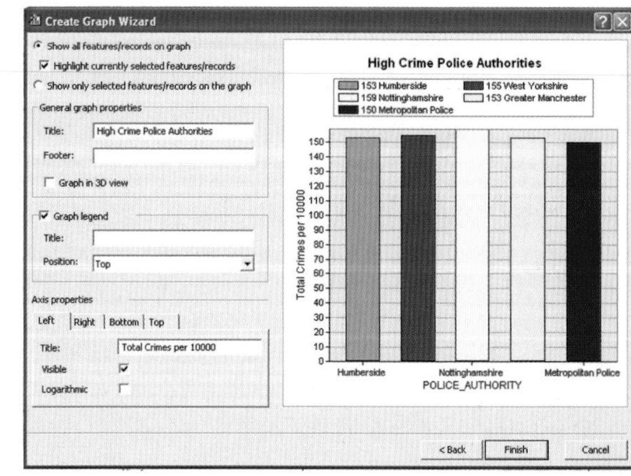

37 Click **Finish** and close the attributes table. You should now see your finished graph.

38 Move your mouse over the graph and click with the right mouse button. From the drop-down menu that appears, click **Add to Layout**.

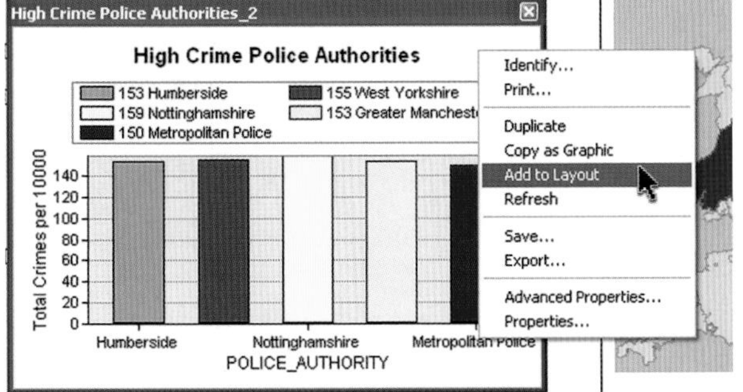

39 The graph will now appear on the layout page. Make sure the graph is selected for editing by clicking on it with the **Select Elements** button from the main menu.

You will know the graph is ready for editing when the graph is highlighted with a blue dashed line.

40 Now place your mouse over the inserted graph and hold down the left mouse button while dragging the graph to the bottom left-hand corner of the page.

41 You can adjust the size of the graph by placing your mouse button over the light-blue 'handles' in the corners of the graph (notice your cursor change to a two-headed arrow when you do so) and dragging with the left mouse button held down.

42 Adjust the size and position of the graph on the layout page until it appears as shown below.

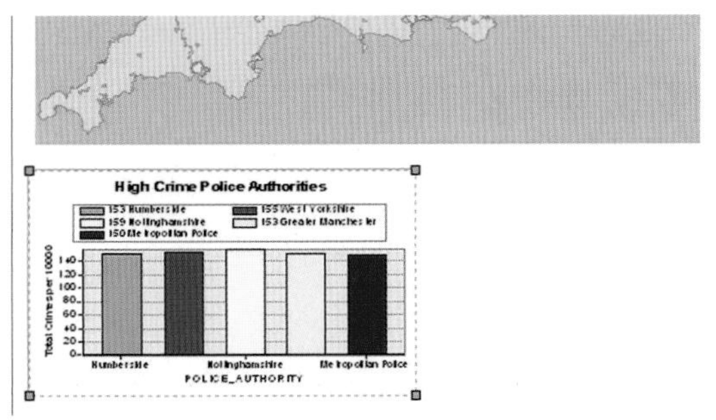

43 In layout view, right-click on the layer called **Low Crime Police Authorities**. From the drop-down menu that appears, click on **Open Attribute Table**.

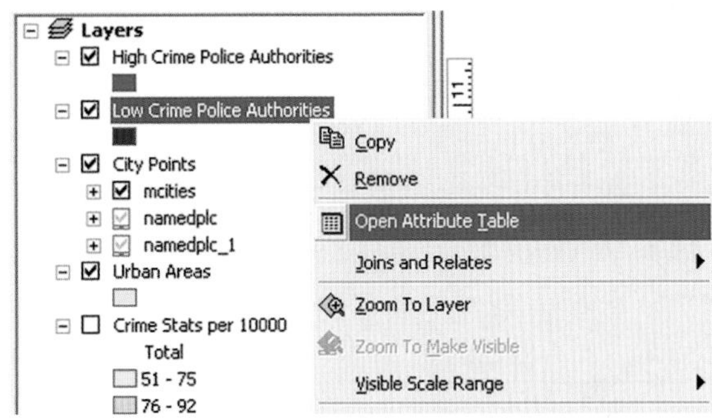

44 With the attributes table open click on the **Options** tab, and from the pop-up menu that appears, select **Create Graph**.

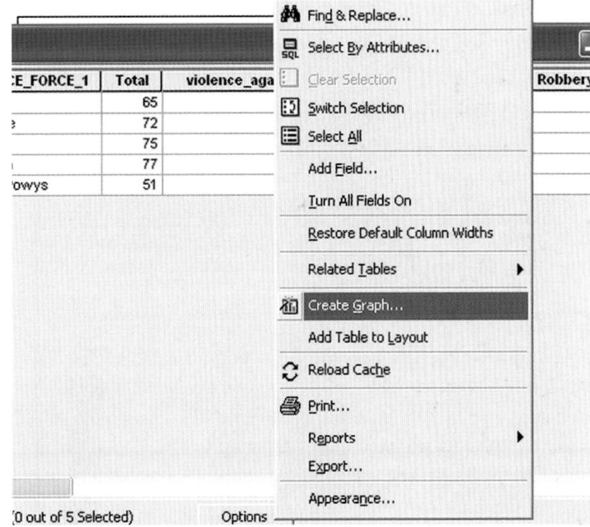

45 Using the **Create Graph Wizard** select the following options:

- for **Graph type:** select **Vertical Bar**
- for **Layer/Table:** select **Low Crime Police Authorities**
- for the **Value field:** select **Total**
- for the **X label field:** select **POLICE_AUTHORITY**
- for **Color:** select **Palette**
- click the check box for the **Show border** option.

46 Click the **Next** button on the **Create Graph Wizard** Menu.

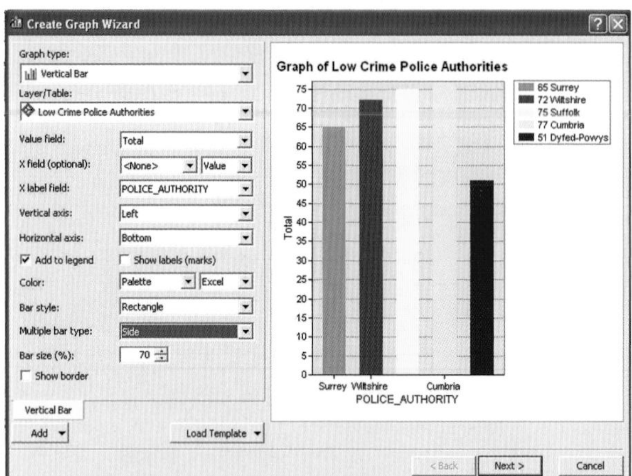

47 In the **General graph properties** box edit the graph title to state **Low Crime Police Authorities**. In the **Graph legend** menu select **Top** from the drop-down **Position** menu. From the **Axis properties** menu click on the left tab and type **Total Crimes per 10000** in the **Title** box.

48 Click **Finish** and close the attributes table. You should now see your finished graph.

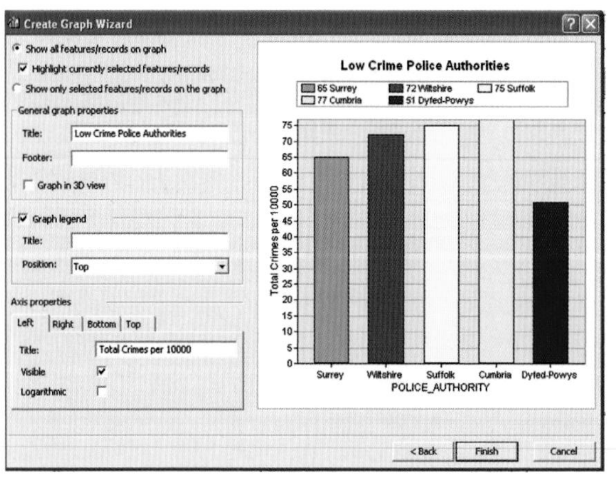

49 Move your mouse over the graph and click with the right mouse button. From the drop-down menu that appears click **Add to Layout**.

50 The graph will now appear on the layout page. Make sure the graph is selected for editing by clicking on it with the **Select Elements** button from the main menu.

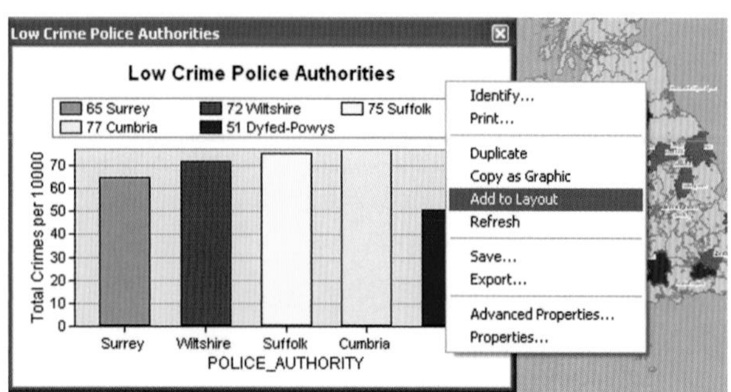

You will know the graph is ready for editing when the graph is highlighted with a blue dashed line.

51 Now place your mouse over the inserted graph and hold down the left mouse button while dragging the graph to the bottom right-hand corner of the page.

52 You can adjust the size of the graph by placing your mouse button over the corners of the graph and dragging with the left mouse button held down. Adjust the size and position of the graph on the layout page until it appears as shown below.

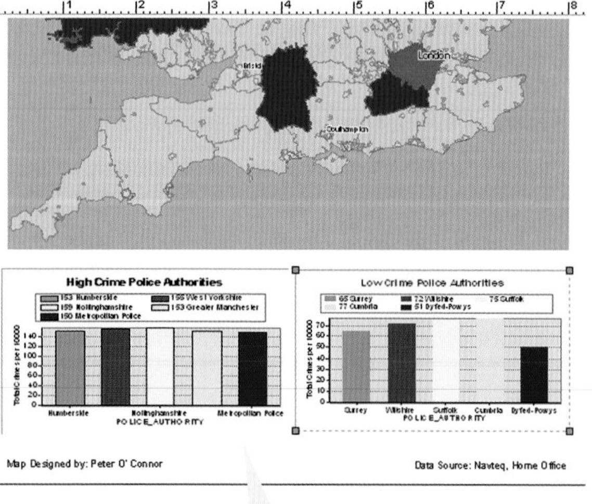

Explain any problems you can identify with the layout of these graphs.

Preparing your map for printing

We now want to add some labels to the mapped locations of high and low-crime police authorities so it will be easy for users of the map to make links between the graphs and mapped data.

53 Right-click on the layer name **Low Crime Police Authorities**, and from the drop-down menu that appears, click **Label Features**. Repeat this labelling process for the **High Crime Police Authorities** layer. You may also want to turn off the **City Points** layer so that your labelling of the police authority areas can be seen more clearly.

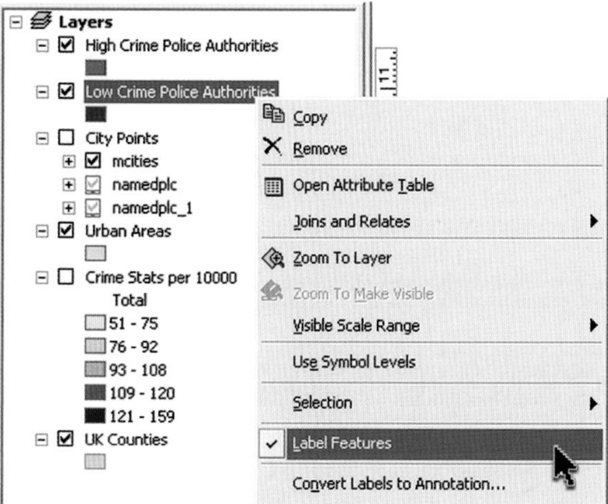

54 The style of the labelling can be edited by double-clicking with the left mouse button on the layer name you want to edit. From the **Layer Properties** menu that appears, click the **Labels** tab. Using the **Text Symbol** options, explore the different label styles.

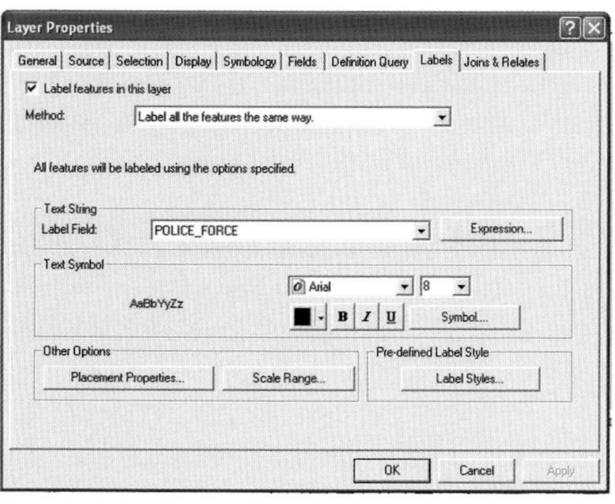

Adding a title to the map

55 From the main menu click **Insert** and then choose **Title** from the drop-down menu.

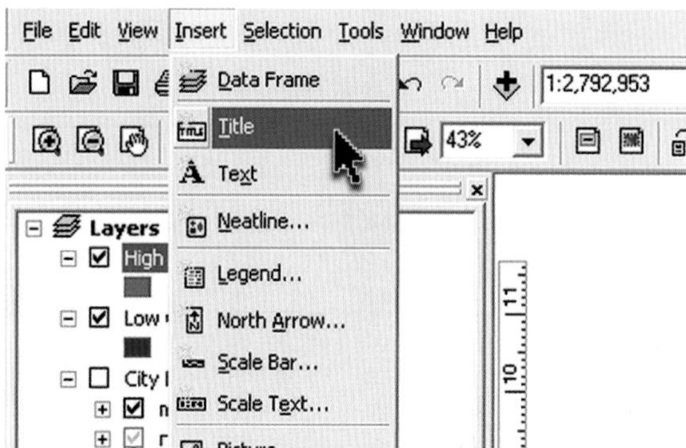

A text box is added to the page. The default title is the name of your ArcMap document.

56 In the text box, type in a well thought-out title that reflects clearly the content of your map (e.g. **High and Low Crime Police Authorities**) and press **Enter**.

57 If you make a mistake and need to change the text after pressing **Enter**, double-click on the title to open its text **Properties**. You can change the properties of the text, including text colour and font, by clicking on the **Change Symbol** button in the **Properties** box.

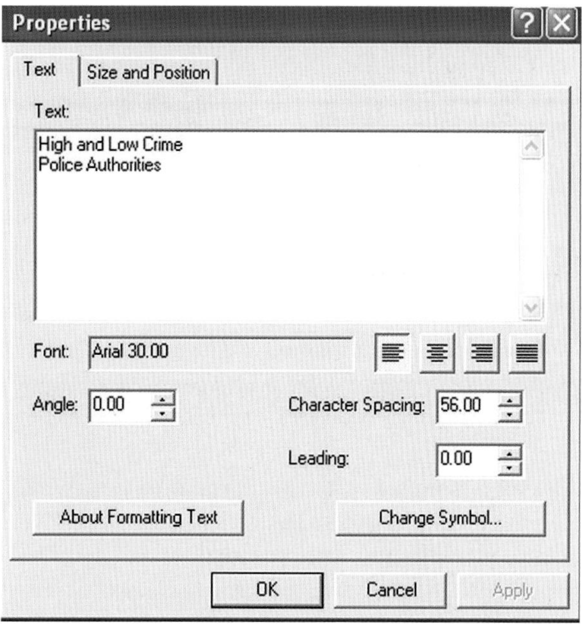

58 You can move the position of the title by clicking and dragging.

59 You can also change the properties of your title by using the **Drawing** toolbar (above).

60 Experiment until you find a style of text that you are happy with.

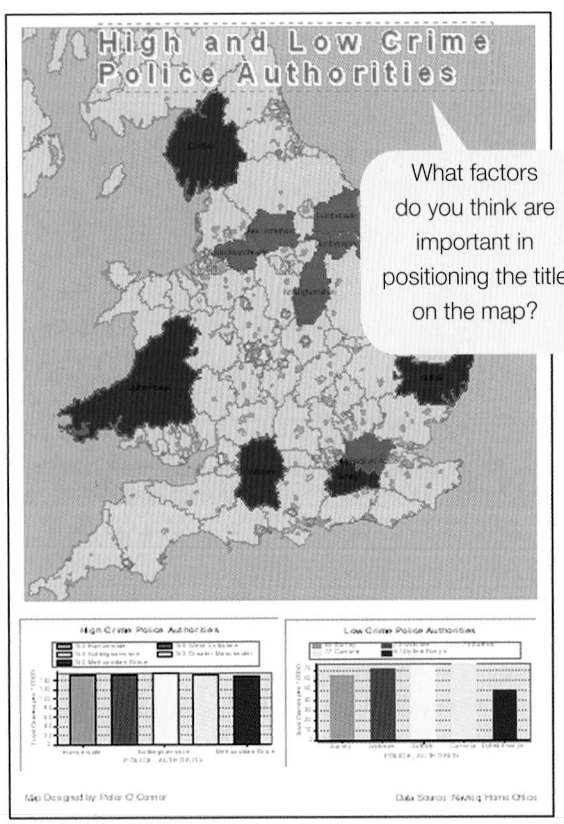

61 Use the **Insert Title** function to add your name (**Map Designed by [your name]**) and the source of the data you are mapping (**Data Source: Navteq, Home Office**).

Now you will need to add a legend/key to your map. Your map needs a key to explain the red and blue colour scheme you have used for high and low-crime police authorities. In ArcMap, keys are called 'legends'.

62 Click the **Insert** menu and click **Legend** to open the **Legend Wizard**.

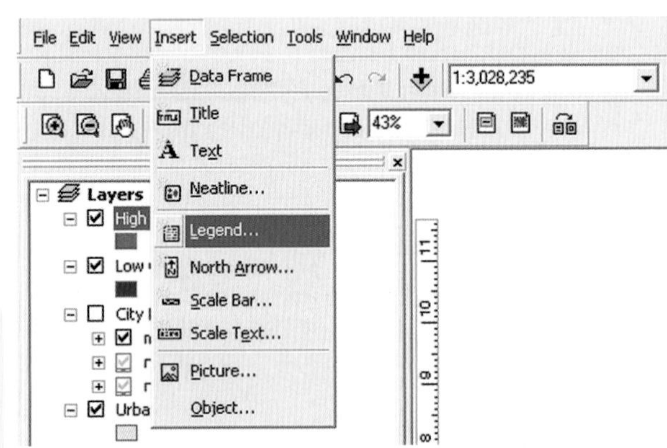

The **Legend Wizard** will open.

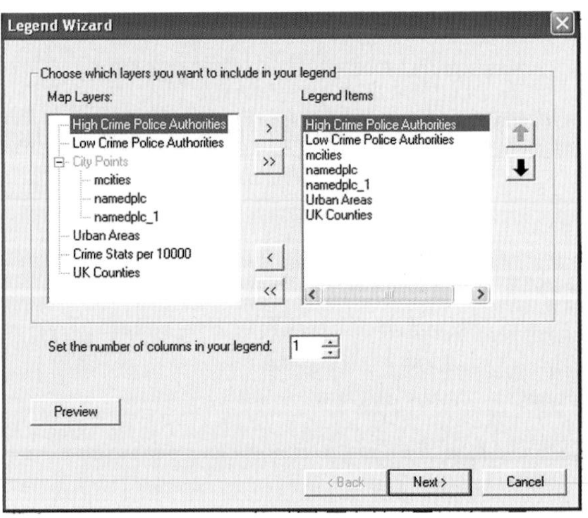

By default, the legend includes all layers from the map and the number of legend columns is set to one.

63 To remove a layer from the items legend, click and highlight it in the column below **Legend Items** on the right, then click the arrow button pointing to the left.

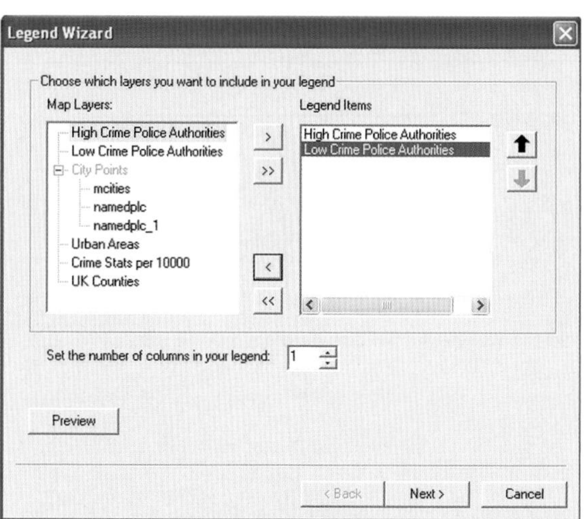

64 Make sure that **High Crime Police Authorities** and **Low Crime Police Authorities** are the only layers in the **Legend** Items column.

65 Click the **Next** button in the **Legend Wizard** four times and then click **Finish**.

66 Make sure you move your legend to an appropriate position on the page.

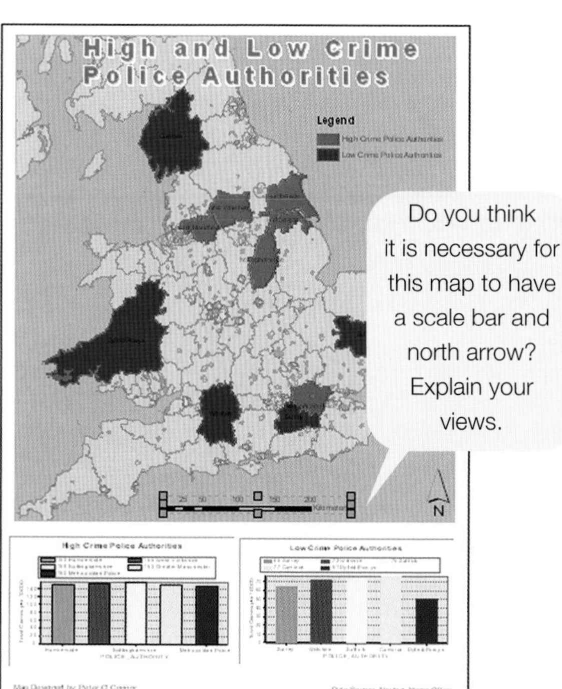

67 You can move the position of your title and legend by using the **Select Elements** button.

68 When you have finished editing your legend, use the **Insert** menu to enter a north arrow and scale bar on your map.

69 If the area of your map appears to be too small on the page, use the **Zoom** tool on the **Tools** toolbar to position the map more like the image shown above.

Once you are happy with the layout of your map and its presentation, it will be ready for printing.

70 From the main menu select **File**. From the drop-down menu that appears, select **Page and Print Setup**.

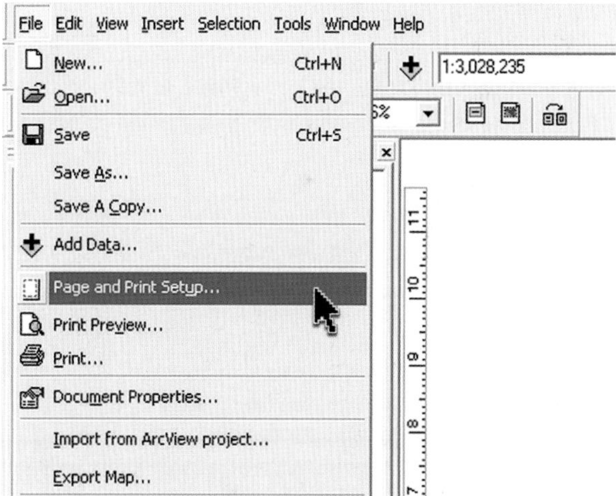

71 From the **Page and Print Setup** menu select the appropriate printer, paper and **Map Page Size** settings. You may need to ask your teacher for advice on what settings to choose. Click **OK**.

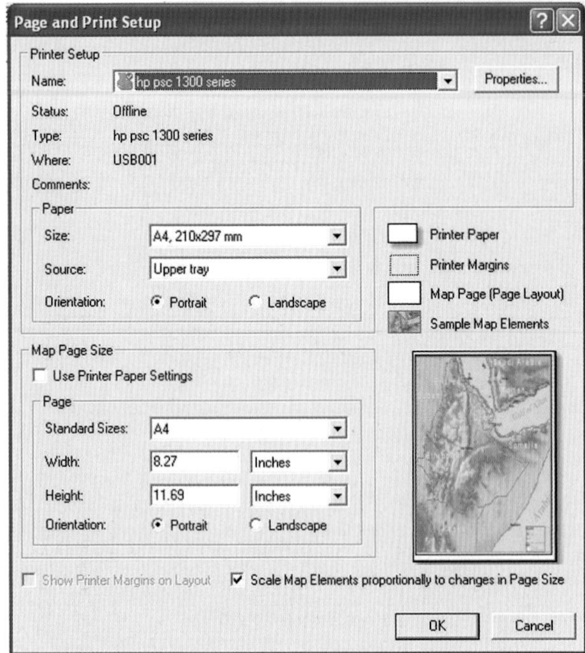

72 Once you have completed your **Page and Print Setup** settings, select **File** from the main menu and click **Print**.

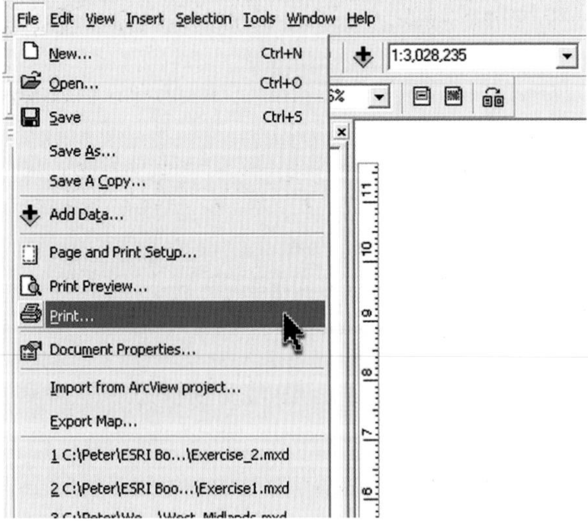

73 Now complete the additional activities associated with exercise 2 on the CD.

Exercise 3

Is there a relationship between crime and levels of urban development?

Aim

- To investigate whether there is a relationship between levels of urban development and the numbers of crimes committed.

Introduction

What types of places are most affected by crime? Where is crime most likely to occur? Which police forces should receive the most funding? At the national scale, answering these types of questions depends partly on whether crime is more likely to occur in an urban or rural setting. This investigation will attempt to map the relationship between urban density and levels of crime in England and Wales.

Launch ArcMap

1 Make sure you have created a folder where you can save all your GIS work. Call it **GIS_Exercises**.

2 From the windows taskbar, click **Start**, **All Programs**, **ArcGIS**, **ArcMap**.

Depending on how ArcGIS and ArcMap have been installed or which Windows operating system you are using, you may have to use a slightly different navigation menu from which to open ArcMap. Ask your teacher for further instructions.

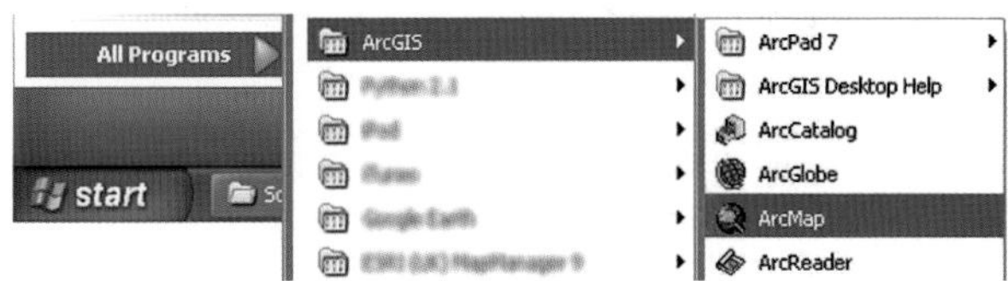

3 In the resulting ArcMap window, click the **An existing map** radio button and click **OK**.

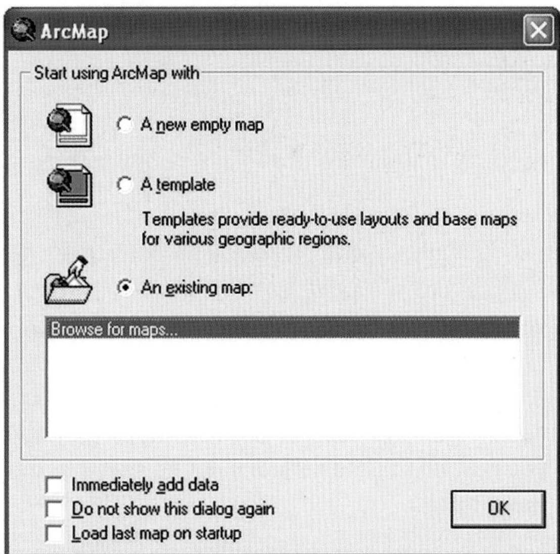

Open an existing map

4 Browse to the drive on which your GIS Exercises have been installed (e.g. GIS_Exercises\Exercise2&3\Map Documents\Exercise3), click the **Exercise_3** icon and click **Open**.

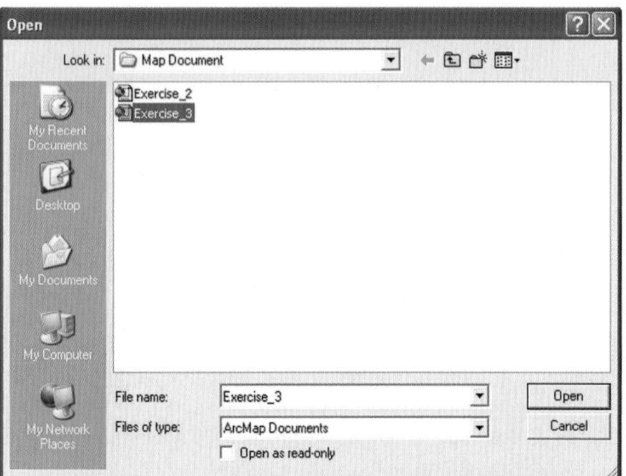

5 The **Exercise_3.mxd** project opens in **ArcMap** showing all the data you have available to complete this exercise.

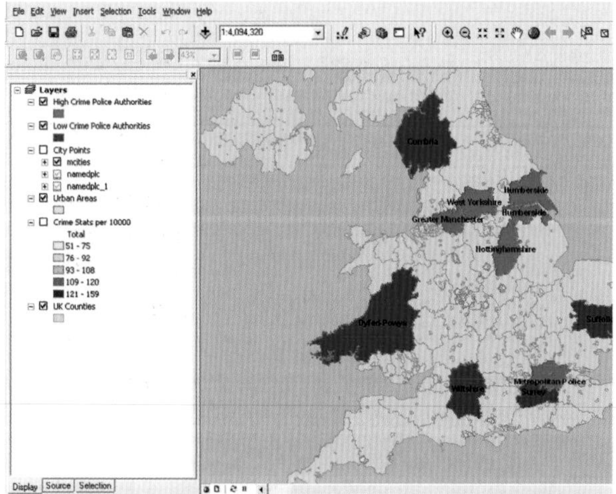

6 **Very important**: As soon as you have opened your Exercise_3 project, save this information to your own drive area (e.g. the new project folder that you have just created called GIS_Exercises). **Everything that you now do for this project must be saved to the same folder.**

Background to the police data

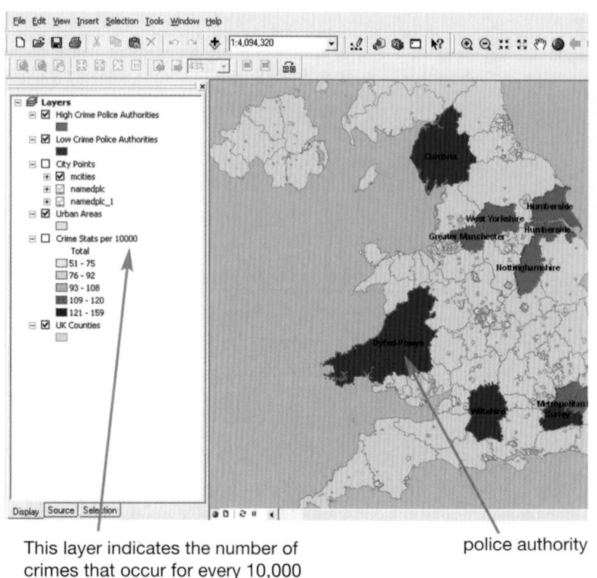

The layer **Crime Stats per 10000** indicates the number of crimes that occur in each police authority for every 10,000 people that live in that area. For example, if the map states that 53 crimes occur for every 10,000 people living in a police authority and the police authority has a population of 50,000, that means 265 criminal incidents have occurred in total in that area. The figures are given in this format in order to take account of variations in population levels between different police authorities. For example, if we simply counted the number of criminal incidents, those areas with the largest populations would nearly always have the largest number of crime incidents. The data is provided by the Home Office, the part of the UK Government which has responsibility for policing.

The layers called **High Crime Police Authorities** and **Low Crime Police Authorities** map the areas in England and Wales with the highest and lowest crimes per 10,000 of the population.

Mapping urban density

To help determine whether there is a relationship between levels of crime and urban development, we are going to create a map showing variations in patterns of urban density across England and Wales.

To do this we first select the urban areas from which we are interested in creating our urban density map.

7 Turn off the layers called **High Crime Police Authorities** and **Low Crime Police Authorities** by unchecking the layer names. Turn on the layer called **City Points**.

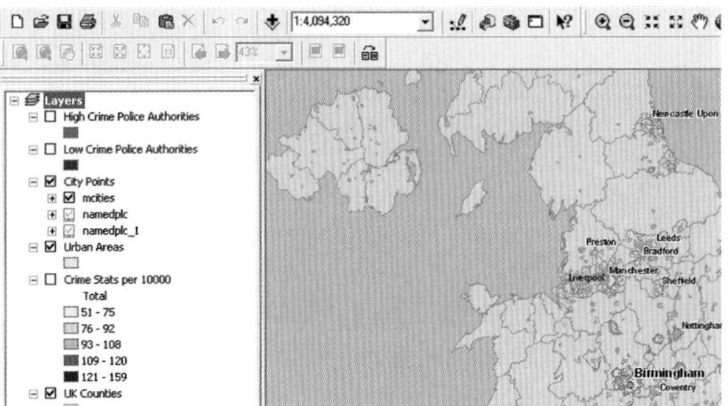

8 From the layer named **City Points**, click on the sub-layer called **namedplc** so that it is highlighted blue.

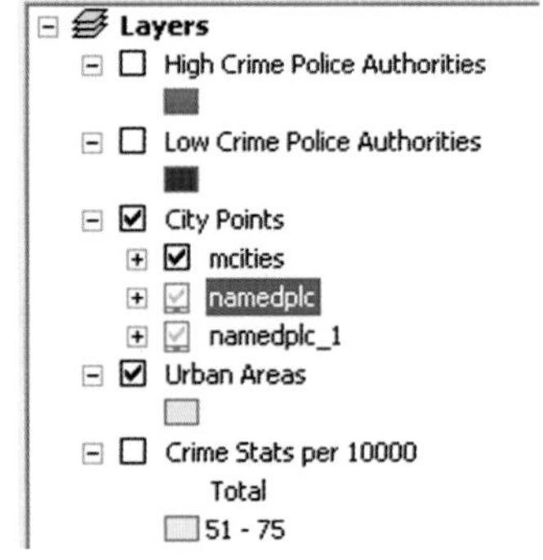

9 From the main menu click **Selection**, and from the drop-down menu that appears click **Select By Attributes**.

10 The **Select By Attributes** menu should now be open. Click on the **Layer** drop-down menu and select **namedplc**.

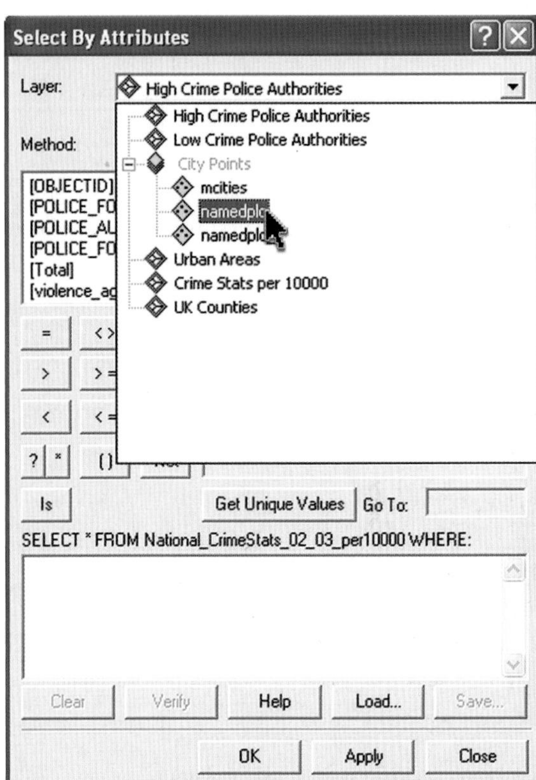

11 In box next to **Method** click **Create a new selection** (see overleaf). Using the scroll bar, scroll down the attribute names till you find **"POPULATION"**. Double-click on the attribute name **"POPULATION"** so that it appears in the bottom white box. Single-click on the 'greater than or equal to' symbol (**> =**) so that it also appears in the bottom white box. Insert the cursor in the bottom white box by clicking immediately after the **> =** symbol, and type in **10000**. Click **OK**. We have just written an attribute query that will select all the towns and cities in England and Wales with a population greater than or equal to 10,000.

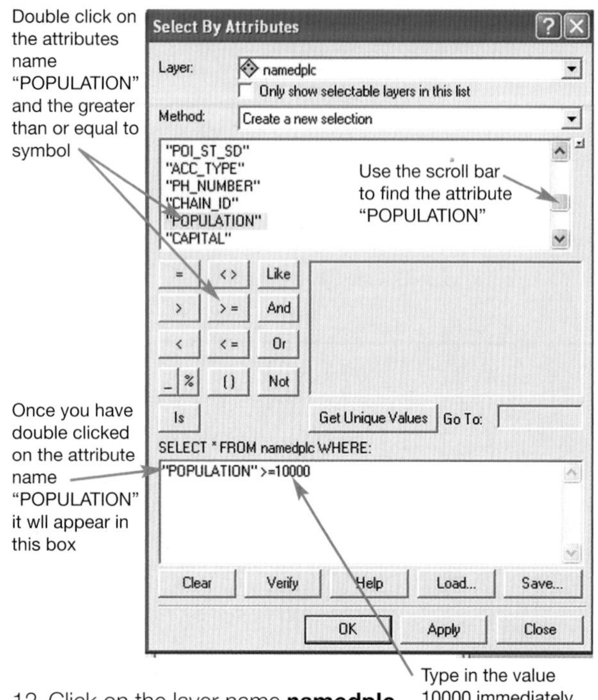

12 Click on the layer name **namedplc** with the right mouse button. From the drop-down menu that appears click on **Open Attribute Table**.

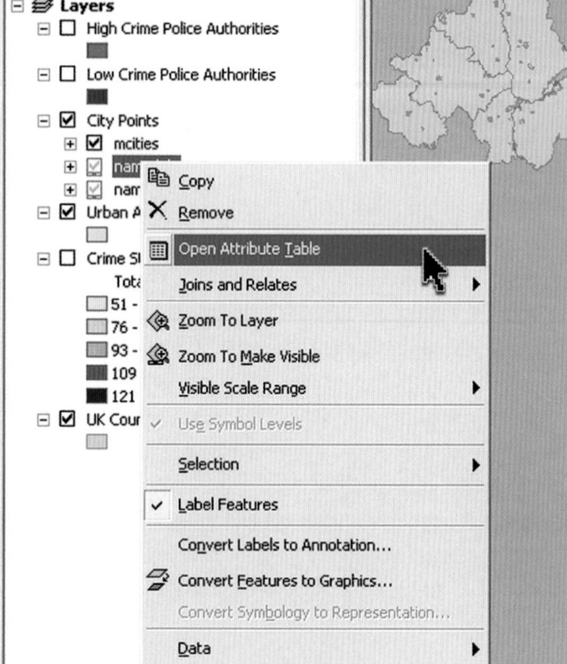

13 Once the attribute table is open, we can see that all towns and cities with a population greater than 10,000 have been selected (highlighted blue). The attributes table also shows that 915 towns have been selected with a population greater than 10,000. Now close the attributes table.

14 From the main menu select **Tools**, and from the drop-

Attributes of namedplc

FID	Shape *	LINK_ID	POI_ID	FAC_TYPE	POI_NAME	POI_LANGCD	POI_NMTYPE	POI_ST_NUM	ST_NAME	ST_LANGCD	POI_:
0	Point	564883627	544867074	4444	Cullyhanna	ENG	B		Freeduff Road	ENG	N
1	Point	564883708	544867077	4444	Crossmaglen	ENG	B		B30	ENG	N
2	Point	564883767	544867078	4444	Cullaville	ENG	B				N
3	Point	564884005	544867082	4444	Silverbridge	ENG	B		B30	ENG	N
4	Point	564884090	544867084	4444	Forkhill	ENG	B		B134	ENG	N
5	Point	564884259	544867092	4444	Meigh	ENG	B		Forkhill Road	ENG	N
6	Point	564886795	544867166	4444	Warrenpoint	ENG	B		Church Street	ENG	N
7	Point	564886889	544867256	4444	Killowen	ENG	B		Killowen Road	ENG	N
8	Point	564886972	544867189	4444	Kilkeel	ENG	B		The Square	ENG	N
9	Point	564887138	544867174	4444	Burren	ENG	B		Milltown Road	ENG	N
10	Point	564887319	544867180	4444	Rostrevor	ENG	B		Kilbroney Road	ENG	N
11	Point	564887434	544867187	4444	Attical	ENG	B		Attical Bog Road	ENG	N
12	Point	564887609	544867257	4444	Ballymartin	ENG	B		Main Road	ENG	N
13	Point	564887653	544867196	4444	Annalong	ENG	B		Glassdrumman Road	ENG	N
14	Point	564890466	544867280	4444	Jonesborough	ENG	B				N
15	Point	19232196	19204868	4444	Buchanhaven	ENG	B		Harbour Street	ENG	N
16	Point	19232808	19204872	4444	Peterhead	ENG	B		West Road	ENG	N
17	Point	19234192	19204874	4444	Boddam	ENG	B		Seaview Road	ENG	N
18	Point	19234293	19205518	4444	Stirling	ENG	B		A90	ENG	N

Record: 1 Show: All Selected Records (915 out of 25038 Selected) Options

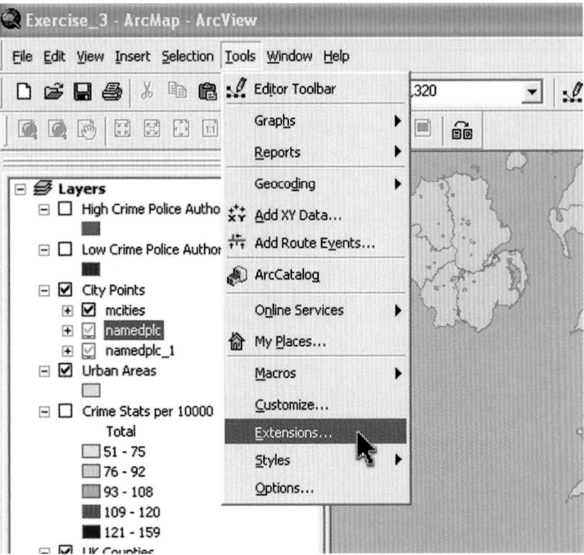

down menu that appears select **Extensions**.

15 In the **Extensions** menu make sure that the **Spatial Analyst** extension is turned on by checking the box

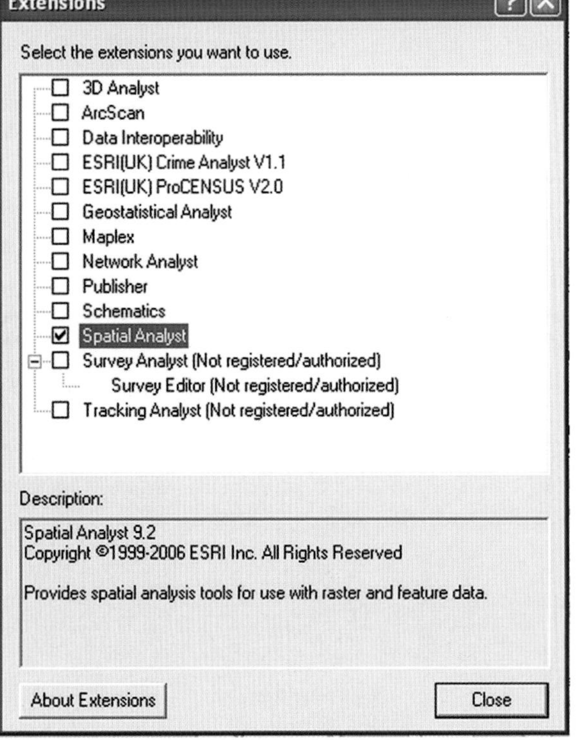

next to it. Now close the **Extensions** menu.

16 From the main menu click on the **Arc Toolbox** icon.

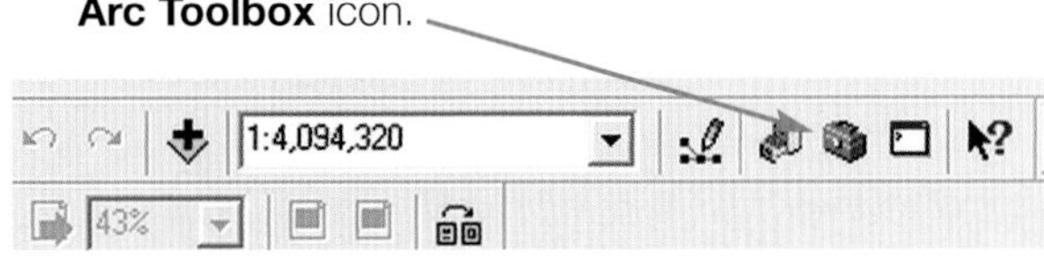

17 The **Arc Toolbox** menu will appear. Expand the **Spatial Analyst Tools** by clicking on the **+** box next to it. Expand the **Density** options by clicking on the relevant **+** box. Double-click with the left mouse button on the **Point Density** tool.

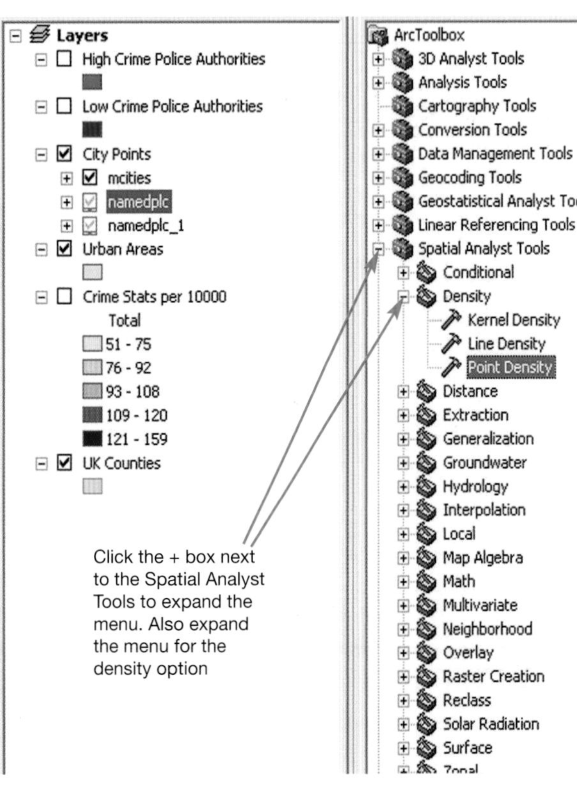

18 From the **Point Density** menu that appears select the layer **namedplc** as the input point feature.

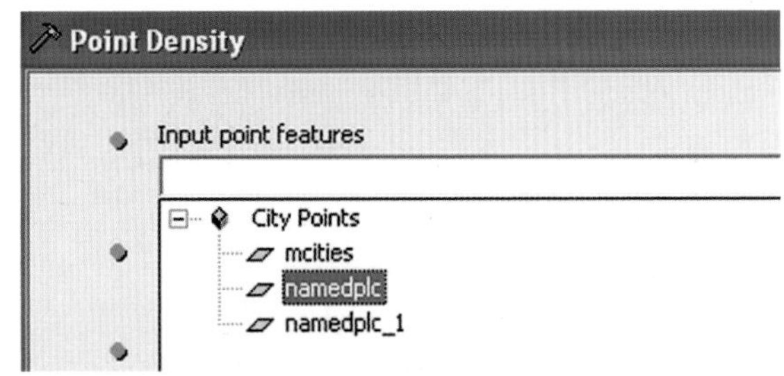

19 Use the **Output raster** field to define an area where you can save the file you are about to create. This should be in your GIS Exercises folder that you created at the start of this exercise. Leave all other options at their default setting and click **OK**.

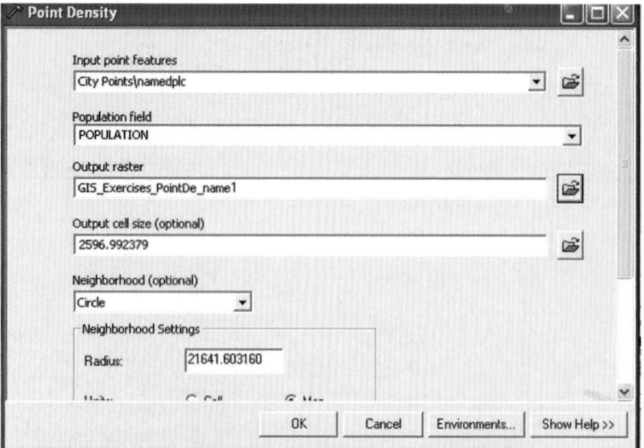

20 Close the **Point Density** dialogue box.

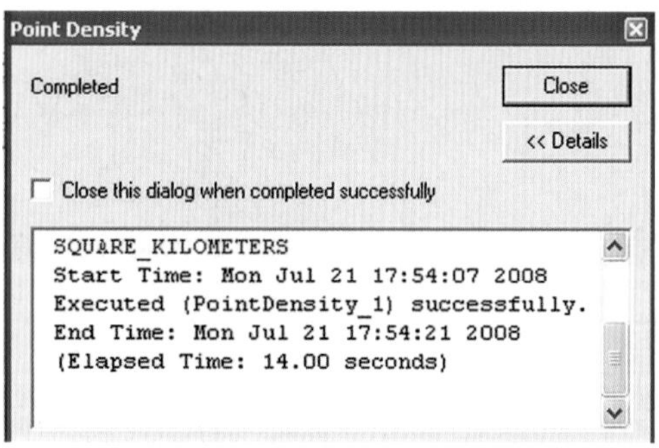

You should now see a new layer appear in the bottom of the table of contents.

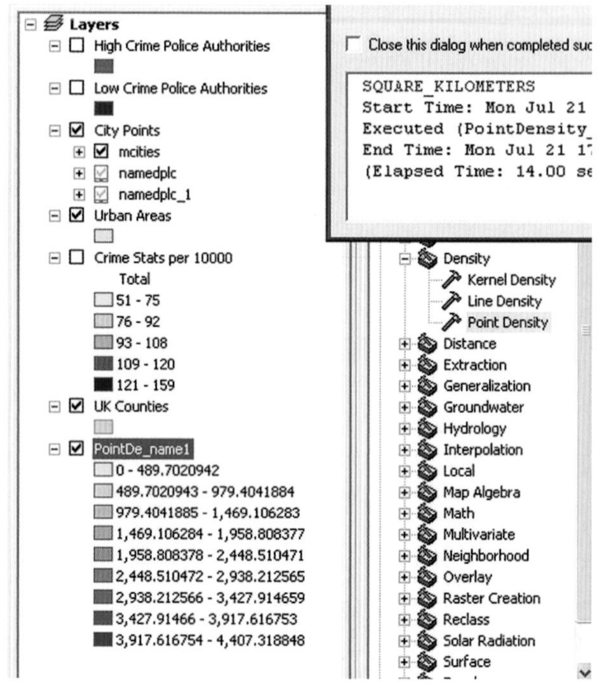

21 A new layer called **PointDe_name1** is produced showing the density of settlements with a population greater than 10,000. Click and hold down the left mouse button on the layer name **PointDe_name1** and drag it up until it appears under the layer called **Urban Areas**. Turn off the layer called **Urban Areas**.

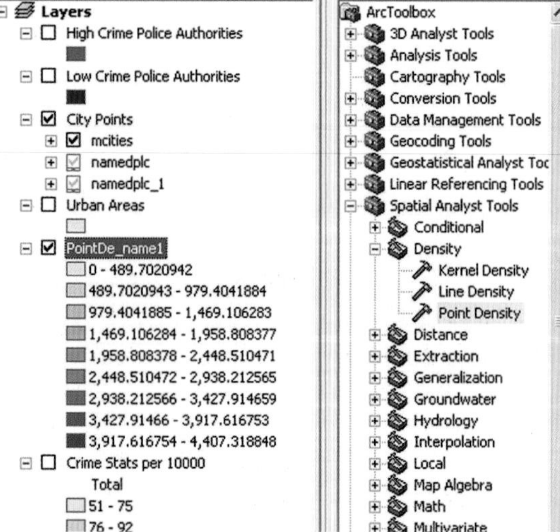

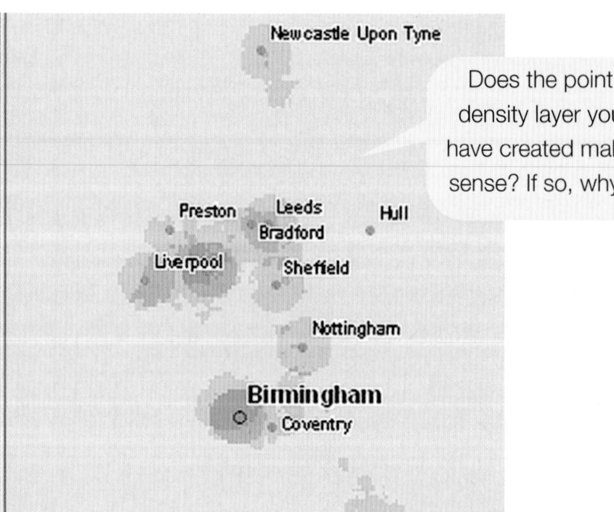

Does the point density layer you have created make sense? If so, why?

22 Close the **Arc Toolbox** menu.

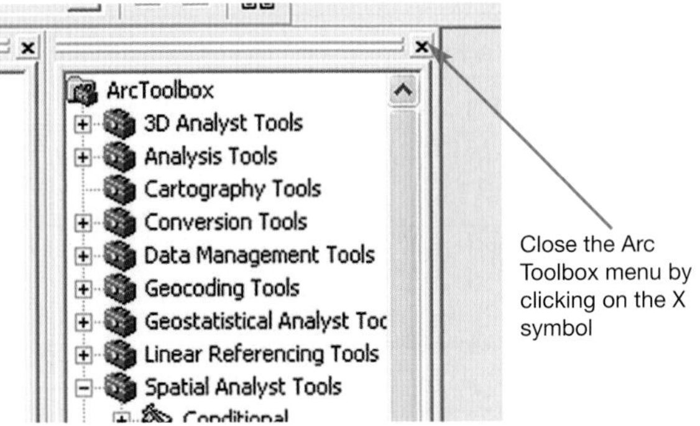

23 We now want to edit the title and legend for the layer **PointDe_Name1**. Click once on the layer name **PointDE_Name1** with the left mouse button and change the name to **Density of Urban Areas**.

24 Next we will make the legend relative rather than using the absolute numbers given by the density calculations. Click on the bottom and top legend values for this layer with the left mouse button and change the labels to **Low Density** and **High Density** as shown below. Delete all the other values.

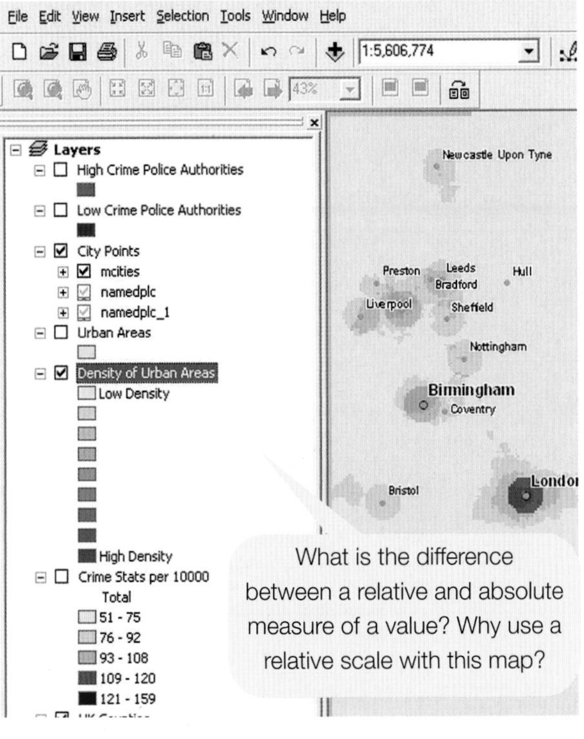

25 The next job is to add an outline map of the UK. From the main menu click the **Add Data** button.

26 Click on the **Connect to Folder** button. Navigate to the directory level where your teacher has saved the data for these exercises. Highlight the layer called **coast.lyr** and click **Add**.

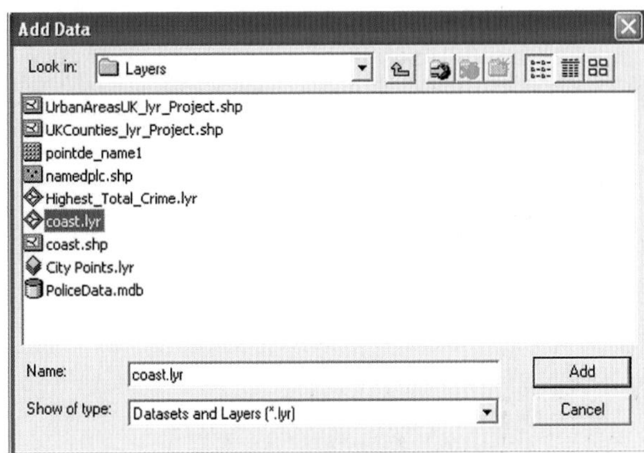

An outline map of the UK should now appear.

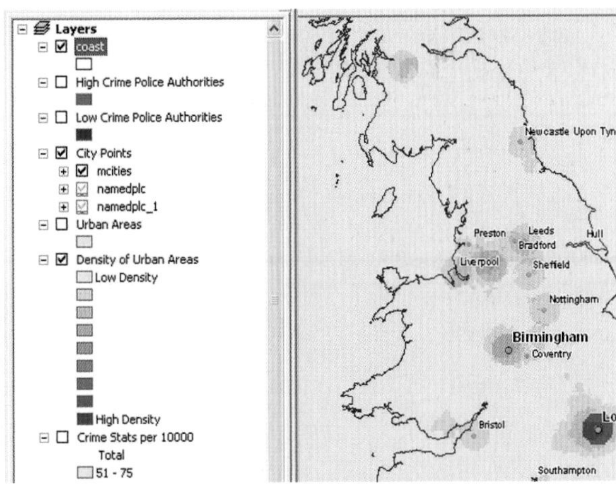

27 Now we need to edit the legends for **High Crime Police Authorities** and **Low Crime Police Authorities**. Single-click with the left mouse button on the symbol for **High Crime Police Authorities**. Once the **Symbol Selector** menu is open, use the drop-down colour ramp associated with the **Fill Color** options and select **No Color**.

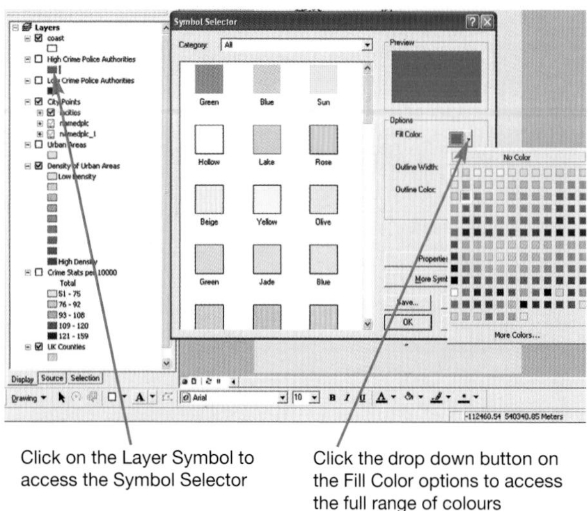

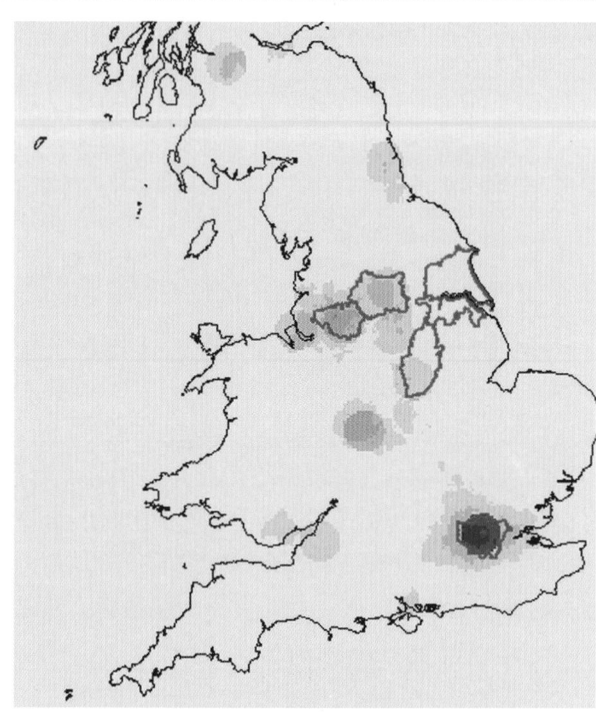

28 Use the drop-down colour ramp associated with the **Outline Color** options to set the colour to **Mars Red**. In the **Outline Width** box type **1.5**. Once you have finished setting these options click **OK**.

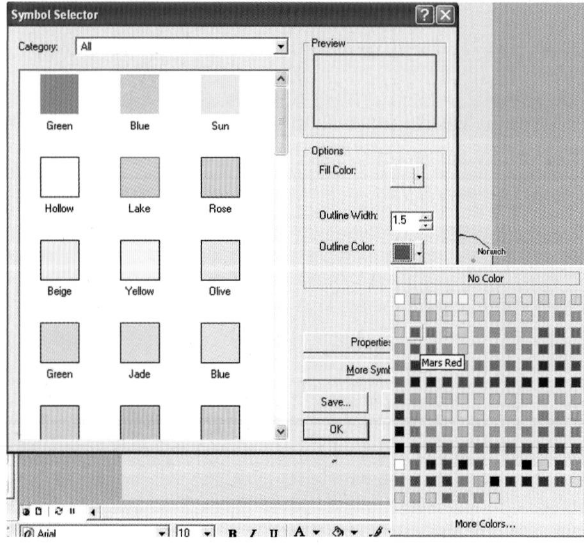

29 Turn on the layer called **High Crime Police Authorities** in the table of contents.

30 Single-click with the left mouse button on the symbol for **Low Crime Police Authorities**. Once the **Symbol Selector** menu is open, use the drop-down colour ramp associated with the **Fill Color** options and select **No Color**.

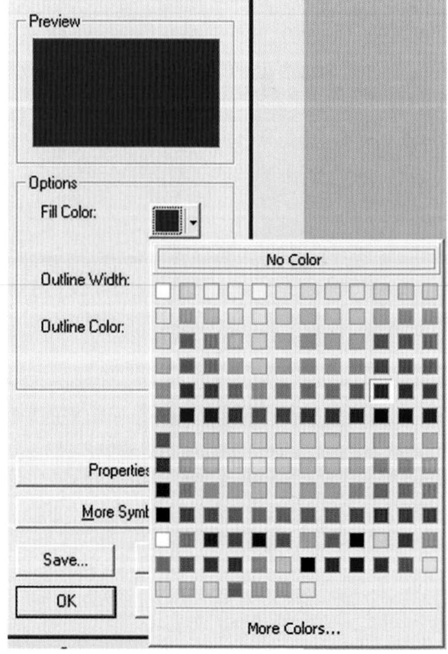

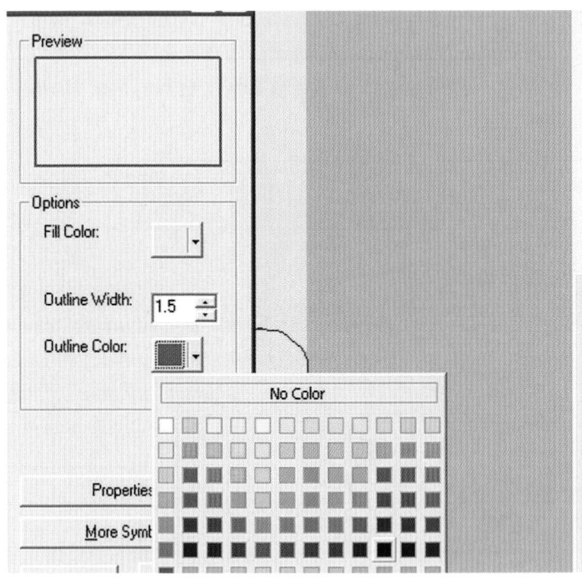

31 Use the drop-down colour ramp associated with the **Outline Color** options to set the colour to **Dark Navy**. In the **Outline Width** box type **1.5**. Once you have finished setting these options, click **OK**.

32 Turn on the layer called **Low Crime Police Authorities** in the table of contents.

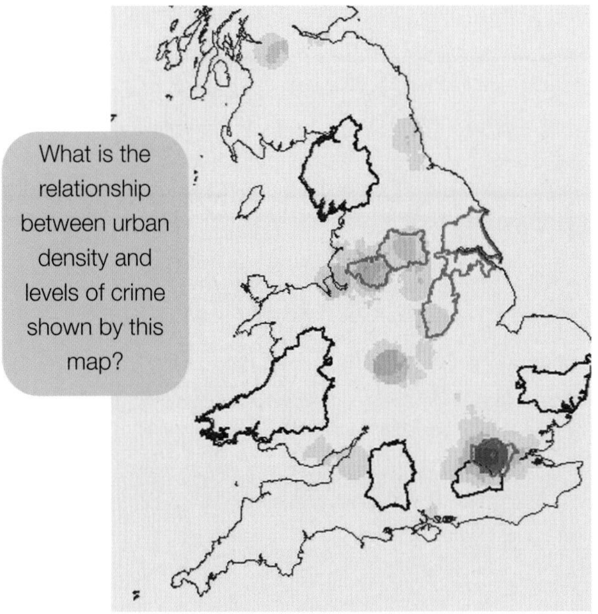

33 You can turn on and off the layers associated with the group layer **City Points** to help you investigate and describe the relationship between crime and urban areas.

***Group layers** are several layers that appear and act as a single layer. Group layers make it easier to organise a map, assign advanced drawing order options and share layers for use in other maps.*

Producing a map for printing

34 Click the **View** menu and click **Layout View**.

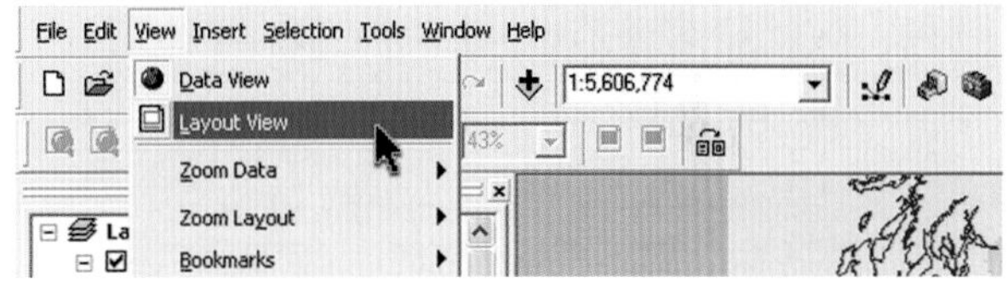

Your map is now sketched on a virtual page. There is also a new navigation toolbar for **Layout View** as shown at the foot of the page.

35 Use the different page symbols to move around your map.

36 In **Layout** view click the **Insert** menu, and click **Title**.

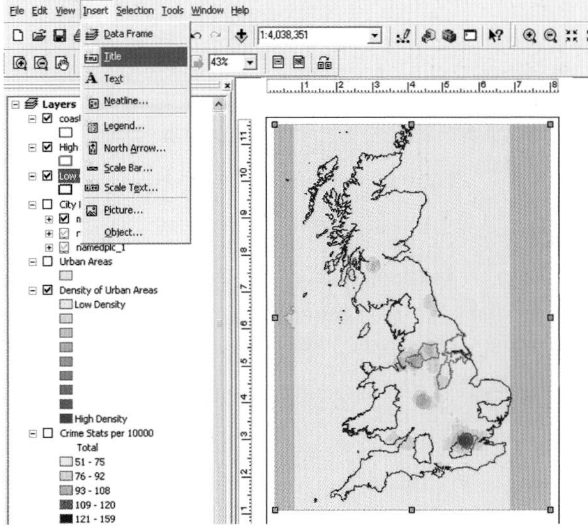

File Edit View Insert Selection Tools Window Help

1:4,038,351

A text box is added to the page. The default title is the name of your ArcMap document.

37 In the text box, type in a well thought-out title that reflects clearly the content of your map (e.g. **Urban Density and Patterns of Crime**) and press **Enter**.

38 If you make a mistake and need to change the text after pressing **Enter**, double-click on the title to open its text **Properties**. You can change the properties of the text, including text colour and font, by clicking on the **Change Symbol** button in the **Properties** box.

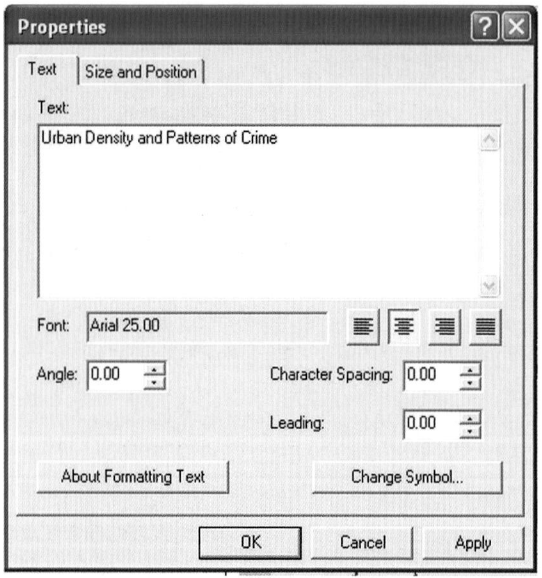

39 You can move the position of the title by and clicking and dragging.

40 You can also change the properties of your title by using the **Drawing** toolbar. (see foot of page)

41 Experiment until you find a style of text that you are happy with.

42 You can add a subtitle like the one shown below by clicking the **Insert** menu and clicking **Title**.

43 Use the **Insert Title** function to add your name (**Map Designed by [your name]**) and the source of the data you are mapping (**Data Source: Navteq, Home Office**).

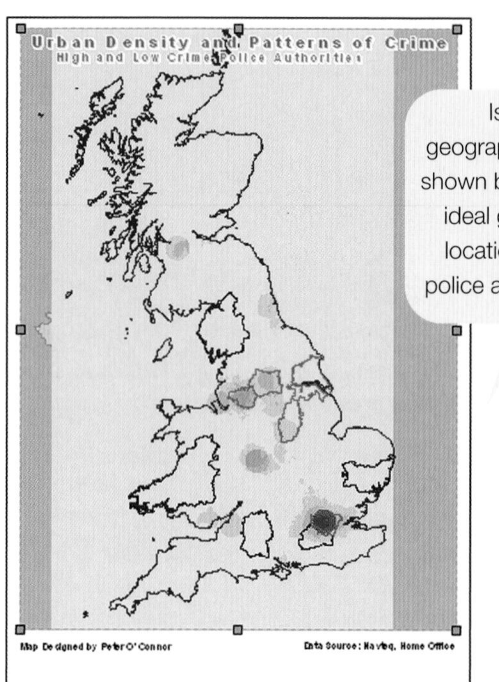

Is the geographical area shown by this map ideal given the location of the police authorities?

Next you will need to add a key to your map. Your map needs a key to explain the meaning of the features drawn on the map. In ArcMap, keys are called 'legends'.

44 Click the **Insert** menu and click **Legend** to open the **Legend Wizard**.

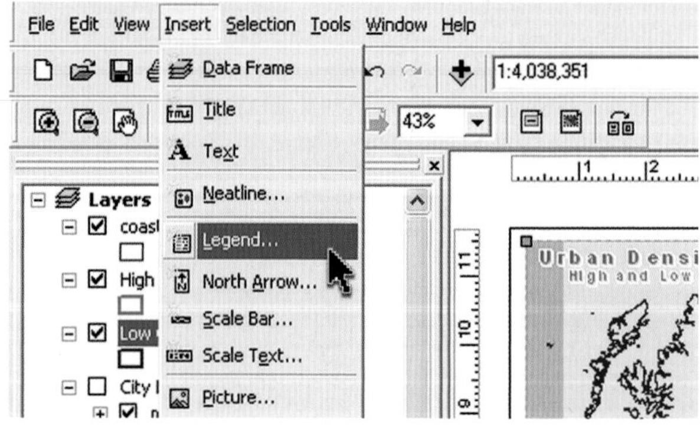

Drawing | Arial | 25 | B | I | U

The **Legend Wizard** will open.

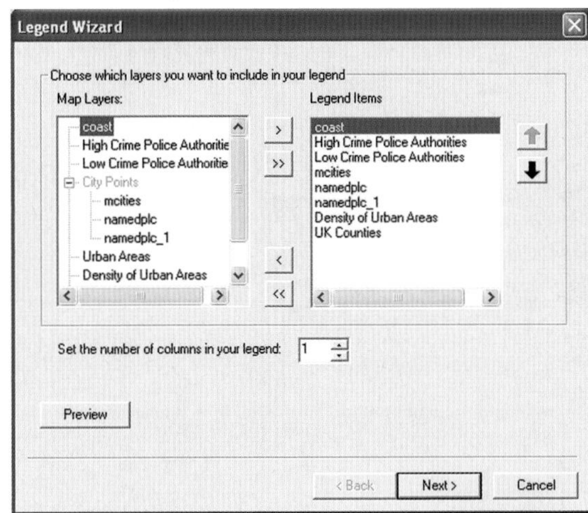

By default, the legend includes all layers from the map and the number of legend columns is set to one.

45 To remove a layer from the items legend, click and highlight it, and then click the arrow button pointing to the left

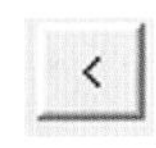

46 Make sure that **High Crime Police Authorities**, **Low Crime Police Authorities** and **Density of Urban Areas** are the only layers in the **Legend Items** column. Click **Next**.

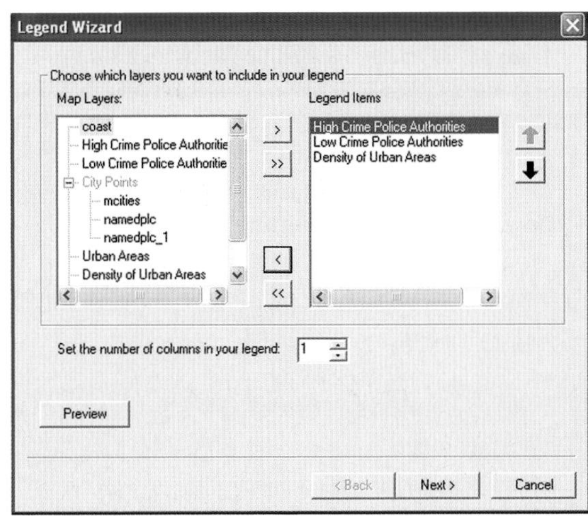

47 In the **Legend Title** box, type in an appropriate title for your legend – for example, **Urban Density and Crime**.

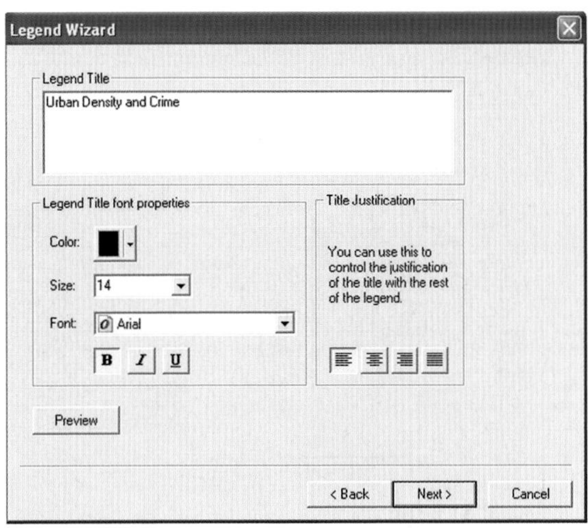

48 In the **Legend Frame** window leave all the options blank and click **Next**.

49 The next two panels set symbols and spacing for the legend, but you will not need to change these, so just click **Next** twice and click **Finish**.

50 Make sure you move your legend to an appropriate position on the page.

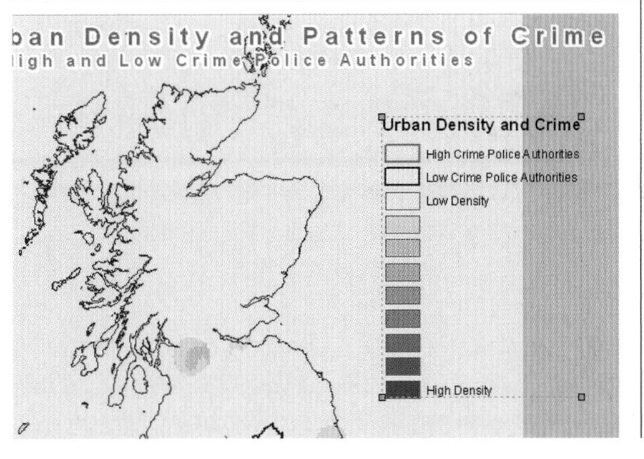

51 You can move the position of your title and legend by using the **Select Elements** button.

52 Use the **Insert** menu to enter a north arrow and scale bar on your map.

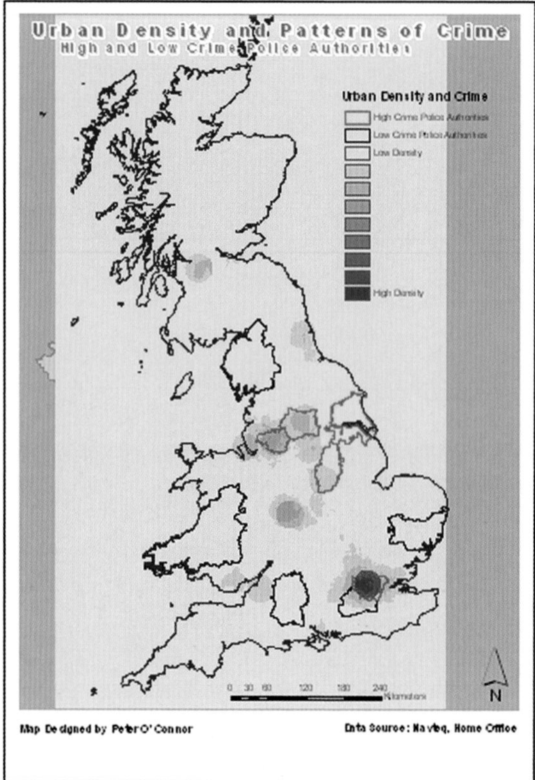

Why do you think the key for this map was placed in the position shown?

53 If the area of your map appears to be too small on the page, use the **Zoom** tool to position the map more like the image shown above.

Once you are happy with the layout of your map and its presentation, export your map as a JPEG file so that it can be easily incorporated into a word-processing package later on.

54 From the **File** menu click **Export Map**.

55 When the directory window appears, navigate to your GIS project folder.

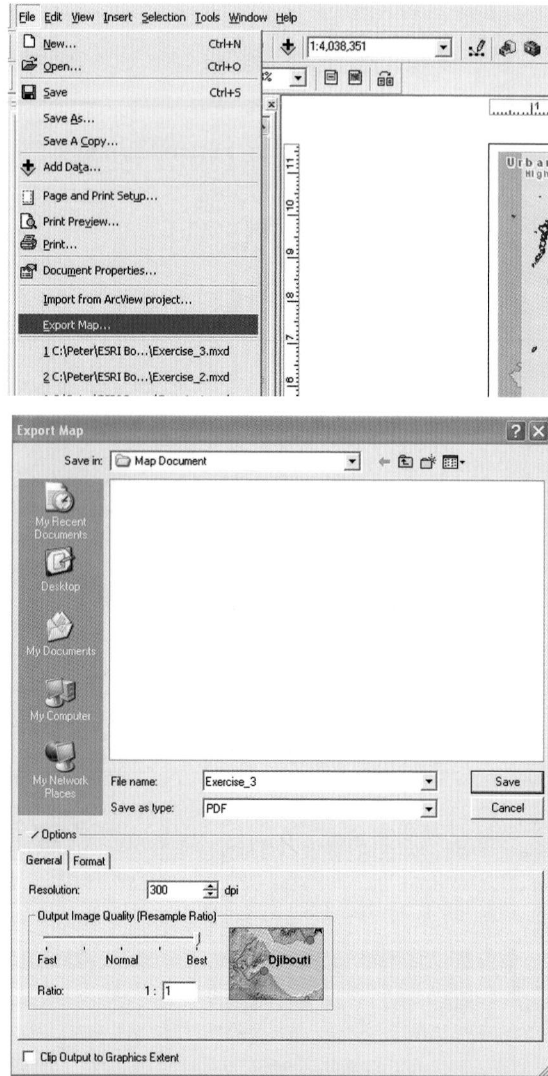

56 Give the map an appropriate file name such as **Urban Density and Patterns of Crime**.

57 From the **Save as type** drop-down menu select **PDF** and click **Save**.

58 Open up the **Adobe Reader** software package from the **Start** menu and then check that the PDF that you have just saved opens correctly.

59 Now complete the additional activities associated with exercise 3 on the CD.

Exercise 4

How does economic and social structure vary across the Cambridge urban–rural fringe?

Aim

- To investigate the nature of social and economic changes across the Cambridge rural–urban fringe.

Introduction

We are often aware that places have a physical structure. However, the places in which we live also have economic and social structures. The places in which we live are not simply characterised by houses, shops and offices, but also by people. People's interactions with one another define social spaces that often have distinct characteristics. For example, people of the same ethnicity or religion can often be found living together. Such grouping can create a recognisable social structure that can ultimately affect how such areas are used and change over time.

Recognising social and economic patterns therefore helps us understand the places in which we live. Gaining an understanding of social and economic patterns can help us to plan efficiently how our cities should evolve. For example, there would be little point in building a large number of detached homes in an area dominated by single people. In this exercise we will look at how social and economic patterns change across the urban–rural fringe in Cambridge and how such changes are likely to define the nature of Cambridge.

Launch ArcMap

1 Make sure you have created a **folder** where you can save all your future GIS work. Call it **GIS_Exercises**.

2 From the windows taskbar, click **Start**, **All Programs**, **ArcGIS**, **ArcMap**.

Depending on how ArcGIS and ArcMap have been installed, or which Windows operating system you are using, you may have to use a slightly different navigation menu from which to open ArcMap. Ask your teacher for further instructions.

3 In the resulting ArcMap window, click the **An existing map** radio button and click **OK**.

Open an existing map

4 Browse to the drive on which your GIS Exercises have been installed (e.g. GIS_Exercises\Exercise4\Map Documents\Exercise4), click the **Exercise4** icon and click **Open**.

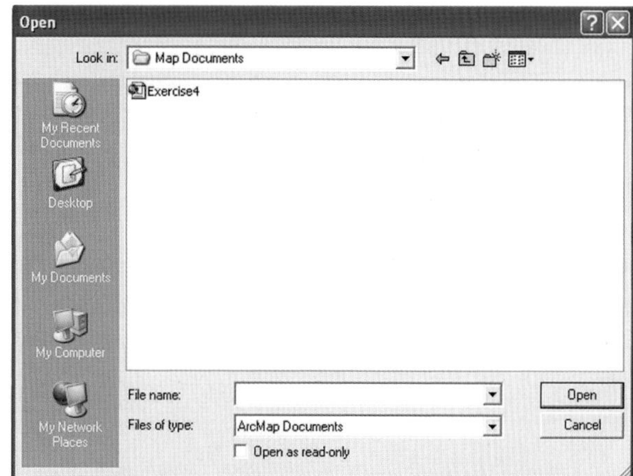

5 The **Exercise4.mxd** project opens in **ArcMap** showing all the data you have available to complete this exercise.

6 **Very Important:** As soon as you have opened the Exercise4.mxd project, save it to your own drive area using **File > Save As…** (e.g. the new project folder that you have just created called **GIS_Exercises**). **Everything that you now do for this project must be saved to the same folder.**

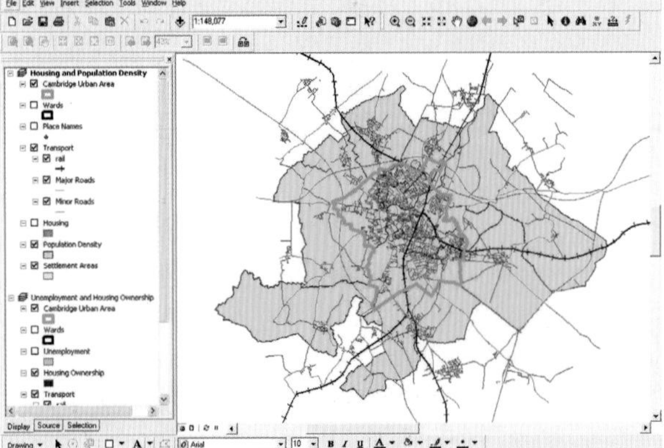

Cambridge data

The layers contained in the table of contents are presented in two separate data frames. Only one data frame can be active at one time. When the exercise opens, the **Housing and Population Density** data frame will be active. You will know it is active because it will be highlighted in bold lettering.

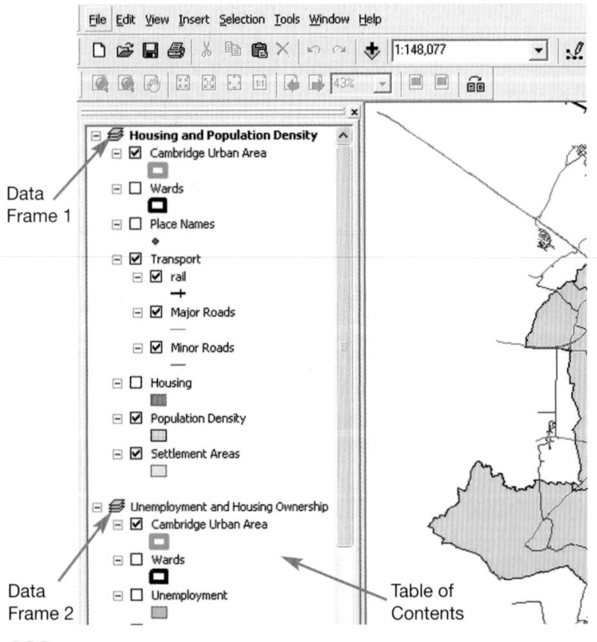

7 From the main menu select **View** and click on **Layout View**.

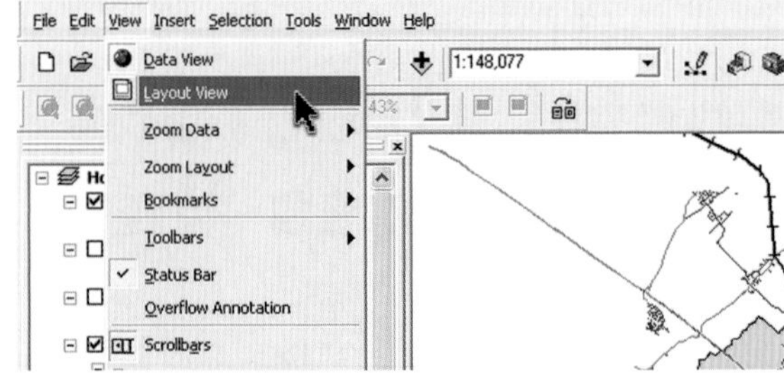

The layout view will appear. In the layout view the page is split into two maps – one for each data frame contained in the table of contents. The active map is highlighted by a dashed line.

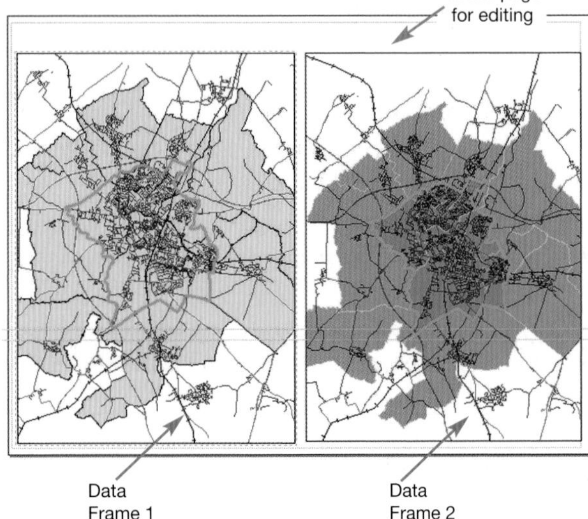

8 From the main menu select **View** and click on **Data View**.

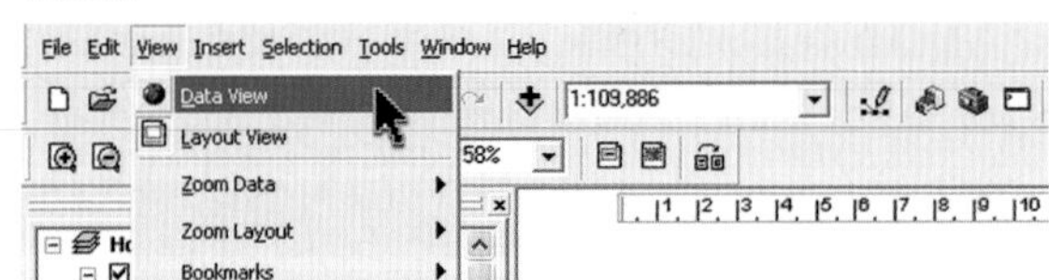

Next we are going to map the relationship between housing type and population density.

9 Double-click with the left mouse button on the layer name **Population Density** to bring up the **Layer Properties** window.

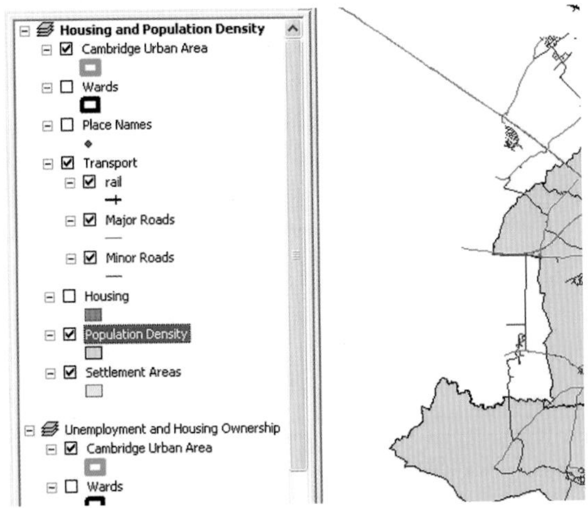

10 In the **Layer Properties** box click on the **Symbology** tab. From the **Layer Properties** dialogue box select **Quantities** and **Graduated colors**. From the **Value** drop-down menu select **TOT_POP**.

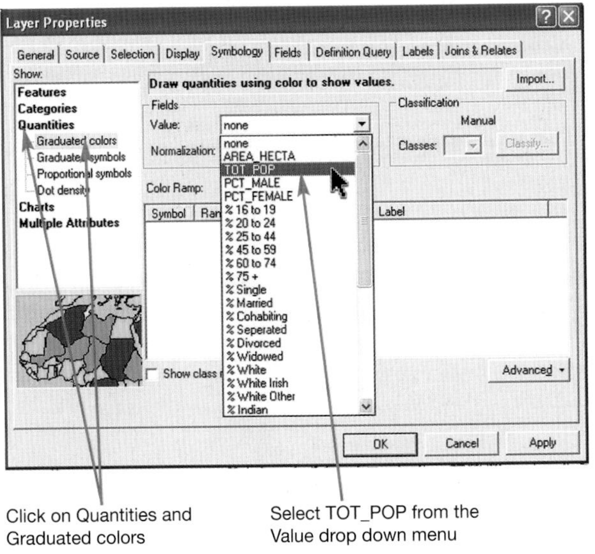

Click on Quantities and Graduated colors

Select TOT_POP from the Value drop down menu

11 From the **Normalization** drop-down menu select **AREA_HECTA**. Click **OK**.

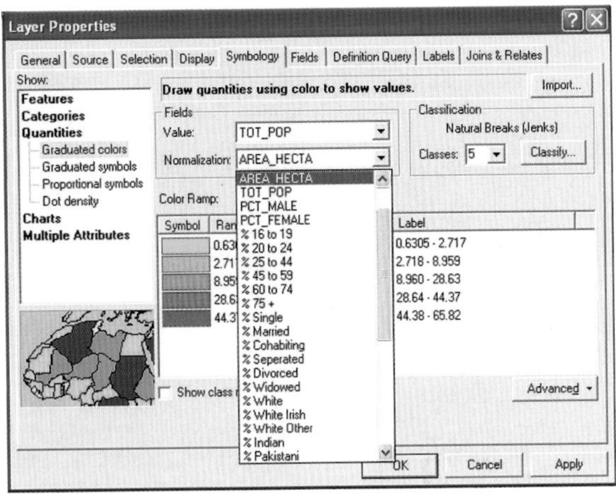

12 Use the **Color Ramp** to set your colour choice to **Green Light to Dark**. If you right-click the **Color Ramp** drop-down menu, you can switch off the graphic to reveal the **Color Ramp** names. When you have finished setting the **Value** and **Color Ramp** options, click **OK**.

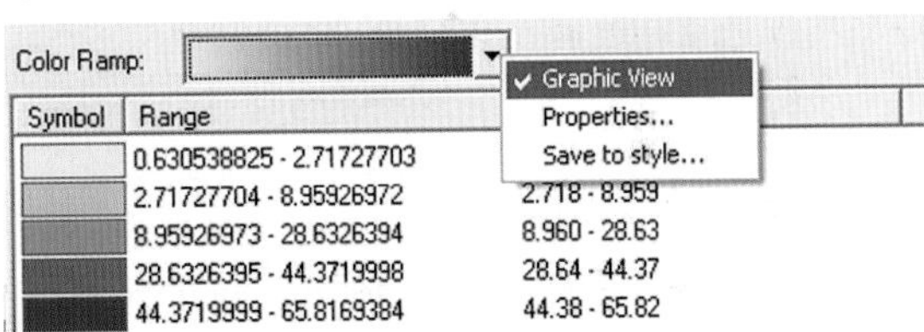

The map produced shows the population density of the city of Cambridge and its surrounding rural areas by ward.

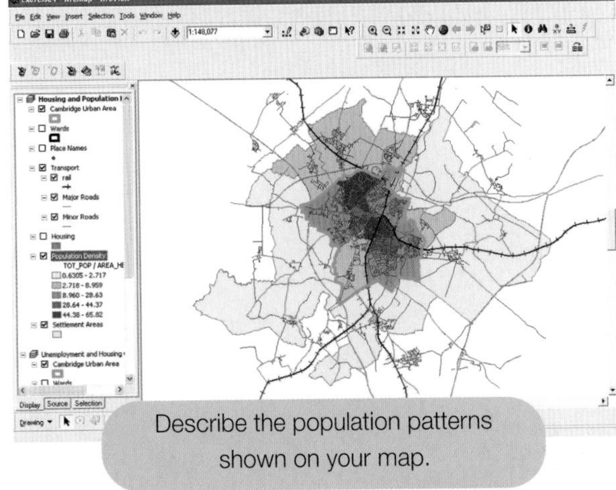

Describe the population patterns shown on your map.

Charting housing type

13 From the table of contents turn on the layer called **Housing**.

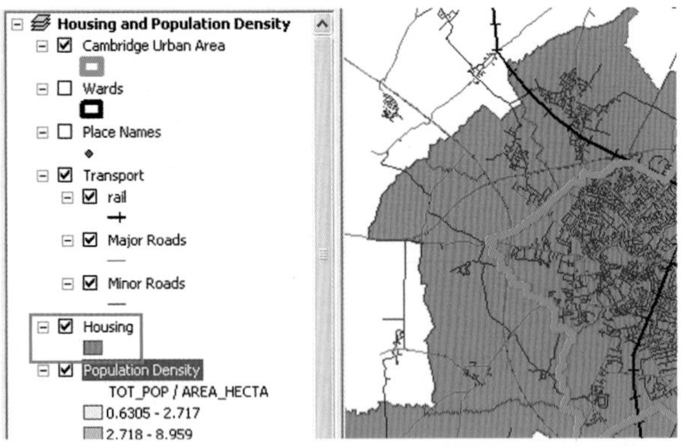

14 Double-click with the left mouse button on the **Housing** layer name.

15 From the **Layer Properties** dialogue box click on the **Symbology** tab and select **Charts** and **Pie**. From the **Field Selection** menu highlight **% Detached**. Add this attribute to the **Symbol** box for the pie chart by clicking the right arrow button.

Click the arrow button to add an attribute to be included in the pie chart

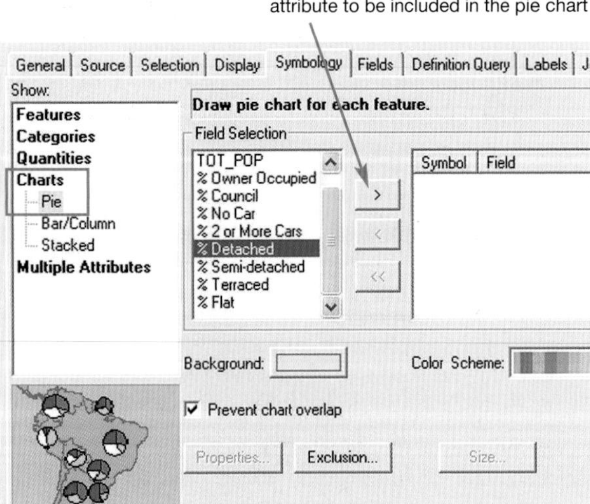

16 Add the four attributes **% Detached**, **% Semi-detached**, **% Terraced** and **% Flat** to the **Symbol** box.

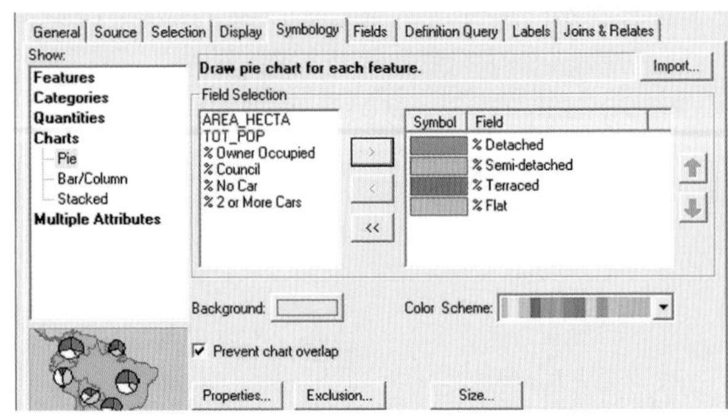

Now we are going to use the symbol editor to define the colours to be used when our pie charts are drawn.

17 Double-click with the left mouse button on the colour currently displayed for **% Flat** in the **Symbol** box. From the **Symbol Selector** dialogue box that appears, use the drop-down menu associated with the **Fill Color** options and select **Mars Red**.

Double click with the left mouse button to access the symbol selector menu

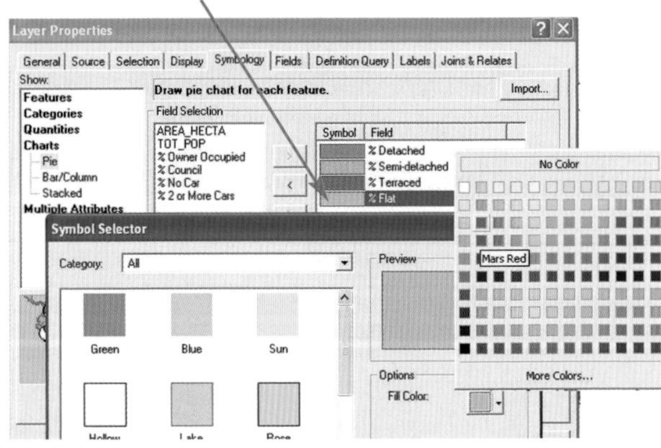

18 Using the same procedure as outlined in step **17**, define each attribute with the following colours:

- **% Flat** – **Mars Red**
- **% Terraced** – **Solar Yellow**
- **% Semi-Detached** – **Quetzel Green**
- **% Detached** – **Dark Navy**.

Why use discrete colours to represent this data?

19 In the **Layers Properties** dialogue box, single-click with the left mouse button on the **Background** symbol.

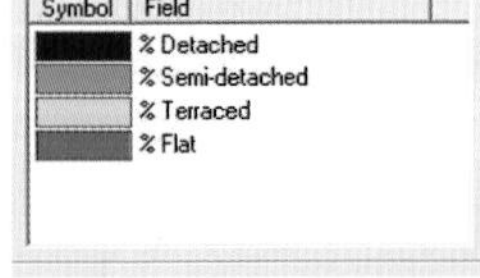

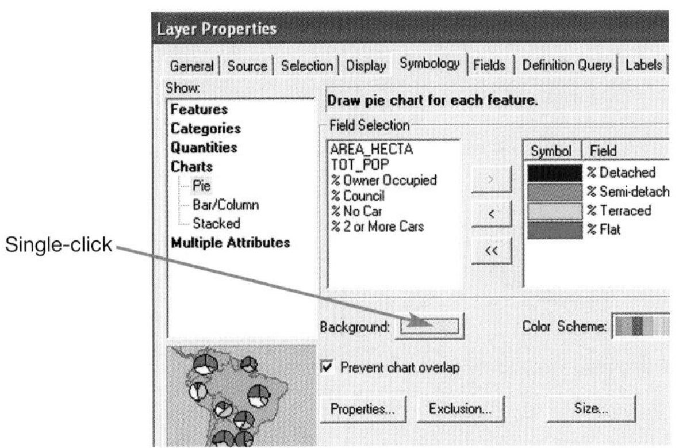

20 From the **Symbol Selector** dialogue box that appears, use the drop-down menu associated with the **Fill Color** option and select **No Color**. Click **OK** and click **OK** again on the **Layers Properties** dialogue box.

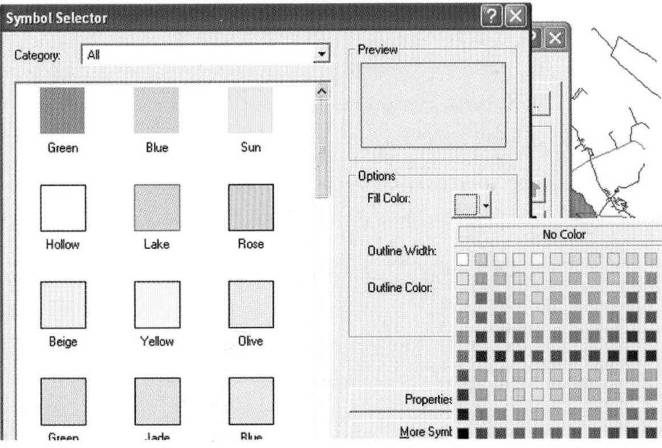

You have now created a map showing the relationship between population density and housing type and how the patterns of these variables change across Cambridge.

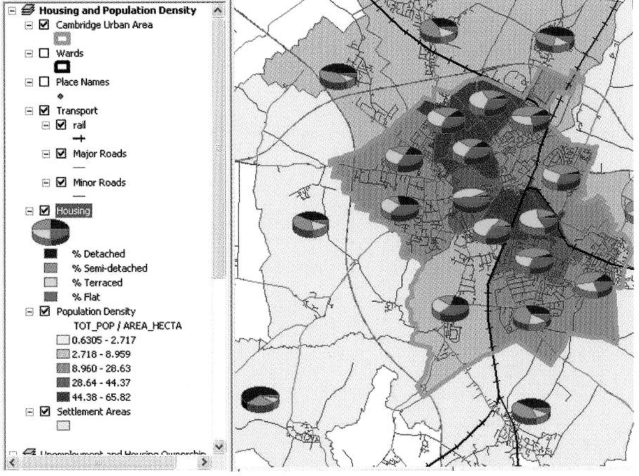

Is there a relationship between housing type and population density?

Mapping housing ownership

21 Click with the left mouse button on the data frame called **Unemployment and Housing Ownership**. Once the data frame is highlighted, click once with the right mouse button. From the drop-down menu that appears, click **Activate**.

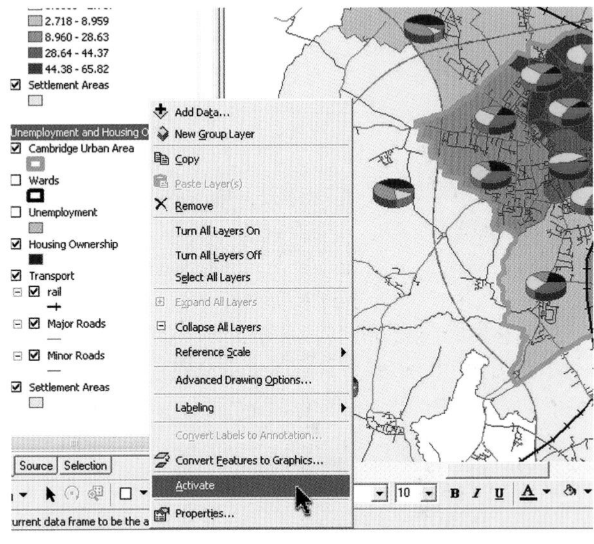

22 In the table of contents double-click on the layer name **Housing Ownership** with the left mouse button.

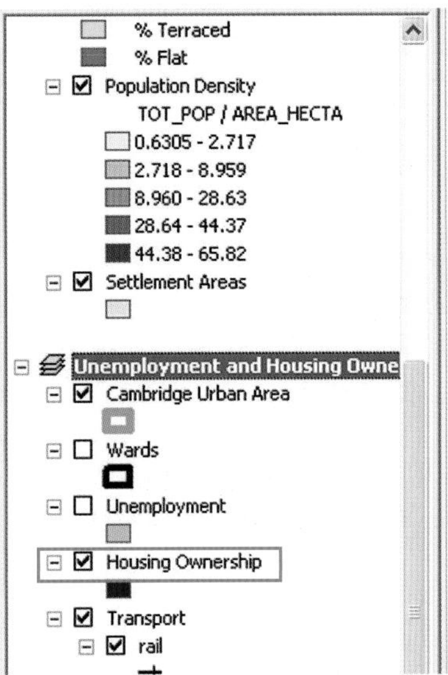

23 From the **Layer Properties** dialogue click on the **Symbology** tab and select **Quantities** and **Graduated colors**. In the **Value** field select the attribute **% Owner Occupied**. Set the **Color Ramp** to **Orange Bright**.

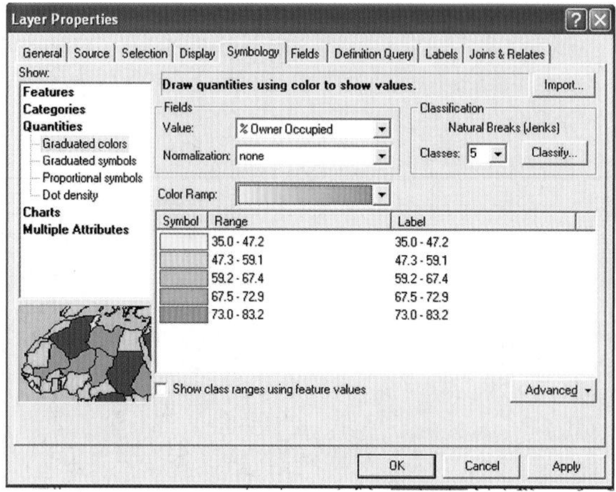

24 Click on the **Display** tab. Place the cursor in the **Transparent** box and type **0**. Click **OK**. This action changes the *transparency* of a layer.

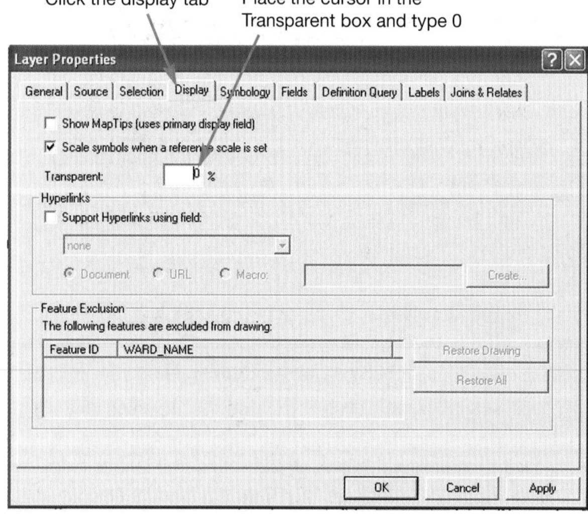

You have now created a map showing variations in the number of people who own or have a mortgage on their home in the Cambridge area.

Creating a map of unemployment

25 In the table of contents double-click on the layer name **Unemployment**.

26 From the **Layer Properties** dialogue box click on the **Symbology** tab and select **Quantities** and **Graduated symbols**. From the **Fields** box use the drop-down menu associated with **Value** and select **% Unemployed**.

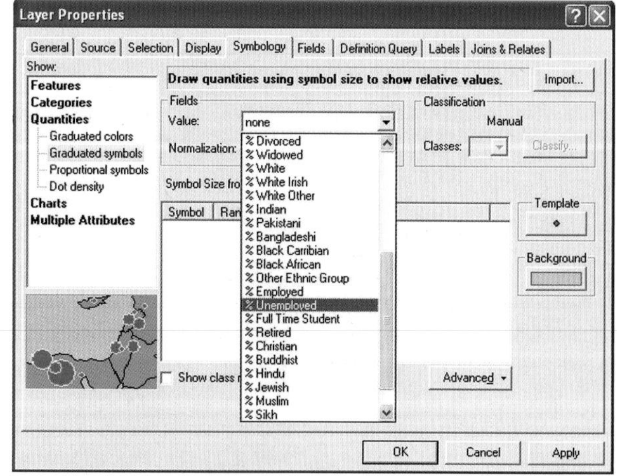

27 Double-click on one of the circles in the **Symbol** box to access the **Symbol Selector**.

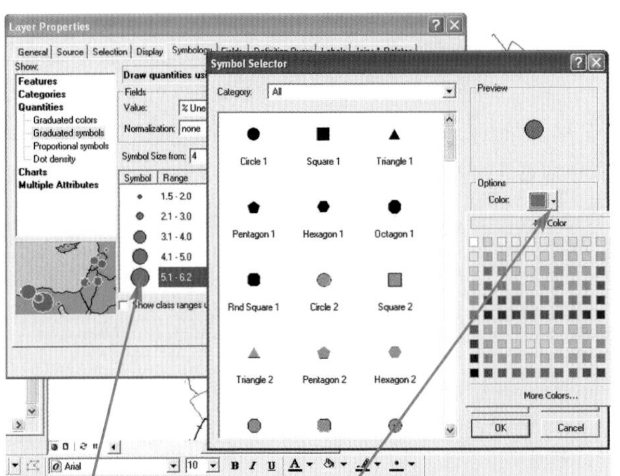

Double-click the symbol to access the Symbol Selector

Use the drop-down colour menu to select new colours

28 Using the method outlined in steps **17** and **18**, select a different colour for each circular symbol.

Do you think it is a good choice to vary both colour and symbol size to represent this variable? Explain your views.

◇	1.5 - 2.0	1.5
○	2.1 - 3.0	2.1
○	3.1 - 4.0	3.1
●	4.1 - 5.0	4.1
●	5.1 - 6.2	5.1

29 In the **Layer Properties** dialogue box, click on **Background**. From the **Fill Color** options on the **Symbol Selector** dialogue box select **No Color**. Click **OK**.

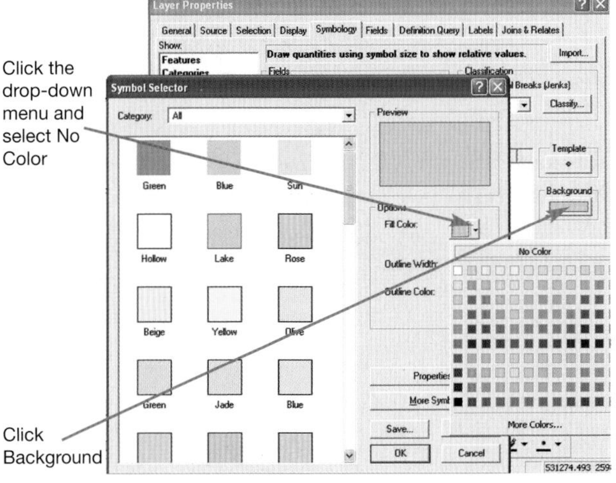

30 From the table of contents window make sure that the layer **Unemployment** is turned on.

You have now produced a map showing the relationship between unemployment and housing ownership.

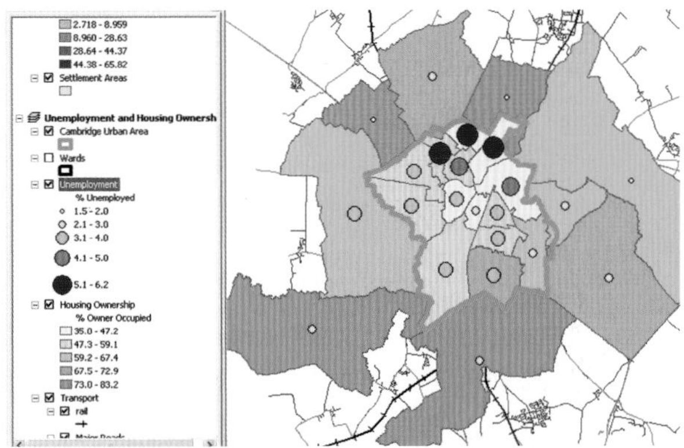

Is there a relationship between housing ownership and unemployment?

Preparing your maps for printing

31 From the main menu select **View**. From the drop-down menu select **Layout View**.

File Edit View Insert Selection Tools Window Help
Data View
Layout View
Zoom Data
Zoom Layout
Bookmarks
Toolbars
Status Bar

You should now see the two maps you have produced side by side on a virtual page.

32 In **Layout View** click the **Insert** menu and then click **Title**.

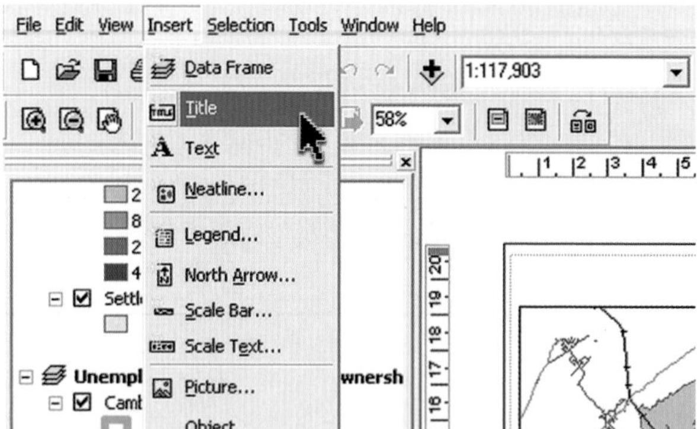

A text box is added to the page. The default title is the name of your ArcMap document.

33 In the text box, type in a well thought-out title that reflects clearly the content of your map (e.g. **Economic and Social Structure of Cambridge**) and press **Enter**.

34 If you make a mistake and need to change the text after pressing **Enter**, double-click on the title to open its text properties. You can change the properties of the text, including text colour and font, by clicking on the **Change Symbol** button in the **Properties** box.

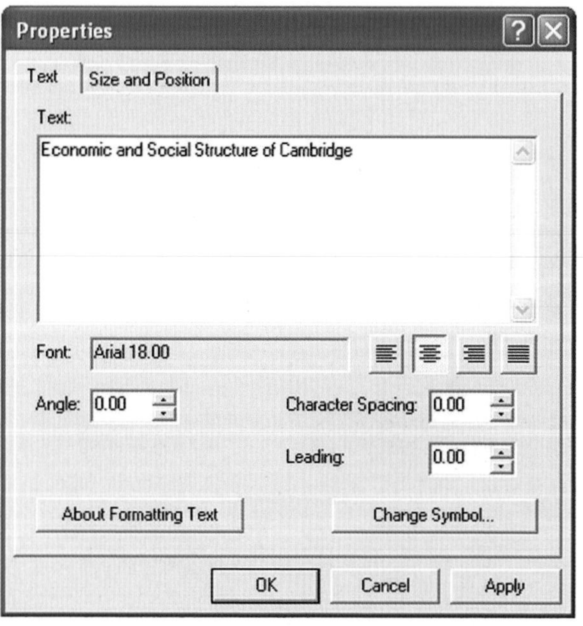

35 You can move the position of the title by and clicking and dragging.

36 You can also change the properties of your title by using the **Drawing** toolbar.

37 Experiment until you find a style of text that you are happy with.

38 Use the **Insert Title** function to add your name (**Map Designed by [your name]**) and the source of the data you are mapping (**Data Source: Navteq, Census 2001**).

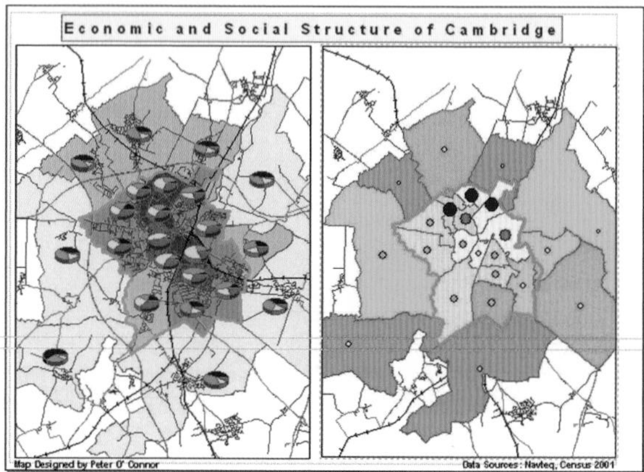

Next you will need to add a legend/key to your map. Your map needs a key to help explain its meaning. In ArcMap, keys are called 'legends'.

39 Activate the Data Frame called **Housing and Population Density**.

40 Click the **Insert** menu and click **Legend** to open the **Legend Wizard**.

The **Legend Wizard** will open.

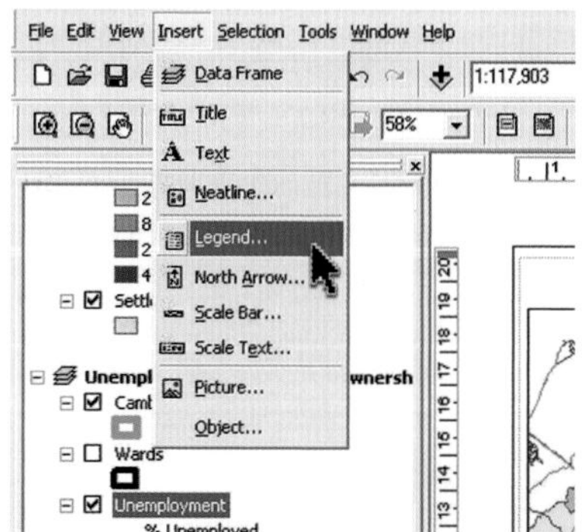

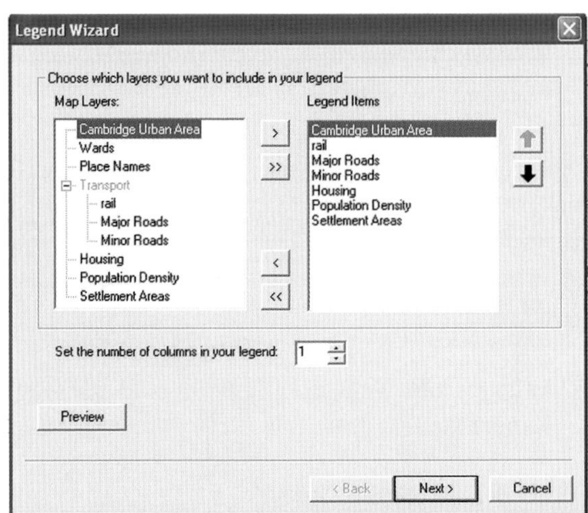

41 By default, the legend includes all layers from the map and the number of legend columns is set to one.

42 Make sure that **Housing** and **Population** Density are the only layers in the Legend Items column. To remove a layer from the items legend, click and highlight it, then click the arrow button pointing to the left.

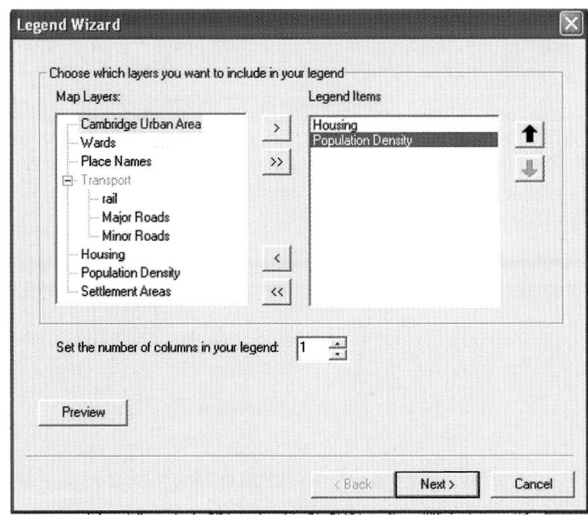

43 Click **Next** in the **Legend Wizard** dialogue box.

44 In the **Legend Title** box add an appropriate title such as **Population Density and Housing Type**. Click **Next**.

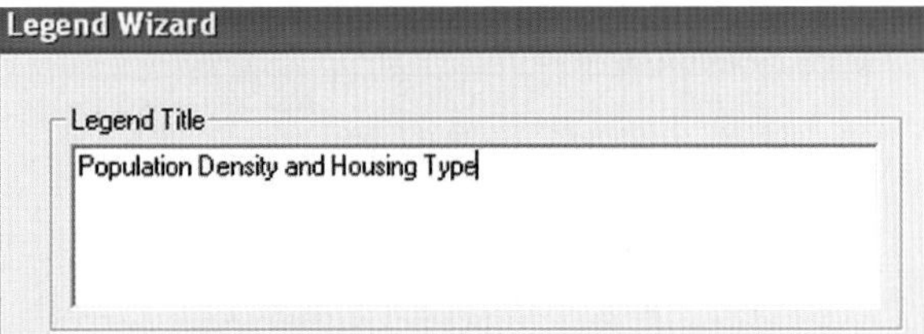

45 From the **Legend Frame** window set the border to **1.5 pt** from the drop-down menu and the background colour to **Sand**.

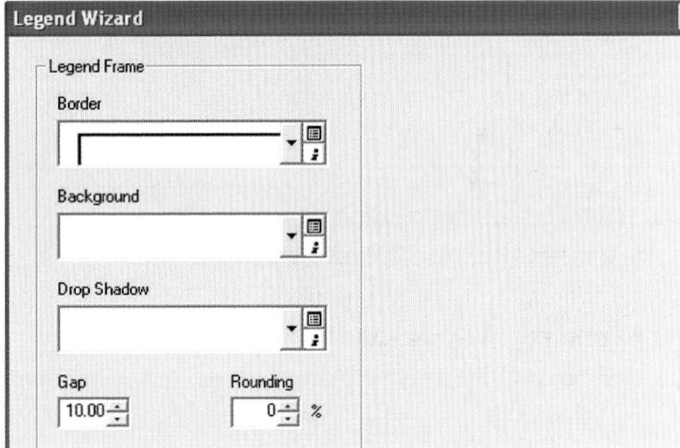

46 The next two panels are for setting symbols and spacing for the legend, but you will not change these, so just click **Next** twice and then click **Finish**.

47 The legend will need reducing in order to fit on the page. Change the size of the legend by holding down the left mouse button on a corner and dragging.

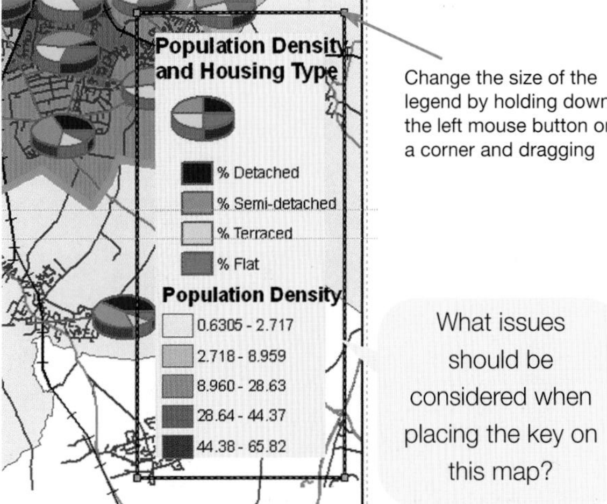

What issues should be considered when placing the key on this map?

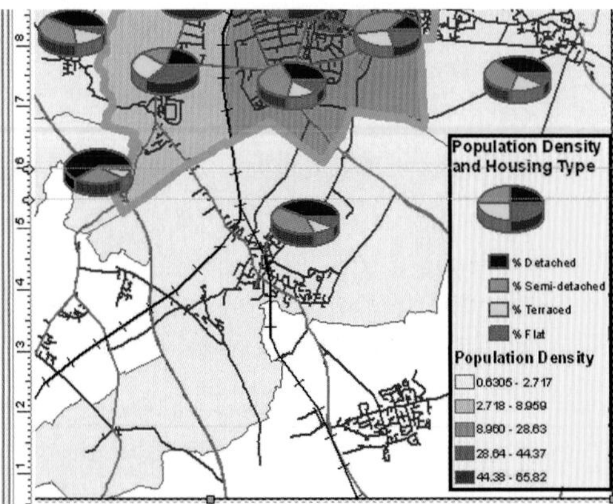

48 Make sure you move your legend to an appropriate position on the page.

49 You can move the position of your title and legend by using the **Select Elements** button.

50 Next we want to remove the **TOT_POP/AREA_HECTA** label from the Key. You can edit this label by using a slow double-click on the title **TOT_POP/AREA_HECTA** in the table of contents. Once you have selected the label, press **Delete**.

51 Once you have finished editing your legend for the first data frame, activate the data frame called **Unemployment and Housing Ownership**. Right-click on the data frame title. From the drop-down menu that appears, click **Activate**.

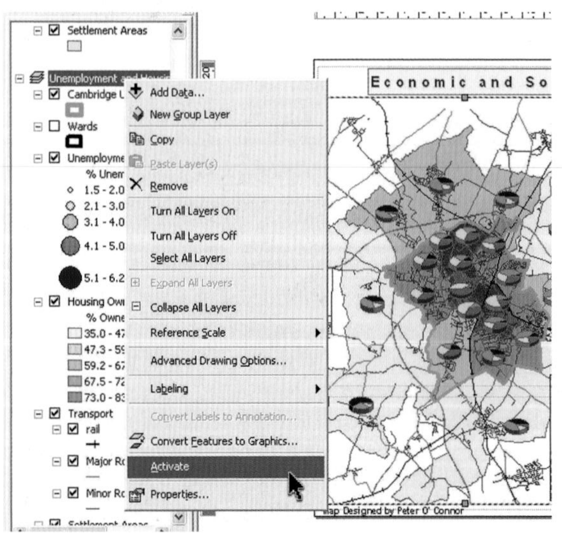

52 With the skills you have learned above, create a legend for the data frame called **Unemployment and Housing Ownership**.

Once you are happy with the layout of your maps and their presentation, you need to export your map as a PDF file so that it permanently saved.

53 From the **File** menu click **Export Map**.

54 When the directory window appears, navigate to your GIS project folder.

55 Give the map an appropriate file name such as **Cambridge Social and Economic Structure**.

56 From the **Save as type** drop-down menu select **PDF** and click **Save**.

57 Open up the **Adobe Reader** software package from the **Start** menu and then check that the PDF that you have just saved opens correctly.

58 Now complete the additional activities associated with exercise 4 on the CD.

Exercise 5

Mapping areas of low flood risk

Aim

- To identify and map urban areas in England with low flood risk.
- To critically evaluate the limitations and errors associated with some GIS data sets.

Introduction

Flooding has become a major issue in the UK and, with people's homes now frequently at risk, this topic has started to have political, economic and social significance.

In this exercise we will attempt to identify urban areas in England that represent a low flood risk. The government could use such information to identify locations for new housing development. Insurance companies may it to determine insurance premiums. So this type of mapping can have a strong influence on decision-making at many levels of government and business. Additionally, as the type of data we are going to use in this exercise becomes widely available, individuals may use it to help decide where they live, which may ultimately affect settlement patterns and the way people make important life decisions.

As spatial data becomes available to the public it is also important to think about the quality of data being used in GIS analysis. This exercise will explore some data quality issues in the context of mapping areas of low flood risk.

Launch ArcMap

1 Make sure you have created a **folder** where you can save all your future GIS work. Call it **GIS_Exercises**.

2 From the windows taskbar, click **Start**, **All Programs**, **ArcGIS**, **ArcMap**.

Depending on how ArcGIS and ArcMap have been installed or which Windows operating system you are using, you may have to use a slightly different navigation menu from which to open ArcMap. Ask your teacher for further instructions.

3 In the resulting ArcMap window, click the **An existing map** radio button and click **OK**.

Open an existing map

4 Browse to the drive on which your GIS Exercises have been installed (e.g. GIS_Exercises\Exercise5\Map Documents\Exercise5), click the **Exercise5** icon and click **Open**.

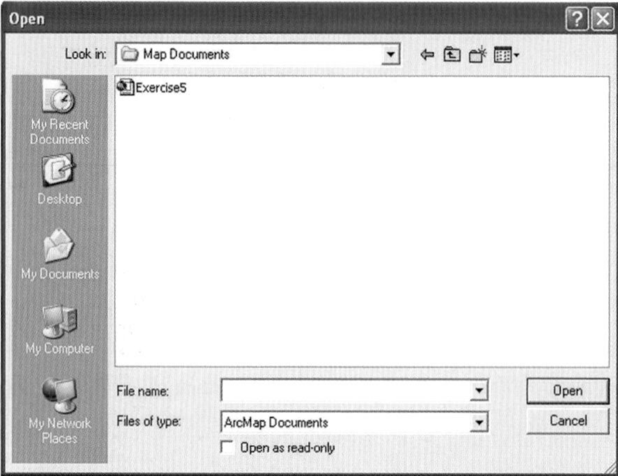

5 The **Exercise5.mxd** project opens in **ArcMap** showing all the data you have available to complete this exercise.

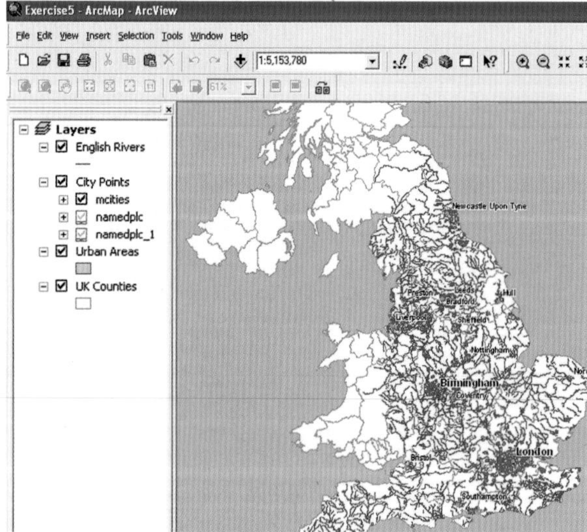

6 **Very Important:** As soon as you have opened the Exercise5.mxd project, save it to your own drive area using **File > Save As...** (e.g. the new project folder that you have just created called **GIS_Exercises**). **Everything that you now do for this project must be saved to the same folder.**

Mapping flood risk areas

The area at risk of flooding surrounding any river will vary considerably depending on catchment size, underlying geology, groundwater conditions and many other factors. For the purposes of this exercise we want to identify urban areas that are at least 1km away from a river course (such areas would be subject to an extremely low flood risk). To do this we need to create a 1km buffer around all rivers in England.

Creating a 1km buffer round English rivers

7 From the main toolbar click on the **Arc Toolbox** icon.

8 From the **Arc Toolbox** menu that appears expand the **Analysis Tools** option. Now expand the **Proximity** tools option and double-click with the left mouse button on **Buffer**.

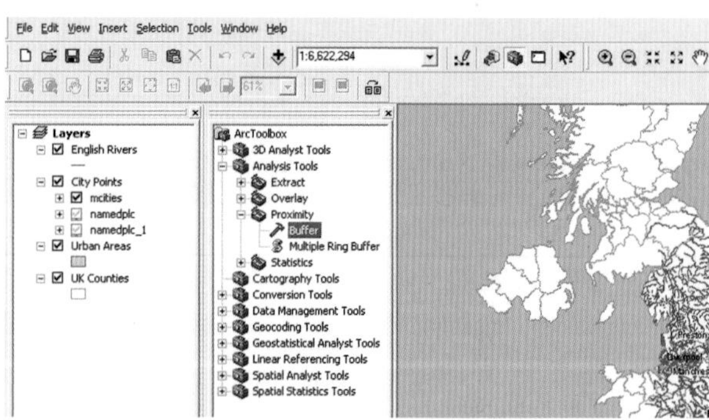

9 In the **Input Features** field, use the drop-down menu to select the layer called **English Rivers**.

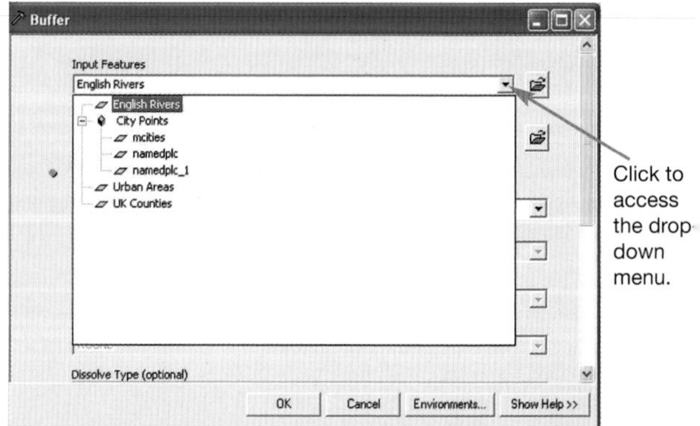

10 In the **Output Feature Class** field, specify the file to be saved in your own work area, that you created at the start of the exercise. In the **Distance** value box, type **1** and set the units to **Kilometers**. Click OK.

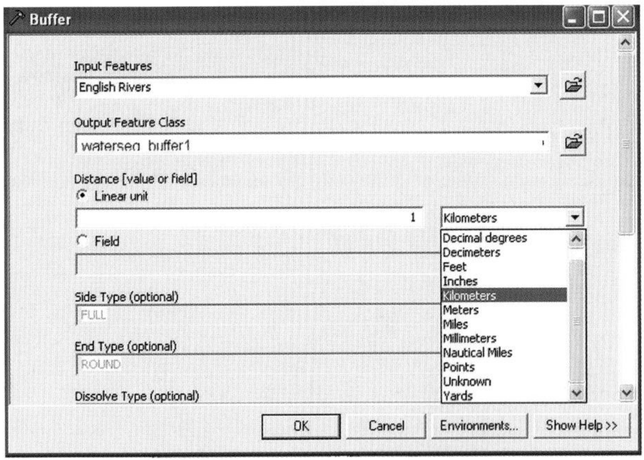

11 Close the **Buffer** dialogue box when the new layer **waterseg_buffer1** has been added to the table of contents.

12 Use the **Zoom** tool to check that a 1km buffer has been drawn around all English rivers.

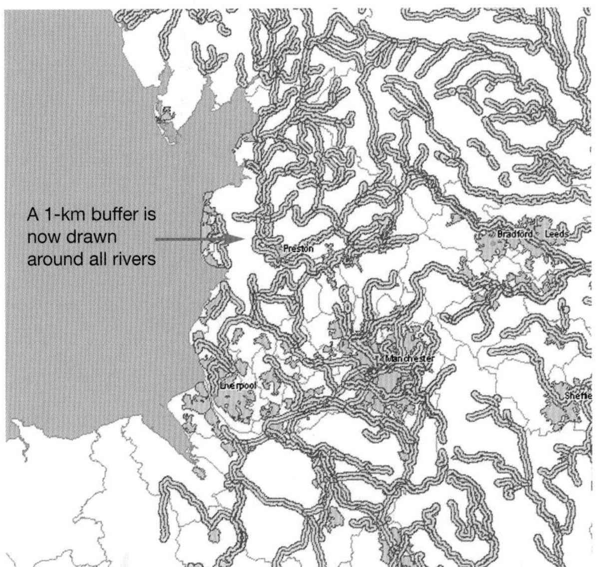

Examine the quality of the vector lines which represent the river features. Are there any data quality issues?

Identifying urban areas that do not fall within the 1km buffer

13 Make sure the layer **Urban Areas** is turned on in the table of contents.

14 In the table of contents window highlight the layer name **Urban Areas**. Click the layer name once with the right mouse button. From the drop-down menu that appears, click **Open Attribute Table**.

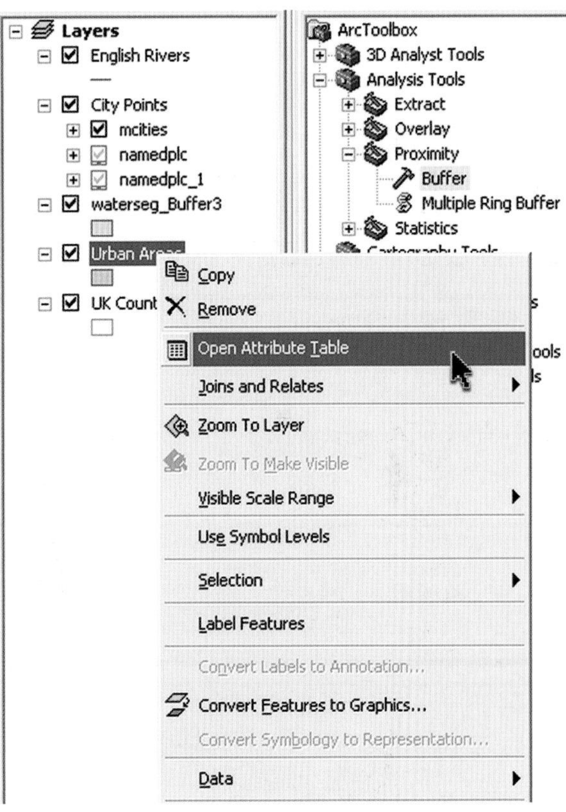

15 At the bottom of the attribute table click **Options**. From the drop-down menu that appears, click **Select All**. Now close the attribute table.

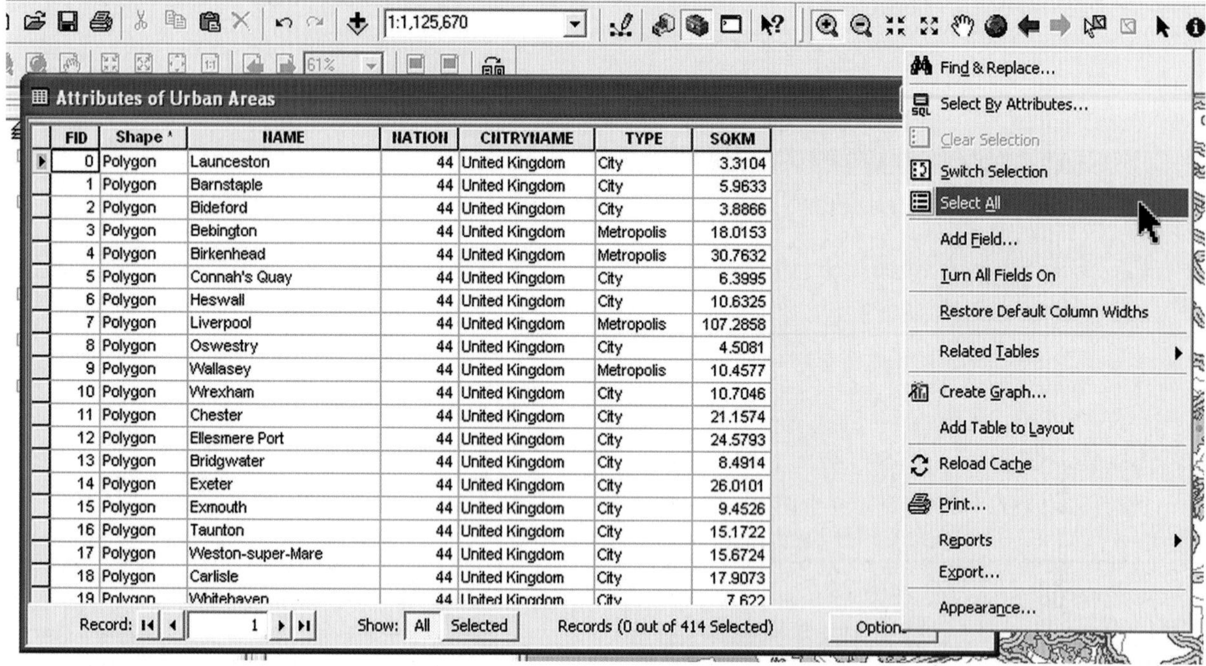

16 Click the **Zoom to Full Extent** button. 

17 In the main menu click on **Selection**. From the drop-down menu that appears click on **Select By Location**.

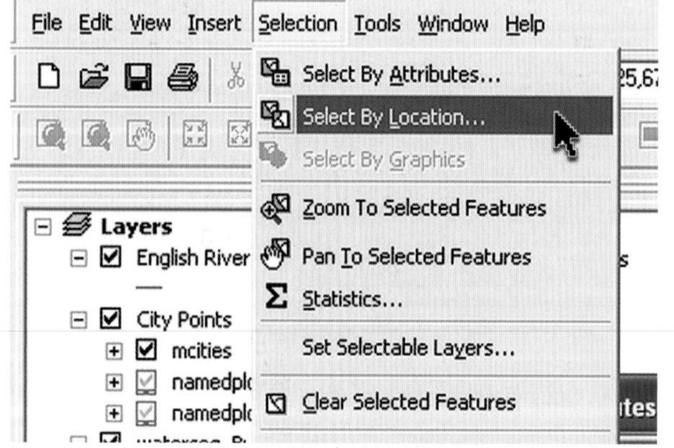

17 In the **I want to:** option box, set the option to **remove from the currently selected features in**. In the **the following layers:** field, click on the **Urban Areas** layer. Set the **that:** option box to **intersect**. Set the **the features in this layer:** field to **waterseg_buffer1**. Click **OK**.

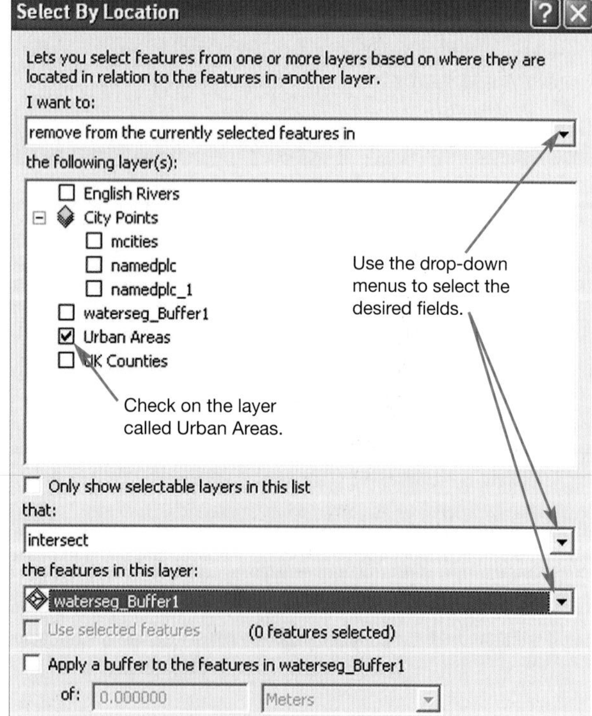

What is the difference between an attribute query and a location query?

We now have a selection of all the major urban areas in the UK that are more than 1km away from a river.

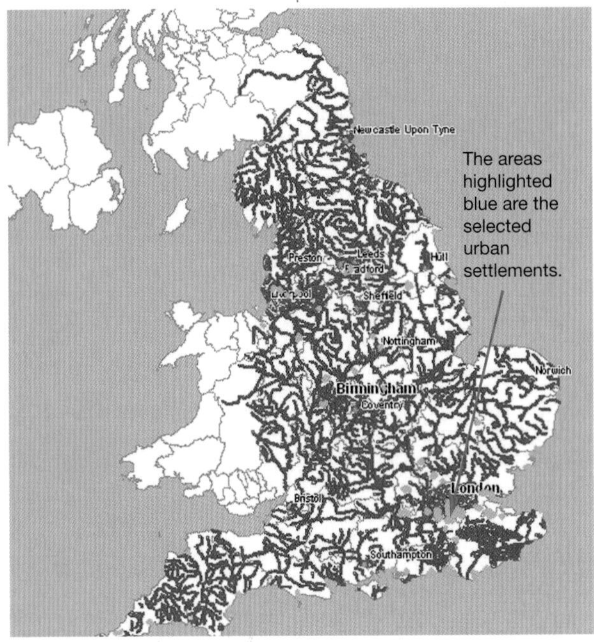

Next we want to identify those settlements that are greater in area than 20km^2.

19 From the main menu click on **Selection** and from the drop-down menu that appears click **Select by Attributes**.

20 Set the **Layer** option to **Urban Areas**. Set the **Method** option to **Select from current selection**. Double-click on the label **"SQKM"**. Single-click on the **> =** symbol. Type in the value **20** after the **>=**. Click **OK**.

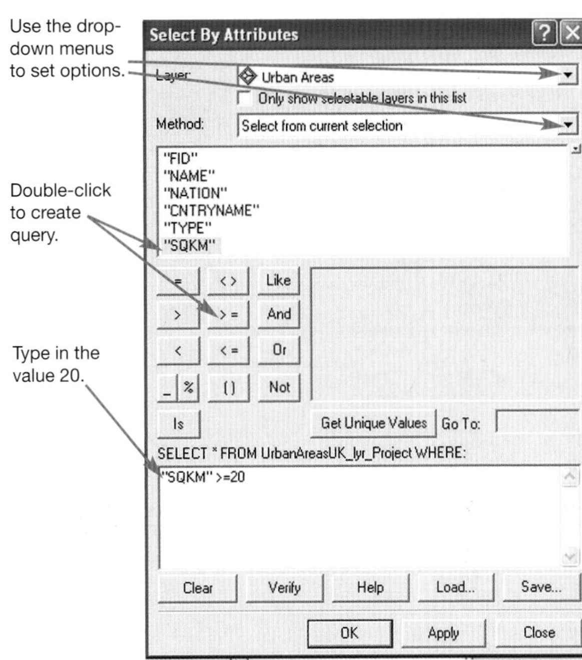

You have now narrowed your selection to show only those urban areas that are larger than 20km^2 and are more than 1km away from a river.

Creating a report

It is often useful to create a report listing the information found from a GIS query. Such reports can be incorporated into word-processed documents or other media, including maps, for presentation to a variety of audiences.

21 Highlight the layer name **Urban Areas**. With the right mouse button click the highlighted layer name once. From the drop-down menu that appears, click on **Open Attribute Table**.

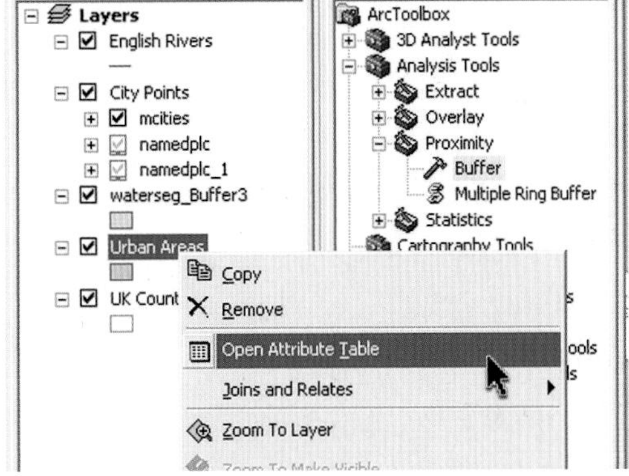

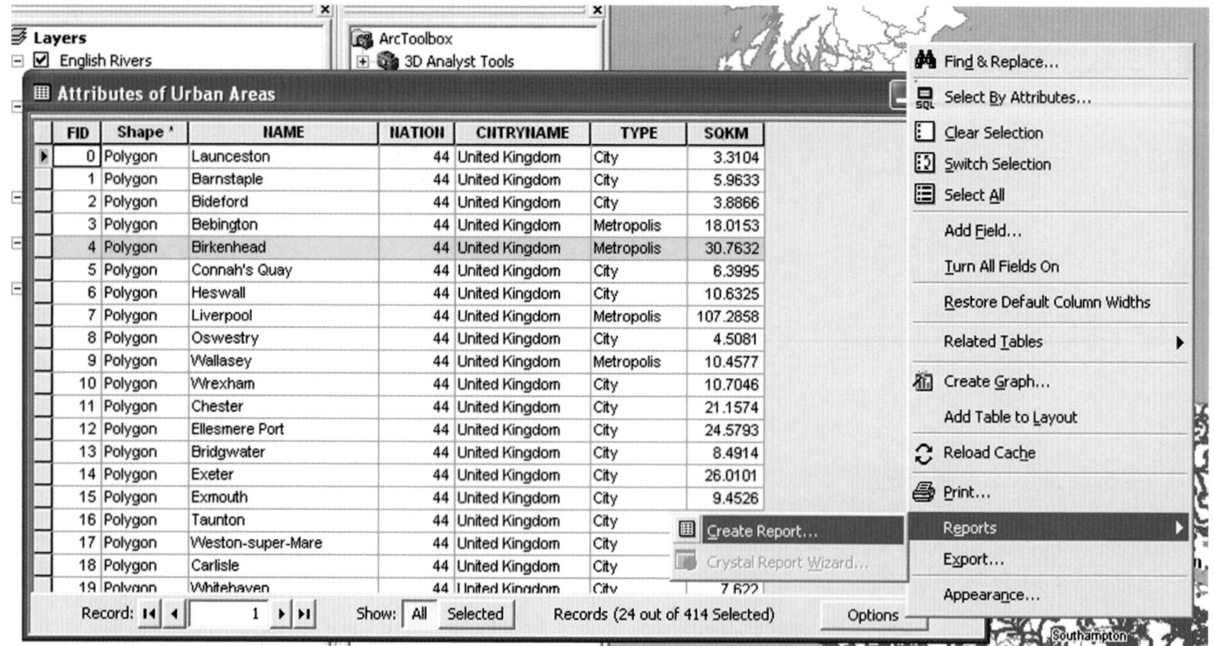

22 From the bottom of the attributes table click **Options**. From the drop-down menu that appears, highlight **Reports** and click on **Create Report**.

23 Ensure the **Fields** tab is selected then set the **Layer/Table** option to **Urban Areas**. In the **Available Fields** box highlight the attribute label **NAME** and click the **Add fields** button. Repeat this process for the attribute label **SQKM**.

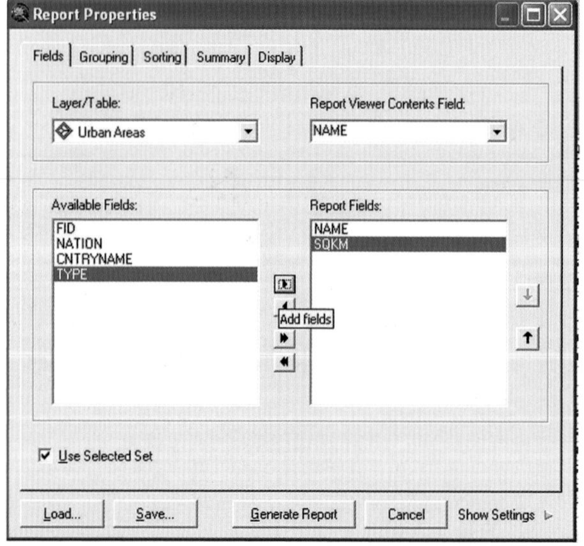

24 Click the **Display** tab in the **Report Properties** dialogue box. In the **Settings** menu click on and highlight the **Title** label. Now type a title for your report into the **Text** field (e.g. **Urban Areas of Low Flood Risk**).

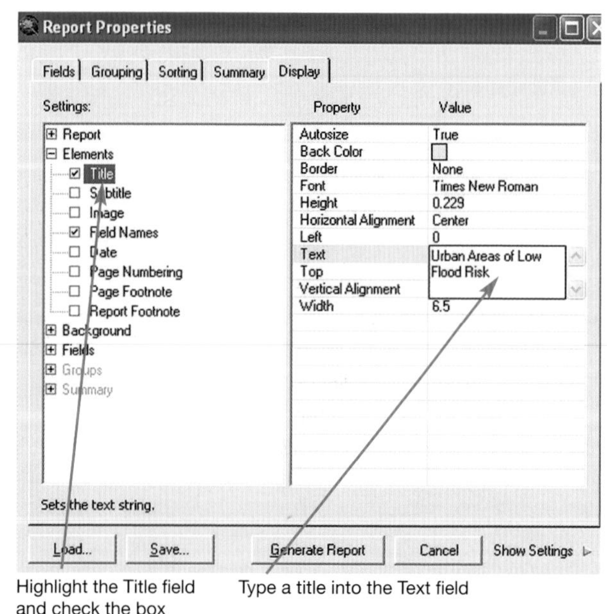

25 Set the **Horizontal Alignment** to **Left**.

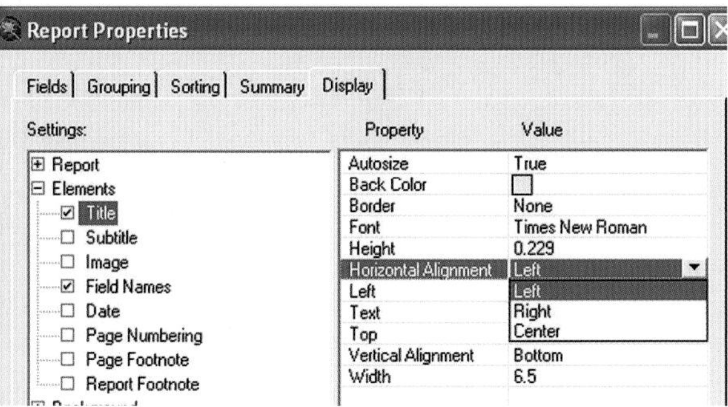

We now want to rank the records that are going to be included in the report according to their area.

26 In the **Report Properties** dialogue box click on the **Sorting** tab. Highlight **SQKM** and use the drop-down menu to set the field to sort **Ascending**. Now click **Generate Report**.

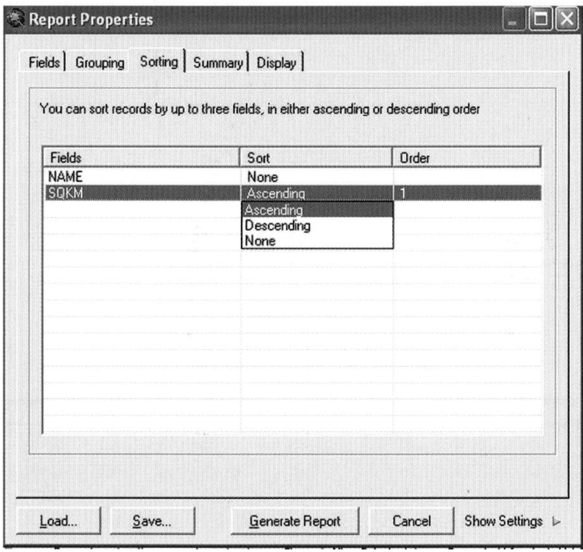

A report is now produced listing all the urban areas in England that are more than 1km away from a river and greater than 20km^2 in area. However, now you need to investigate the quality of this dataset to see if you can trust the results!

Report Viewer

Print... Export... Add... Copy 100% Stop 1/1

Urban Areas of Low Flood Risk

NAME	SQKM
Gillingham	22.021
High Wycombe	22.198
Scunthorpe	22.6445
Worthing	24.0116
Basildon	25.2227
Eastbourne	26.0591
Lambeth	26.1433
Kingston upon Thames	27.0056
Portsmouth	29.1992
Birkenhead	30.7632
South Shields	34.9788
Poole	37.1118
Sunderland	38.7946
Brighton	44.5971
Croydon	62.4569
Bromley	65.8011

What could be the value of this list to planners?

Are there any anomalous results in this list? If so, why have they occurred?

If your computer is connected to a printer, you can print your report.

27 At the top of the **Report Viewer** select your printer, click the **Print** button. Then click **Print** to print the report.

28 Close the **Report Viewer** dialogue. In the **Report Properties** dialogue box, click Close.

You are then asked whether you wish to save your report.

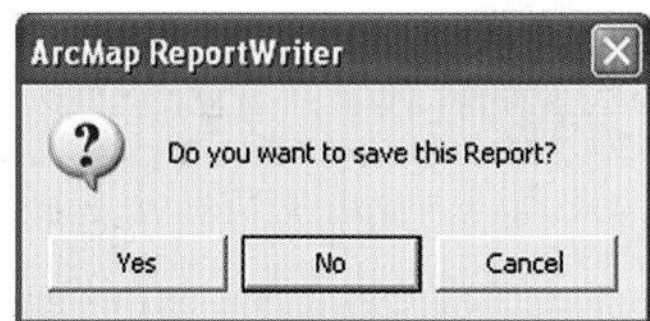

29 If you want to save your report, click **Yes** and navigate to the work area you set up at the start of this exercise. If you don't want to save the report, click **No**.

30 Now complete the additional activities associated with exercise 5 on the CD.

references

The references below have been used extensively by the author to develop the chapters in this book.

Appleton, K. J. and Lovett, A. A. (2005) 'GIS-based visualisation of development proposals: reactions from planning and related professionals', *Computers, Environment and Urban Systems* 29, pp. 321–339.

Arima, E. Y., Walker, R. T., Perz, S. G. and Caldas, M. (2005) 'Loggers and forest fragmentation: behavioral models of road building in the Amazon Basin', *Annals of the Association of American Geographers* 95, 3, pp. 525–541.

ASET (2005) ASET Level 3 GIS Qualification Topic Materials. These topic materials are available from ASET to support the teacher of their Level 3 qualification in GIS. Further information can be found at http://www.aset.ac.uk/view page.php?id=programmes%2Fqualifications%2F geographical-information-systems-l3%2F

Askew, D., Evans, S., Matthews, R. and Swanton, P. (2005) 'MAGIC: a geoportal for the English countryside', *Computers, Environment and Urban Systems* 29, pp. 71–85.

Baldi, P., Fabris, M., Marsella, M. and Monticelli, R. (2005) 'Monitoring the morphological evolution of the Sciara del Fuoco during the 2002–2003 Stromboli eruption using multi-temporal photogrammetry', *ISPRS Journal of Photogrammetry and Remote Sensing* 59, pp. 199–211.

Beaumont, P., Longley, P. A. and Maguire, D. J. (2005) 'Geographic information portals: a UK perspective', *Computers, Environment and Urban Systems* 29, pp. 49–69.

Bedford, M. (2004). *GIS for Water Management in Europe*. ESRI Press.

Birmingham Community Safety Partnership (2002) *Birmingham Crime and Disorder Audit 2002*.

Burrough, P. A. and McDonnell, R. A. (2000) *Principles of Geographical Information Systems*. Oxford: OUP.

Clark, C. D., Evans, D. J. A, Khatwa, A., Bradwell, T., Jordan, C. J., Marsh, S. H., Mitchell, W. A. and Bateman, M. D. (2004) 'Map and GIS database of landforms and features related to the last British ice sheet', *Boreas* 33, 4, pp. 359–375.

Cossman, R. E., Cossman, J. S., Jackson, R. and Cosby, A. (2003) 'Mapping high or low mortality places across time in the United States: a research note on a health visualization and analysis project', *Health and Place* 9, pp. 361–369.

Crampton, J. (2001) Maps as social constructions: power, communication, and visualization', *Progress in Human Geography* 25, 2, pp. 235–252.

DeMers, M. N. (2005) *Fundamentals of Geographic Information Systems*. New York: Wiley.

Di, K., Xu, F., Wang, J., Agarwal, S., Brodyagina, E., Li, R. and Matthies, L. (2008) 'Photogrammetric processing of rover imagery of the 2003 Mars Exploration Rover mission', *ISPRS Journal of Photogrammetry and Remote Sensing* 63, 2, pp. 155–282.

Durham County Council (1999) *County Durham Structure Plan (adopted) 1991–2006*. Durham County Council.

ESRI (2004a) *What is ArcGIS?*. ESRI Press.

ESRI (2004b) *ArcGIS 9: Using ArcGIS Spatial Analyst*. ESRI Press.

ESRI (2004c) *Understanding Map Projections*. ESRI Press.

ESRI (2004d) *Using ArcGIS Geostatistical Analyst*. ESRI Press.

ESRI (2004e) *ArcGIS 9: Using ArcGIS 3D Analyst*. ESRI Press.

ESRI (2004f) *ArcGIS 9: Using ArcGIS Tracking Analyst*. ESRI Press.

ESRI (2004g) *Geographic Information Systems*. ESRI Press.

Forest, B. (2004) 'Information sovereignty and GIS: the evolution of "communities of interest" in political redistricting', *Political Geography* 23, pp. 425–451.

Gastner, M. T., Shalizi, C. R. and Newman, M. E. J. (2005) 'Maps and cartograms of the 2004 US presidential election results', *Advances in Complex Systems* 8, pp. 117–123.

Goodchild, M. F., Anselin, L., Appelbaum, R. P. and Harthorn, B. H. (2000) 'Towards spatially integrated social science', *International Regional Science Review* 23, 2, pp. 139–159.

Graham, S.D.N. (2005). 'Software-sorted geographies.' *Progress in Human Geography* 29, 5, pp. 562-580.

Heywood, I., Cornelius, S. and Carver, S. (2006) *An Introduction to Geographical Information Systems*. Pearson/Prentice Hall.

Hudson-Smith, A. (2008) *The digital geography: Geographic visualisation for urban environments*. CASA at UCL.

Huggel, C., Schneider, D., Julio Miranda, P., Delgado Granados, H. and Kääb, A. (in press) 'Evaluation of ASTER and SRTM DEM data for lahar modeling: a case study on lahars from Popocatépetl volcano', *Journal of Volcanology and Geothermal Research*.

Jensen, J. R. and Cowen, D. C. (1999) 'Remote sensing of urban/suburban infrastructure and socioeconomic attributes', *Photogrammetric Engineering and Remote Sensing* 65, pp. 611–622.

Kaiser, W. L. and Wood, D. (2001) *Seeing Through Maps: The Power of Images to Shape Our World View*. Amherst, MA: ODT, Inc.

Kevany, M. J. (2003) 'GIS in the World Trade Center attack: trial by fire', *Computers, Environment and Urban Systems* 27, pp. 571–583.

Kwan, M.-P. and Lee, J. (2005) 'Emergency response after 9/11: the potential of real-time 3D GIS for quick emergency response in micro-spatial environments', *Computers, Environment and Urban Systems* 29, pp. 93–113.

le Blanc, D. and Perez, R. (2008) 'The relationship between rainfall and human density and its implications for future water stress in Sub-Saharan Africa', *Ecological Economics*, 66, 2-3, pp. 319-36.

Liang, H., Arangarasan, R. and Theller, L. (2007) 'Dynamic visualization of high resolution GIS dataset on multi-panel display using ArcGIS engine', *Computers and Electronics in Agriculture* 58, pp. 174–188.

Loboda, T. V. and Csiszar, I. A. (2007) 'Reconstruction of fire spread within wildland fire events in Northern Eurasia from the MODIS active fire product', *Global and Planetary Change* 56, pp. 258–273.

Longley, P. A., Goodchild, M. F., Maguire, D. J. and Rind, D. W. (2005) *Geographic Information Systems and Science*. New York: Wiley.

Martin, C., Curtis, B., Fraser, C. and Sharp, B. (2002) 'The use of a GIS-based malaria information system for malaria research and control in South Africa', *Health and Place* 8, pp. 227–236.

Monmonier, M. S. (2002) *Spying with Maps: Surveillance Technologies and the Future of Privacy*. Chicago: University of Chicago Press.

Morad, M. and Connolly, T. (2001) *A Concise Introduction to Geographic Information Systems and Science*. Kingston Centre for GIS, Kingston University.

Napieralski, J., Harbor, J. and Li, Y. (2007) 'Glacial geomorphology and geographic information systems', *Earth-Science Reviews* 85, pp. 1–22.

Ó Dochartaigh, B. E., Ball, D. F., MacDonald, A. M., Lilly, A., Fitzsimons, V. Del Rio, M. and Auton, C. A. (2005). 'Mapping groundwater vulnerability in Scotland: a new approach for the Water Framework Directive', *Scottish Journal of Geology* 41, 1, pp. 21–30.

OEDC (2004) *OEDC Information Technology Outlook*. OEDC.

Office for National Statistics (2004). *Census 2001: Key Statistics for postcode sectors in England and Wales*. HMSO.

Ordnance Survey (2002) *A Guide to Coordinate Systems in Great Britain: An Introduction to Mapping Coordinate Systems and the Use of GPS Datasets with Ordnance Survey Mapping*. Ordnance Survey.

Sparkes, A. and Kidner, D. (1996) A GIS for the Environmental Impact of Wind Farms. ESRI (http://gis.esri.com/library/userconf/europroc96/papers/pn26/pn26f.htm).

Stirling Council (2005) *Stirling Council Structure Plan*. Stirling Council.

Sustainable Development Commission (2005) *Wind Power in the UK*. Sustainable Development Commission (www.sd-commission.org.uk/publications.php?id=234).

Tralli, D. M., Blom, R. G., Zlotnicki, V. Donnellan, A. and Evans, D. L. (2005) 'Satellite remote sensing of earthquake, volcano, flood, landslide and coastal inundation hazards', *ISPRS Journal of Photogrammetry and Remote Sensing* 59, pp. 185–198.

Tyrvainen, L., Makinen, K. and Schipperijn, J. (2007) 'Tools for mapping social values of urban woodlands and other green areas', *Landscape and Urban Planning* 79, pp. 5–19.

Weeks, J. R., Getis, A. Hill, A. G., Gadalla, M. S. and Rashed, T. (2004) 'The fertility transition in Egypt: intraurban patterns in Cairo', *Annals of the Association of American Geographers* 94, 1, pp. 74–93.

Wood, J. (2005) '"How green is my valley?': desktop geographic information systems as a community-based participatory mapping tool', *Area* 37, 2, pp. 159–170.

Wyatt, P. and Ralphs, M. (2003) *GIS in Land and Property Management*. London: Spon Press.

Xiao, X. M., Boles, S., Liu J., Zhuang D., Frolking, S., Li, C. S., Salas, W. and Moore, B. (2005) 'Mapping paddy rice agriculture in southern China using multi-temporal MODIS images', *Remote Sensing of Environment* 95, pp. 480–492.

Zhou, Qiming (1999) *Digital Image Processing and Interpretation*. Department of Geography, Hong Kong Baptist University Kowloon Tong, Kowloon, Hong Kong (http://geog.hkbu.edu.hk/geog3610/image_processing.pdf).

acknowledgements

The author and publishers would like to thank for the following organisations for supplying materials for this book:
ESRI Inc, for the *ArcView* 9.2 software
ESRI (UK) for numerous images and data
Navteq, for the base mapping data for England and Wales used in the exercises
The Home Office Research and Development Statistics Directorate, for crime data and police boundaries. Further data can be downloaded from: *http://rds.homeoffice.gov.uk/rds/crimeew0607.html*
The Office for National Statistics, for census data and boundaries. Further census data can be downloaded from: *http://neighbourhood.statistics.gov.uk/dissemination/Download1.do?bhcp=1*

We have made every effort to contact the original sources of copyright material, but if there have been any inadvertent breaches of copyright we apologise. The majority of copyright owners are credited where their material appears; however, where the attribution is very long we have recorded it here instead:
Figure 1.5 is reprinted from *ISPRS Journal of Photogrammetry and Remote Sensing*, 63, 2, Di, K., Xu, F., Wang, J., Agarwal, S., Brodyagina, E., Li, R. and Matthies, L., 'Photogrammetric processing of rover imagery of the 2003 Mars Exploration Rover Mission', pp. 181-201, © 2008, with permission from Elsevier.
Figure 3.2 is reprinted from *Computers, Environment and Urban Systems*, 27, 6, Kevany, M.J., 'GIS in the World Trade Centre attack – trial by fire', pp. 571-83, © 2003, with permission from Elsevier.
Figure 3.4 is reprinted from the *Annals of the Association of American Geographers*, 95, 3, Arima, E.Y., Walker, R.T. and Perz, S.G., 'Loggers and Forest Fragmentation: Behavioral Models of Road Building in the Amazon Basin', pp. 525-541, © 2005, with permission from Taylor & Francis Ltd (www.tandf.co.uk/journals).
Figure 3.5 is reprinted from the *Scottish Journal of Geology*, 41, Ó Dochartaigh *et al* (2005). Reproduced by permission of the British Geological Survey. © NERC. All rights reserved. IPR/103-21CA.
Figure 3.6 is reprinted from *ISPRS Journal of Photogrammetry and Remote Sensing*, 59, 4, Tralli, D.M., Blom, R.G., Zlotnicki, V., Donnellan, A. and Evans, D.L., 'Satellite remote sensing of earthquake, volcano, flood, landslide and coastal inundation hazards', pp. 185-98, © 2005, with permission from Elsevier.
Figure 3.7 is reprinted from *Remote Sensing of Environment*, 95, 4, Xiao, X., Boles, S., Liu, J., Zhuang, D., Frolking, S., Li, C., Salas, W. and Moore, B., 'Mapping paddy rice agriculture in Southern China using multi-temporal MODIS images', pp. 480-92, © 2005, with permission from Elsevier.
Figure 3.8 is reprinted from the *Annals of the Association of American Geographers*, 94, 1, Weeks, J.R., Getis, A. and Hill, G., 'The fertility transition in Egypt: intraurban patterns in Cairo', pp. 74-93, © 2004, with permission from Taylor & Francis Ltd (www.tandf.co.uk/journals).
Figure 3.9 is Figure 7 (page 11) 'The human face on four different projections' from *Seeing Through Maps* (2006) by Wood, Kaiser and Abramms. Rights available from ODTmaps.com or USA 413-549-1293.
Figure 3.10 is Figure 4 (page 7) 'Areal distortion on Mercator's projection' from *A New View of the World*, Ward L. Kaiser, ODTmaps.com (Amherst MA); 1987, 1993 (page 12) and used in *Seeing Through Maps* (2006) by Wood, Kaiser and Abramms.
Figure 3.11 is Figure 2 (page 4) 'The Mercator projection' from *Map Projections - A Working Manual*, John P. Snyder, USGS Professional Paper 1395, 1987, Washington D.C. (page 40). Image prepared by ODTmaps.com and used in *Seeing Through Maps* (2006) by Wood, Kaiser and Abramms.
Figures 3.19 and 3.20 are reprinted from *Health and Place*, 9, 4, Cossman, R.E., Cossman, J.S., Jackson, R. and Cosby, A., 'Mapping high or low mortality places across time in the United States: a research note on a health visualisation and analysis project', pp. 361-9, © 2003, with permission from Elsevier.
Figure 4.1 is reproduced by permission of the Office of National Statistics and Ordnance Survey on behalf of HMSO. © Crown copyright 2008. All rights reserved. Ordnance Survey Licence number 100017849.
Figure 5.2 is reproduced by permission of Ordnance Survey on behalf of HMSO. © Crown copyright 2008. All rights reserved. Ordnance Survey Licence number 100017849.
Figure 13.4 is reprinted with permission from the American Society for Photogrammetry and Remote Sensing.
Figures 19.3 and 19.4 are reprinted from *ISPRS Journal of Photogrammetry and Remote Sensing*, 59, 4, Baldi, P., Fabris, M., Marsella, M. and Monticelli, R., 'Monitoring the morphological evolution of the Sciara del Fuoco during the 2002-2003 Stromboli eruption using multi-temporal photogrammetry', pp. 199-211, © 2005, with permission from Elsevier.
Figures 19.6 and 19.7 are reprinted from *Ecological Economics*, 66, 2-3, le Blanc, D. and Perez, R., 'The relationship between rainfall and human density and its implications for future water stress in Sub-Saharan Africa', pp. 319-36, © 2008, with permission from Elsevier.
Figure 20.4 is reprinted from from *ISPRS Journal of Photogrammetry and Remote Sensing*, 59, 4, Tralli, D.M., Blom, R.G., Zlotnicki, V., Donnellan, A. and Evans, D.L., 'Satellite remote sensing of earthquake, volcano, flood, landslide and coastal inundation hazards', pp. 185-98, © 2005, with permission from Elsevier.
Figure 22.2 is reproduced by permission of Ordnance Survey on behalf of HMSO. © Crown copyright 2008. All rights reserved. Ordnance Survey Licence number 100017849.
Figures 22.3 and 22.4 are reprinted from *Health and Place*, 8, 2, Martin, C., Curtis, B., Fraser, C. and Sharp, B., 'The use of a GIS-based malaria information system for malaria research and control in South Africa', pp. 227-36, © 2002, with permission from Elsevier.
Figures 25.7, 25.8 and 25.9 are reprinted from *Computers, Environment and Urban Systems*, 29, 3, Appleton, K., and Lovett, A., 'GIS-based visualisation of development proposals: reactions from planning and related professionals', pp. 321-39, © 2005, with permission from Elsevier.
Figure 26.4 is reprinted from *Global and Planetary Change*, 56, 3-4, Loboda, T.V. and Csiszar, I.A., 'Reconstruction of fire spread within wildland fire events in Northern Eurasia from the MODIS active fire product', pp. 258-73, © 2007, with permission from Elsevier.
Figure 27.5 is reprinted from Hudson-Smith, A. (2008) *The digital geography: Geographic visualisation for urban environments.* CASA at UCL.
Figure 27.6 is reprinted from *Computers and Electronics in Agriculture*, 58, 2, Liang, H., Arangaransan, R. and Theller, L., 'Dynamic visualisation of high resolution GIS dataset on multipanel display using ArcGIS engine', pp. 174-88, © 2007, with permission from Elsevier.
Figure 27.7 is reprinted from *Earth-Sciences Reviews*, 85, 1-2, Napieralski, J., Harbor, J. and Li, Y., 'Glacial geomorphology and geographic information systems', pp. 1-22, © 2007, with permission from Elsevier.
Table 29.1 is reprinted from *Computers, Environment and Urban Systems*, 29, 1, Beaumont, P., Longley, P.A. and Maguire, D.J., 'Geographic information portals – a UK perspective', pp. 49-69, © 2005, with permission from Elsevier.
Figure 33.8 is reproduced by permission of Ordnance Survey on behalf of HMSO. © Crown copyright 2008. All rights reserved. Ordnance Survey Licence number 100017849.
Figures 35.1-35.5 are reprinted from *Landscape and Urban Planning*, 79, 1, Tyrväinen, L., Mäkinen, K. and Schipperijn, J., 'Tools for mapping social values of urban woodlands and other green areas', pp. 5-19, © 2007, with permission from Elsevier.
Figures 36.1-36-5 are reprinted from *Journal of Volcanology and Geo-thermal Research*, 170, 1-2, Huggel, C., Schneider, D., Julio Miranda, P., Delgado Granados, H. and Kääb, A., 'Evaluation of ASTER and SRTMDEM data for lahar modelling: A case study on lahars from Popocatépetl Volcano, Mexico', pp. 99-110, © 2008, with permission from Elsevier.
Figures 34.1 and 34.2 are reprinted from Clark, C.D., Evans, D.J.A., Khatwa, A., Bradwell, T., Jordan, C.J., Marsh, S.H., Mitchell, W.A. and Bateman, M.D. (2004) 'Map and GIS database of landforms and features related to the last British ice sheet', *Boreas*, 33, 4, pp. 359-75. Copyright 2004. Reproduced with permission of Blackwell Publishing Ltd.